D0282650

A NONPARAMETRIC INTRODUCTION TO STATISTICS

A NONPARAMETRIC INTRODUCTION TO STATISTICS

CHARLES H. KRAFT and CONSTANCE VAN EEDEN
UNIVERSITÉ DE MONTRÉAL

THE MACMILLAN COMPANY, *New York*
COLLIER-MACMILLAN LIMITED, *London*

First Printing

Library of Congress catalog card number: 68-13213

The Macmillan Company, New York
Collier-Macmillan Canada, Ltd., Toronto, Ontario

Printed in the United States of America

To Professor J. Neyman

PREFACE

Part I of this text is designed as a one-term introduction to statistics. We chose nonparametric methods as the principal vehicle for this introduction because of the simplicity of their basic probability theory. This simplicity permits an introduction to inference, that is, to the establishment of a relationship between observations and a family of models, to precede a discussion of probability. The contributions that the knowledge of the probabilistic properties of observations can make, both to the usefulness and to the understanding of inferential statements, is then explored, first for simple randomizations, and then for samples from populations.

We have attempted to make this introduction comprehensible to a reader who is willing to gain insight by studying both the rationale for, and the arithmetic details of, the numerous examples and exercises. Although we have given verbal descriptions of computations, formulas become necessary and a reader should, at least, be willing to learn to read and use them.

Part II contains brief descriptions of particular tests and their exact and approximate distributions. These were selected to provide an introduction to the more common designs and their analyses. With supplementation, by examples from experimental sciences, Part II could serve as a basis for a second course.

Part III consists of tables and introductions to tables. We have recommended, in Parts I and II, the use, as a descriptive statistic, of what would be, with certain randomizations, the family of all confidence intervals for given families of tests. Consequently, the tables give complete distributions and not only certain levels of significance.

Some of the work on this book was done while the authors were at the University of Montreal and part was done while they were at the University of Minnesota. We wish to thank both universities for their encouragement of the work. We received support from the National Research Council of Canada while at the University of Montreal and from the National Science

Foundation of the United States of America while at the University of Minnesota. We are grateful to these agencies for this support. The computing centers at both universities were very helpful. We thank M. Norman Buckle, who programmed the computations for the extension of the tables for the Wilcoxon, Mann-Whitney tests and the Kruskal-Wallis, Rijkoort tests. We are indebted to Dr. Siegfried Schach, who read the entire manuscript and made many valuable comments and suggestions. We wish to express our appreciation to Miss Jean Havlish and to Mme. Francine Marigaux for their expert typing and tireless retyping of the manuscript. Finally, we thank our publishers, The Macmillan Company, for their help and encouragement.

Charles H. Kraft
Constance van Eeden

CONTENTS

PART I. ELEMENTARY THEORY OF STATISTICAL ANALYSIS 1

PART II. DESCRIPTIONS OF PARTICULAR ANALYSES 133

PART III. TABLES 183

PART I

ELEMENTARY THEORY OF STATISTICAL ANALYSIS

CHAPTER 1

A TREATMENT AND CONTROL DESIGN

It often occurs that information relevant to questions such as the following is sought.

1. How does a certain quantity of a given dietary supplement affect weight gains?
2. How does an advertising campaign, conducted before the introduction of a new product, affect sales when the product is introduced?
3. What difference is there, in the performance of pupils, between a proposed new method of teaching and the one presently used?

An approach to obtaining information about such questions is to observe the behavior of two groups of subjects. One group, called the *treatment group*, will have experienced the treatment (the dietary supplement, the advertising campaign, or the new teaching method) during the observation period. The other group, called the *control group*, will not have experienced the treatment. Aside from this difference, the experiences and conditions for both groups should be as alike as possible.

Since "to observe the behavior of the subjects" is too vague, it will be supposed that a particular aspect of behavior has been singled out and that the observation of this aspect can be expressed by a number for each subject. When such observations have been made, it is useful to present them in some tabular form together with a description of the circumstances under which the observations were made. There is no general rule as to how detailed such a description should be; a good goal is to give a description sufficiently detailed so that a reader can carry out a nearly equivalent experiment.

In the examples to follow, descriptions of these circumstances (fictitious anyway) will be grossly abbreviated. The concern will be with the two sets of numerical measurements $(t_1, t_2, \ldots, t_n)$ for the n treatment subjects, and $(c_1, c_2, \ldots, c_m)$ for the m control subjects. The numbers of subjects, n and m, will be smaller than are often used.

Example 1. To learn about the effect of a dietary supplement a litter of 5 young rats was randomly divided into two groups. The weight gains, in grams, during their third and fourth weeks from birth were

Supplement		*No supplement*	
Rat 1	52	Rat 3	40
Rat 2	35	Rat 4	21
Rat 5	43		

In the notation of the preceding paragraph, $n = 3$ and $t_1 = 52$, $t_2 = 35$, $t_3 = 43$, and $m = 2$ and $c_1 = 40$, $c_2 = 21$. Or, more briefly, $(t_1, t_2, t_3) = (52, 35, 43)$ and $(c_1, c_2) = (40, 21)$.

Example 2. For a study to gain information about the effect of an advertising campaign before the introduction of a new product, six towns were used. Because towns *A*, *B*, and *C* had a resident company representative, preadvertising was conducted there. In towns *D*, *E*, and *F* there was no representative and no advertising before the introduction of the product. The number of units sold during the first two weeks after the introduction of the product were

Preadvertising		*No preadvertising*	
Town *A*	3250	Town *D*	3120
Town *B*	3780	Town *E*	2540
Town *C*	2915	Town *F*	2760

Here $(t_1, t_2, t_3) = (3250, 3780, 2915)$ and $(c_1, c_2, c_3) = (3120, 2540, 2760)$.

Example 3. In an experiment to assess a new method of instruction, seven students were divided into two groups. The first group was taught by the new method and the second group was taught "conventionally." The differences between the posttest score and the pretest score were

	New method				*Standard method*		
	Pre	*Post*	*Gain*		*Pre*	*Post*	*Gain*
Brown	80	86	6	Olsen	82	92	10
Evans	82	92	10	Peters	67	65	−2
Jones	76	91	15	Smith	75	76	1
				Roberts	76	81	5

or $(t_1, t_2, t_3) = (6, 10, 15)$ and $(c_1, c_2, c_3, c_4) = (10, -2, 1, 5)$.

For each of the above examples the method of division of the subjects into two groups was different. The method was random for the first, according to the presence of a representative for the second, and alphabetically for the third.

Clearly, for Example 2, a question will exist whether any difference between the two groups will be due to the advertising or to the presence of the representative (or both). In such cases the two treatments are said to be confounded and no way exists to separately assess their effects from the present observations. It may be that an argument that one of the two, say, the representative, has no effect on sales can be based on past, or future, experience, so as to make it reasonable to attribute an observed difference to the advertising.

In Example 3, the presence of confounding is less obvious. In many cases it can be argued that there should be no relation between the first letter in a student's last name and his difference in test scores. Still it is easy to give examples where it might matter; socioeconomic level and name could be associated. In any case, it is not going to be clear, from the present observations, whether any observed difference is to be attributed to the difference in teaching method or to the first letter of the student's last name.

In Example 1 the presence of confounding is even more subtle, but it is there. Although selected at random, rats 1, 2, and 5 were the treatment subjects and rats 3 and 4 were the control subjects. Just as in the other two examples, it is not going to be possible, from the present observations, to decide whether an observed difference in gains is due to the supplement or is due to some factor present in rats 1, 2, and 5 and absent in rats 3 and 4.

Randomization has advantages; over a series of experiments it will "average out" confoundings, and for a particular experiment it will assure that there has been no deliberate (conscious or unconscious) confounding. However, any experiment is necessarily conducted with certain subjects and the possibility that an observed difference is due to peculiarities of these subjects, rather than to the treatment, will always exist. It is for this reason that careful experimentation always calls for replication of experiments and for comparison of observed results with the experience accumulated from similar experiments.

In the three examples, one group was a treatment group, the other group was a control group. For many experiments the purpose is to compare two treatments, in which case it is more appropriate to refer to a treatment effect as a treatment difference. The distinction is more apparent than real (even the control group receives some treatment during an experiment), and it will be convenient to usually refer to the groups as treatment and control.

EXERCISES

1.1. From the recent issues of an experimental journal in your field of interest find several examples of treatment and control experiments, or two treatment experiments. (*Science*, published by the American Association for the Advancement of Science, has descriptions of experiments from many fields.) From the description given, try to find out exactly what was done and observed. How were the subjects selected? How were they divided into two groups? What were the environmental differences between the two groups during the course of the experiment? Exactly what was measured and how? How are any conclusions based on these measurements? Could you, given the time and facilities, repeat the experiment from the description given? Describe how, in detail. (Notice that you could not replicate the "experiments" described in Examples 1, 2, and 3.)

1.2. Choose a convenient scale and draw a graph of the observations, for each of Examples 1, 2, and 3, as

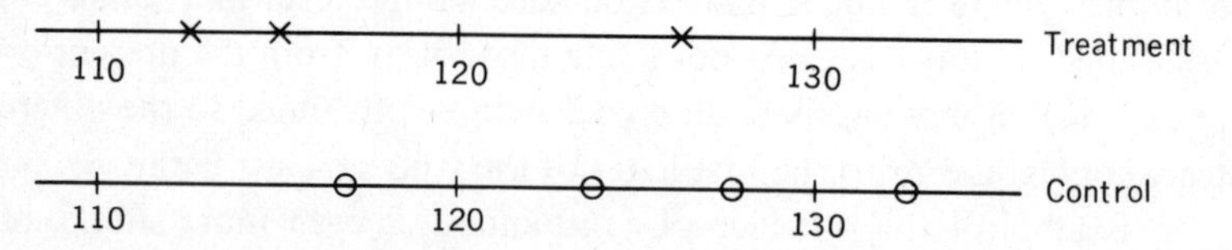

1.3. For each of the Examples list the possible assignments of subjects to treatment and control. There will be 10 such assignments for Example 1, 20 for Example 2, and 35 for Example 3. A simple way to enumerate these possible assignments is to identify each subject with a different letter. Then each possible assignment of subjects to, say, treatment corresponds to an n-letter word from the $(m + n)$-letter alphabet if no two letters in each n-letter word are the same and if the letters in each n-letter word are in increasing (alphabetic) order. It is a simple matter to enumerate the n-letter words, whose letters are in increasing order, from an $(m + n)$-letter alphabet if the words themselves are enumerated in alphabetical order.

Example for $n = 2$, $m = 2$. If the four subjects, say, Smith, Brown, Jones, and Johnson are identified with a = Smith, b = Brown, c = Jones, and d = Johnson, the possible assignments are

Treatment	*Control*
(a, b)	(c, d)
(a, c)	(b, d)
(a, d)	(b, c)
(b, c)	(a, d)
(b, d)	(a, c)
(c, d)	(a, b)

CHAPTER 2

MODELS FOR THE EFFECT OF TREATMENT

MODELS

The question "How does the treatment affect the observations?" admits a complete and precise answer if one is willing to suppose that experiments with an infinite number of subjects can be conducted in a fixed environment. Even though such experiments do not exist, it will be useful to consider what a complete and precise answer to the question could be.

There is a choice of observing a given subject under either of two circumstances, as a control subject with no treatment or as an experimental subject with treatment. Suppose that, for each subject, there is a pair of numbers, (t, c), where t represents the measurement that would be made if the subject were a treatment subject and c represents the measurement that would be made if the subject were a control subject. If all subjects with the same value of c also have the same value of t, these pairs of numbers define a function h whose value at c is $h(c)$, or, as is often written, $t = h(c)$. Such a function, h, is a complete description of a treatment effect in that it states, for any subject, the score that would be observed under the control conditions and under the experimental conditions. That t and c are not both observable will be ignored in this chapter.

A function h will be called a *model* for the treatment effect. There are other sorts of models; for instance, it is easy to imagine that the treatment scores would differ even for subjects who all would have the same control scores, or to imagine that the control scores and the treatment scores are not a fixed property of the subject. Models appropriate for this last case will be discussed in Chapter 11. However, most of the analyses to be proposed for the present model are equally applicable for the models of Chapter 11.

If, for a given experiment, the function h could be determined, its interpretation would be straightforward. This can be seen by considering a few examples.

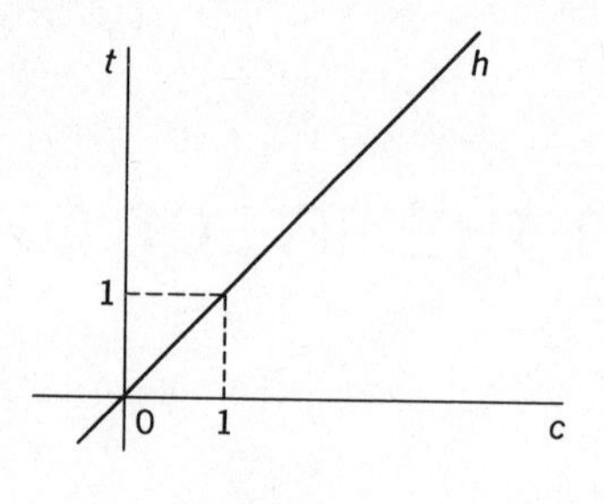

Figure 2.1.

One of the simplest functions is that defined by $h(c) = c$. This function, h, expresses what is referred to as, "no-treatment effect." That is, for a given subject, the same score would be observed under either the treatment conditions or the control conditions. The graph of the function is the main diagonal, as in Figure 2.1.

A model which expresses the statement that the effect of treatment is to increase the score of any subject is a function h whose graph is everywhere above the main diagonal. Three such functions are shown in Figure 2.2. The function h_1 in Figure 2.2*a* states that the increase due to treatment in score is the same amount, 5, in the units measured, no matter what a subject's control score would have been. The function h_2 in Figure 2.2*b* represents a situation where the increase due to treatment is greater for subjects with higher control scores. In Figure 2.2*c* the increase due to treatment is smaller for subjects with higher control scores.

One might expect a treatment effect like h_2 if the subjects with lower control scores could not respond to treatment while the subjects with higher control scores could respond. For example, a fertilizer might increase yields on fields that were already fairly fertile but have no effect on fields whose fertility is below a certain minimum.

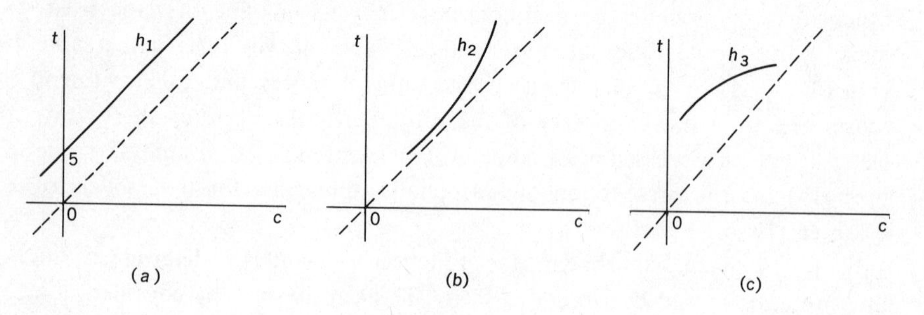

Figure 2.2.

A treatment effect like h_3 could be expected if the subjects with higher control scores had nearly attained a maximum, while subjects with lower scores could still respond. Again, this could be the case with the treatment consisting of a fertilizer.

Treatments whose effects can be described by h_1, that is, treatments whose effect is the same for any subject, are more difficult to imagine. Yet models like h_1 are the most often used. The reasons for this are simple. First, the no-treatment scores, c, can usually be considered to be restricted to a bounded range. An experimenter is usually only interested in a subset of all possible subjects, and the subjects in this subset will usually have their no-treatment scores in a limited range. Second, a treatment effect such as h_1 is often a good first approximation to a more complicated treatment effect over such a

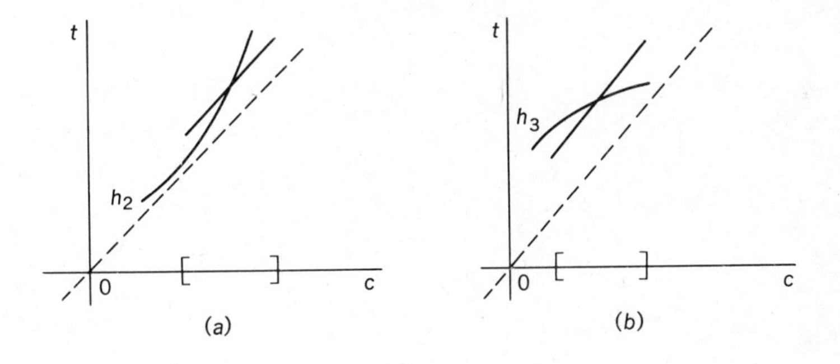

Figure 2.3.

limited range. In Figure 2.3 the functions h_2 and h_3 are each so approximated by a simple function like h_1 over the ranges shown.

Particularly in preliminary experiments, the practice is to assume that the treatment effect, if any, is simple, like h_1, and to attempt to establish its existence—postponing to future and larger experiments a detailed description of the treatment effect. This practice is usually successful, although occasionally it can be misleading. (An example will be given later in this chapter.)

Models like h_1 are simple to describe. Each can be identified with a number, θ, where θ is defined by $h_\theta(c) = c + \theta$. Then θ represents the change due to treatment in a subject's score. If θ is positive, the effect of the treatment is to increase scores; if θ is negative, the effect of treatment is to decrease scores. Models corresponding to $\theta = 10$, 0, and -5 are shown in Figure 2.4. h_{10} is the model $c \to c + 10$; that is, the effect of treatment is to increase any subject's score by 10 ($\theta = 10$). h_0 is the model $c \to c$; that is, the treatment leaves the subjects' scores unchanged ($\theta = 0$). h_{-5} is the model $c \to c - 5$; that is, the effect of treatment is to decrease each subject's score by 5 ($\theta = -5$). The models $c \to c + \theta$ are called *additive*; the constant θ is the parameter of the model. Note that, if an additive model obtains, it would be sufficient to observe, for one subject, both his no-treatment score c, and his treatment score t, to find θ. [Since $t = h(c) = c + \theta$, θ could be found from $t - c = \theta$.] However, it is inherently impossible to observe both t and c for the same subject for the experiments considered here.

Even if it were possible, it would not generally be expected that the treatment effect would be a constant, regardless of the subject's no-treatment

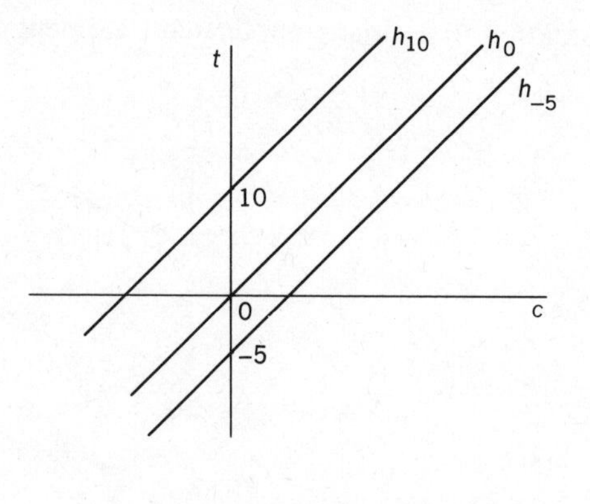

Figure 2.4.

score. As mentioned above, the assumption of an additive model is a first approximation and departures from it are to be expected. The following example describes a situation in which departures would be grossly misleading.

Suppose it were desired to investigate the effect of exercise on recovery of patients during a given postoperative period. It could be that patients who would have recovered by an amount z_0 or more during the period without exercise would recover still more with exercise, while patients who would have recovered less than z_0 without exercise would recover still less with exercise. A function h expressing such a treatment effect is shown in Figure 2.5. If the subjects' no-treatment scores were in a range symmetric about z_0, the assumption of an additive effect would result in approximating h with a section of the main diagonal, as shown. In other words, within the class of additive models the best conclusion would be that there is no treatment effect.

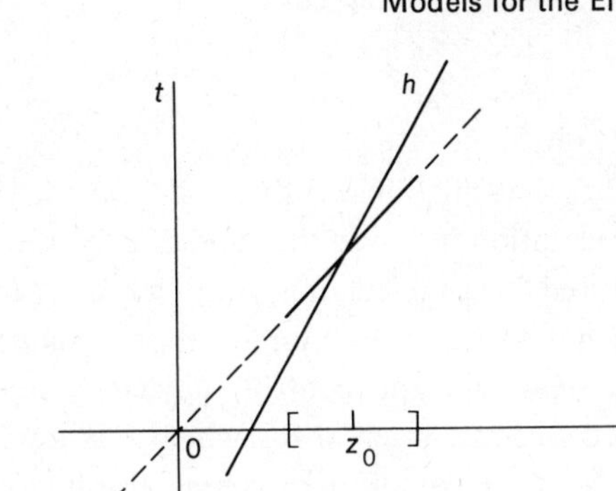

Figure 2.5.

If the subjects' no-treatment scores would have been in a range to one side of z_0, the assumption of an additive effect would still have resulted in an approximation too high for some subjects and two low for others, as in Figure 2.6.

However, the conclusion that the treatment effect is θ for all subjects in the range would be consistent with the fact that their treatment scores are higher than their no-treatment scores. The dangers of extending this conclusion to subjects not in the range of those studied is very apparent here.

In this introductory text the existence of an additive model will be assumed. In Chapters 16 and 17, additive models in which θ is possibly different for different groups of subjects will be considered.

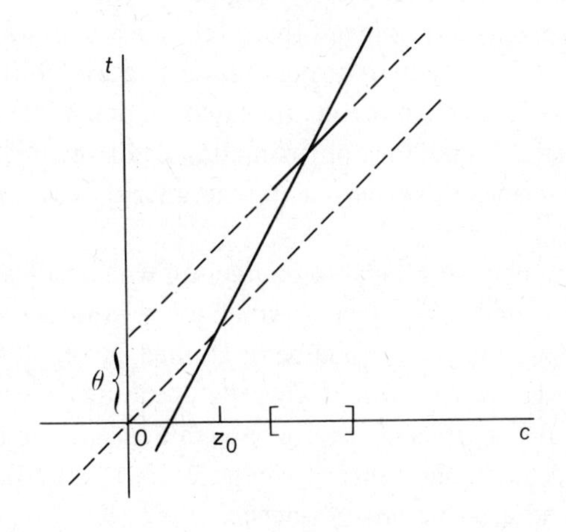

Figure 2.6.

CLASSES OF MODELS

If it can be assumed that a function h is the model for the treatment effect, the purpose of experimentation is to find this model. Even though only one of c and $h(c)$ can be measured for a subject, it is intuitively clear that, from a very large experiment, the model h can be closely approximated. It would be enough that both the treatment and control subjects were such that their scores c were restricted to some interval for which h is monotone, and the scores c for either group were equally well spread throughout this interval. From a relatively small experiment, such an attempt to find h will usually result in an approximation which is highly dependent upon the subjects used.

The usual practice is to suppose that the treatment effect belongs to a restricted class of models. A class that is often assumed is the class of additive models, that is, the class of functions h each of which can be written as $h(c) = c + \theta$ for some θ. A less restricted class that is often used is the class of linear models: those h which are of the form $h(c) = ac + \theta$ for some pair of numbers (a, θ). Still larger classes can, of course, be considered.

An analogy can be made with a search for a particular straw in a straw-stack. A search throughout the entire stack would be difficult, that is, require a very large experiment. If only a portion of the stack is searched, the search will be simpler, but clearly the particular straw might not be in the portion searched and not be found. This risk would be intolerable if it were not for the possibility that a straw exists in the portion searched which can at least approximate the particular one being sought.

The examples given above suggest that, if the class of models to be searched is taken as the additive class, it is possible to find an additive model which reasonably approximates a more complicated model. What must be remembered is that, even if found, the approximating additive model may not be the model which describes the experiment. The uncritical assumption that it is can be misleading.

The problem of choosing a class of models in which to search is not simple and will not be treated in this text. A satisfactory solution calls for considerable experience with the phenomena being studied as well as skill in formulating this knowledge into models. Generally speaking, a start is made with some class and, over a series of experiments, this class is enlarged or restricted as appropriate. The recognitions of where to start and what is appropriate are the artistic and creative acts of science.

Here it will be assumed that the class of models has been determined, so that the problem will be to use the observations to distinguish among the models in the class. The class of models assumed will be the additive class (until Chapter 10).

EXERCISES

2.1. Sketch graphs of the following models.

a. The effect of treatment is to increase each subject's score by 16.
b. The effect of treatment is to decrease each subject's score by 7.
c. The effect of treatment is to increase each subject's control score by an amount equal to one half of his control score.
d. The treatment score for any subject is 60.

2.2. Write an equation for the function h representing the treatment effect for each of the models in Exercise 2.1.

2.3. Which of the models in Exercise 2.1 are additive?

2.4. Suppose that in an experiment with five treatment and five control subjects the following scores were obtained:

Control	*Treatment*
117	147
126	153
108	131
132	139
119	142

If it is assumed that the treatment effect is additive, that is, $h(c) = c + \theta$, what would you guess θ to be?

2.5. Suppose $(t_1, t_2) = (19, 15)$ and $(c_1, c_2) = (6, 9)$ are observed. Then, if $\theta = 8$ is the additive treatment effect, $(t_1 - \theta, t_2 - \theta) = (19 - 8, 15 - 8) = (11, 7)$, and $(c_1, c_2) = (6, 9)$ are an observation of a no-treatment $(\theta = 0)$ experiment. With these subjects there were five other no-treatment experiments which could have been carried out—those corresponding to the five other assignments of these subjects, with these no-treatment scores, to the treatment and control groups. These are listed, with graphs, in the following figure. The observed experiment is marked and in the first row.

Of these, select the two which "look most like" a no-treatment experiment. Also, select the two which "look most like" there was some nonzero (either positive or negative) treatment effect.

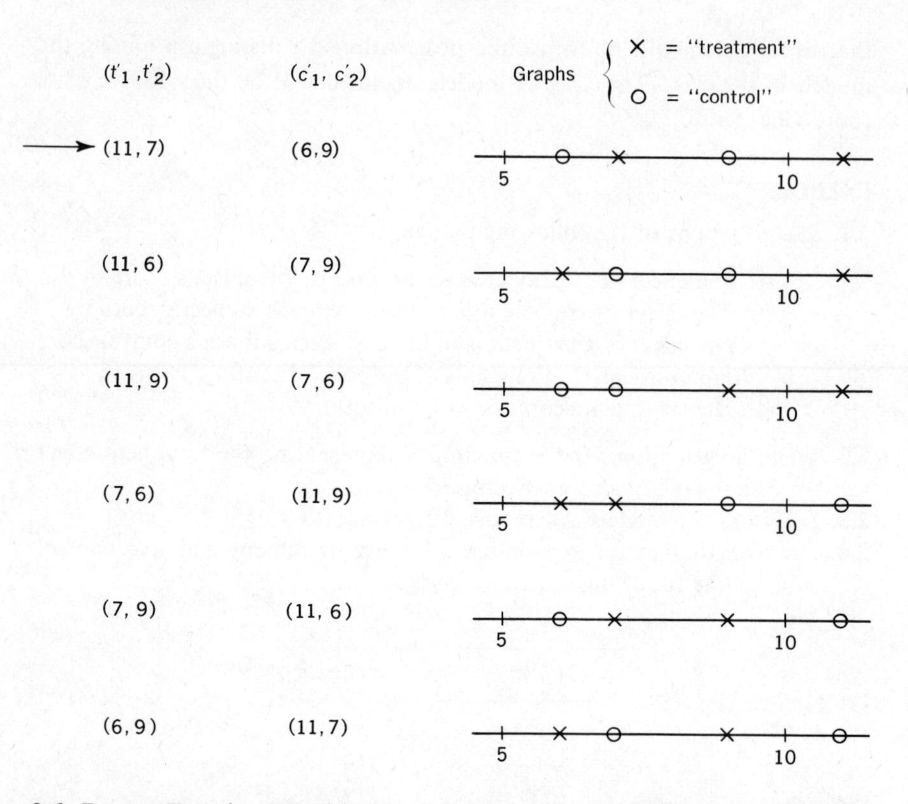

2.6. Repeat Exercise 2.5 with $\theta = 5$ for Example 1 of Chapter 1. [The list made, or its method, for Exercise 1.3 will be helpful in enumerating the possible assignments of $(t_1 - \theta, t_2 - \theta, t_3 - \theta, c_1, c_2) = (52 - 5, 35 - 5, 43 - 5, 40, 21) = (47, 30, 38, 40, 21)$ to a "treatment" group of three and a "control" group of two.]

CHAPTER 3

RELATING THE OBSERVATIONS TO THE CLASS OF MODELS

Given the observations $(t_1, t_2, \ldots, t_n)$ and $(c_1, c_2, \ldots, c_m)$ and a class of models, here the additive class indexed by θ, the problem is to relate the observations to the class of models. The relationship to be described here will, for each fixed θ, state how much agreement, in a certain sense, there is between the observations and the assumption "The treatment effect is θ." More precisely, it will state how much more the observations, $(t_1, \ldots, t_n)$ and $(c_1, \ldots, c_m)$, suggest that the treatment effect is θ than they suggest that the treatment effect is not θ. Such a description supposes that a number can be assigned to $(t_1, \ldots, t_n)$ and $(c_1, \ldots, c_m)$ which expresses how much more these observations suggest some other model in the additive class of models than they suggest the model θ. Low values of this number will thus express disagreement, high values agreement. More accurately, this number will express relative agreement within the class of models. That it has the value 1 for a particular model will indicate that this model is among those in the class which are most in agreement with the observations. If a wider class of models is taken, it will often be the case that a model for which the agreement is 1 relative to the original class will have an agreement considerably smaller than 1 relative to the wider class.

The number expressing agreement will be computed from the no-treatment scores $(t_1 - \theta, t_2 - \theta, \ldots, t_n - \theta)$ and $(c_1, \ldots, c_m)$, which are implied by the observations $(t_1, \ldots, t_n)$ and $(c_1, \ldots, c_m)$, and the assumption that the (additive) model is θ. [When the adjective "additive" occurs here it is in parentheses because the additive class has been assumed and the adjective (here) is redundant. Whenever the term "model" or "treatment effect" occurs, it is to be understood as modified by any assumptions concerning the class of models.] For these implied no-treatment observations, the question will be how much more strongly they suggest that the treatment effect is not zero than they suggest that it is zero.

Before describing how this number is to be computed, a semantic caution is in order. The words "agreement" and "suggest" have been used above. The arithmetic procedure to follow will yield a number expressing agreement after certain possible sets of observations have been placed in an order according as they suggest the presence of a treatment effect. Although such an ordering will be made in accord with intuitive and everyday meanings of "suggest" and "agreement," there will be more than one ordering with this accord. Each of them will, in fact, constitute a definition of the words "suggest" and "agreement" and, once a particular ordering is given, the ordering will be the only basis for the meaning of "suggest" and "agreement." Whether this particular meaning will be useful will depend, of course, upon the ordering as well as upon the use to be made of the number expressing agreement.

These reservations are not at all peculiar to the present context. They apply to any reduction, precision, or abstraction of intuitive concepts to a number. "Width" is a good example. In everyday words, many objects have width; a table, for instance, has width. If a method of expressing the width as a number is given, then for a certain table the method may be applied and result in the statement "The table is 3 feet wide." At this point the only meaning of the statement is the method used to arrive at "3 feet wide" for the table. How useful the statement is depends upon this method as well as on the use intended for the statement. If it is intended as an answer to the question "Will the table go through a 4-foot-wide door?" the statement "The table is 3 feet wide" will give a useful answer even if the method used to obtain the statement is quite crude or gross. If the statement is intended as an answer to the question "Will the table go through a 3-foot-wide door?" the statement will only be useful if the method has a certain precision. It might even be that no method of measurement (that is, reducing the property of width to abstract form) will suffice and the only answer available is to try to get the table through the door.

This analogy cannot be pursued for the present context until it is known how the number expressing agreement is to be computed and until the uses to which it can be put are known. However, the analogy exists and the caution is to rely, for the meaning of agreement, on the manner in which it is computed and to expect its usefulness to depend upon for what, and in what circumstances, it is used.

The computation of a number expressing the agreement between $(t_1, \ldots, t_n)$ and $(c_1, \ldots, c_m)$ and the assumption "The treatment effect is θ" can most easily be described in several steps.

1. The number θ is subtracted from the treatment scores to give the implied no-treatment scores $(t_1 - \theta, \ldots, t_n - \theta)$ and $(c_1, \ldots, c_m)$.

2. The possible ways that these numbers can be divided into a group of n "treatment scores" and m "control scores" are listed.

3. These possible sets of scores are ordered (with those that are more suggestive of no-treatment effect to the left and those more suggestive of a treatment effect to the right). This ordering is denoted by f.

4. In this ordering, the number of implied, possible no-treatment observations which are as far, or farther, to the right than that corresponding to the original observations is divided by the total number of implied, possible no-treatment observations. The resulting number, $A_f(\theta)$, is called the agreement between the observations and the assumption that θ is the treatment effect.

This number, $A_f(\theta)$, depends upon the observations $(t_1, \ldots, t_n)$ and $(c_1, \ldots, c_m)$, the value of θ, the ordering f, and the class of models.

Example 1. Suppose that $(t_1, t_2) = (25, 27)$ and $(c_1) = (31)$. If the model in question is $\theta = 5$, $(t_1 - \theta, t_2 - \theta) = (20, 22)$ and $(c_1) = (31)$. These are to be divided into a set of two "treatment observations" and one "control observation" in all possible ways. These, with their graphs, are shown in Figure 3.1, where the division corresponding to the observations is marked and in the first row.

The following statements are based on inspection of the three graphs:

① strongly suggests a negative (additive) treatment effect.
③ suggests a positive (additive) treatment effect.

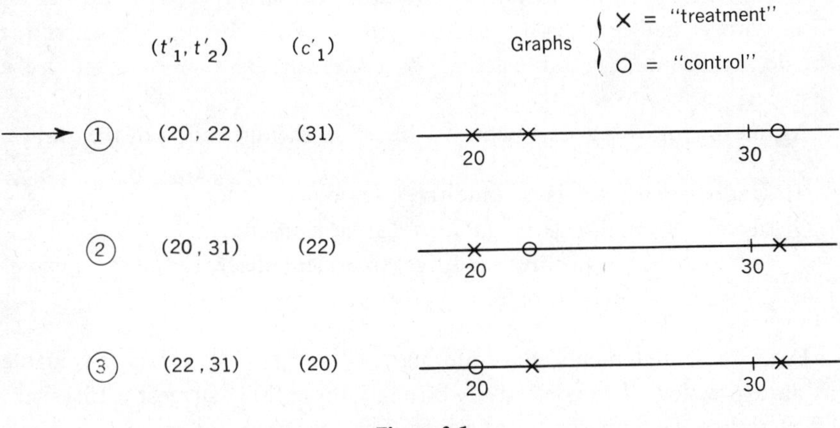

Figure 3.1.

② also suggests a positive (additive) treatment effect, but somewhat less so than ③.

From these statements, the ordering, f: ② < ③ < ①, according as the three suggest some (nonzero) treatment effect rather than zero treatment effect, seems reasonable. Since ① corresponds to the observations actually obtained and it alone is as far to the right in the ordering, by definition $A_f(5) = 1/3$.

Example 2. For the same observations, $(t_1, t_2) = (25, 27)$ and $(c_1) = (31)$, consider the assumption "$\theta = -5$." Then $(t_1 - \theta, t_2 - \theta) = (30, 32)$ and

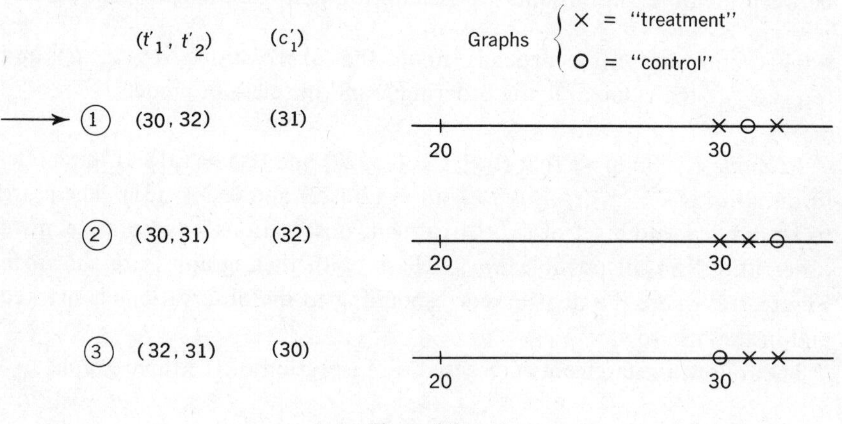

Figure 3.2.

$(c_1) = (31)$. The possible divisions of these scores into groups of two "treatment scores" and one "control score" are shown in Figure 3.2, where the division corresponding to the actual observations is again marked and in the first row.

Again, the following statements are based on the inspection of the graphs.

① suggests that there is no (additive) treatment effect.
② suggests a small negative (additive) treatment effect.
③ suggests a small positive (additive) treatment effect (to the same extent that ② suggests a negative one).

From these statements, the ordering f, ① < ② = ③, seems reasonable as an expression of how relatively strongly these three suggest a treatment effect rather than no treatment effect. For this ordering and for $\theta = -5$, by definition, $A_f(-5) = 3/3$, since all three implied (by $\theta = -5$) no-treatment experiments are more suggestive of some treatment effect than is that corresponding to the observations $(t_1, t_2) = (25, 27)$ and $(c_1) = (31)$.

These examples show the steps for computing $A_f(\theta)$ for a given θ and given observations $(t_1, \ldots, t_n)$ and $(c_1, \ldots, c_m)$.

1. Undo the model, that is, compute the no-treatment scores implied by the assumption "θ is the additive model." These scores are $(t_1 - \theta, \ldots, t_n - \theta)$ and $(c_1, \ldots, c_m)$.
2. Divide these no-treatment scores into two sets of n and m scores in each possible way.
3. Order, from left to right, these ways according as they more strongly suggest a treatment effect rather than a no-treatment effect. Call the ordering f.
4. In this ordering f, count how many are farther or as far to the right as is that corresponding to the observations.
5. $A_f(\theta)$ is the proportion of this number to the number of ways.

Of these five steps, the first and fifth present no problem. Given the second and the third, the fourth is routine. The second is only tedious when m and n are large. The third, even after the second has been done, presents special problems in that it requires that comparisons be made directly among the possible no-treatment experiments. In many cases, and particularly when m or n is large, these comparisons can be very subtle. It is useful to have some method of producing the ordering without making all the judgments involved in the direct comparisons. There are at least two advantages to the methods of producing the orderings now to be discussed. These are that they will be (a) quicker in that they avoid direct comparisons of the possible no-treatment experiments, and, more important, (b) more objective; that is, with their use, different persons (or the same person at different times) will arrive at the same ordering.

These methods of producing an ordering, f, of the possible no-treatment experiments, implied by the assumption of a particular model, can be described as follows. Let f denote a function, $f[(t_1', \ldots, t_n'), (c_1', \ldots, c_m')]$, of the possible observations. If f is chosen so that it has a higher value for those $(t_1', \ldots, t_n'), (c_1', \ldots, c_m')$ which more strongly suggest a treatment effect other than $\theta = 0$, then the ordering defined by $[(t_1', \ldots, t_n'), (c_1', \ldots, c_m')] \leq [(t_1'', \ldots, t_n''), (c_1'', \ldots, c_m'')]$ if $f[(t_1', \ldots, t_n'), (c_1', \ldots, c_m')] \leq f[(t_1'', \ldots, t_n''), (c_1'', \ldots, c_m'')]$ will be an ordering of the sort desired.

Example 3. Consider the function

$$f[(t_1', t_2'), (c_1')] = |\bar{t}' - \bar{c}'| = \left|\frac{t_1' + t_2'}{2} - c_1'\right|.$$

The three no-treatment experiments implied by $\theta = 5$ and the observations $(t_1, t_2) = (25, 27)$, $(c_1) = (31)$, appear, along with the values of this function, in Table 3.1.

Table 3.1

	(t_1', t_2')	(c_1')	$\bar{t}' - \bar{c}'$	$\lvert\bar{t}' - \bar{c}'\rvert = f$
①	(20, 22)	(31)	$\frac{20 + 22}{2} - 31 = -10$	10
②	(20, 31)	(22)	$\frac{20 + 31}{2} - 22 = 3.5$	3.5
③	(22, 31)	(20)	$\frac{22 + 31}{2} - 20 = 6.5$	6.5

Since the values of f are in the order $3.5 < 6.5 < 10$, the corresponding order of the possible no-treatment experiments is ② < ③ < ①. This is the same ordering as that which was constructed, by inspection, above (Figure 3.1) for $\theta = 5$ and $A_f(5) = 1/3$.

For Example 2 the calculations for the ordering given by $f = |\bar{t}' - \bar{c}'|$ are shown in Table 3.2.

Table 3.2

	(t_1', t_2')	(c_1')	$\bar{t}' - \bar{c}'$	$\lvert\bar{t}' - \bar{c}'\rvert = f$
①	(30, 32)	(31)	$\frac{30 + 32}{2} - 31 = 0$	0
②	(30, 31)	(32)	$\frac{30 + 31}{2} - 32 = -1.5$	1.5
③	(32, 31)	(30)	$\frac{32 + 31}{2} - 30 = 1.5$	1.5

The values of $f = |\bar{t}' - \bar{c}'|$ are in the order $0 < 1.5 = 1.5$, so that the corresponding order for the no-treatment observations is ① < ② = ③. Again this agrees with the one produced by inspection (Figure 3.2) for $\theta = -5$ and $A_f(-5) = 1$.

There are many functions f that can be used to order the possible no-treatment observations for any given θ. (In fact, there are, effectively, exactly as many functions as there are arbitrary orderings.) The problem of choosing among them is not elementary. Some indications of a possible basis for choice, after further assumptions about the source of the data, are given in Chapter 13. At present, three functions which are widely used and have generally good properties will be discussed. A choice among these on purely arithmetic grounds will be indicated.

The examples above with two treatment scores and one control score are too small to show much distinction among these three functions. The orderings they give, for Example 1 of Chapter 1, where $(t_1, t_2, t_3) = (52, 35, 43)$, $(c_1, c_2) = (40, 21)$, will be found below for $\theta = 5$. Although some computational short cuts are possible, their use and explanation will be postponed and the computations done here directly from the definition.

The first function, $f_1 = |\bar{t}' - \bar{c}'|$, has already been used to produce an ordering. Here, if $\theta = 5$, the implied no-treatment scores are $(t_1 - \theta, t_2 - \theta, t_3 - \theta) = (52 - 5, 35 - 5, 43 - 5) = (47, 30, 38)$ and $(c_1, c_2) = (40, 21)$. The 10 possible ways these scores can be rearranged into a "treatment" group of three scores and "control" group of two scores are listed in Table 3.3 together with the calculation of $f_1 = |\bar{t}' - \bar{c}'|$.

Table 3.3

	(t_1', t_2', t_3')	(c_1', c_2')	$\bar{t}' - \bar{c}'$	$\lvert\bar{t}' - \bar{c}'\rvert = f_1$
→①	(47, 30, 38)	(40, 21)	7.83	7.83
②	(47, 30, 40)	(38, 21)	9.50	9.50
③	(47, 40, 38)	(30, 21)	16.17	16.17
④	(40, 30, 38)	(47, 21)	2.00	2.00
⑤	(47, 30, 21)	(38, 40)	−6.33	6.33
⑥	(47, 21, 38)	(30, 40)	.33	.33
⑦	(21, 30, 38)	(47, 40)	−13.83	13.83
⑧	(47, 40, 21)	(30, 38)	2.00	2.00
⑨	(40, 30, 21)	(47, 38)	−12.17	12.17
⑩	(40, 21, 38)	(47, 30)	−5.50	5.50

The ordering f_1 given by $f_1 = |\bar{t}' - \bar{c}'|$ to these 10 possible divisions is

f_1: ⑥ < ④ = ⑧ < ⑩ < ⑤ < ① < ② < ⑨ < ⑦ < ③
↑ (under ①)

since ⑥ has the lowest value, .33, of f_1 and the values increase to 16.17 for ③. Because the arrangement corresponding to the original arrangement is ①, which is fifth from the right, $A_{f_1}(5) = 5/10$.

A second example of an ordering is given by replacing, in each division, the numbers $(t_1', \ldots, t_n')$, $(c_1', \ldots, c_m')$ by their ranks (of a set of numbers, the smallest has rank 1, the second smallest has rank 2, etc.) in $(t_1', \ldots, t_n', c_1', \ldots, c_m')$ and ordering the divisions by the absolute value of the difference of the mean ranks. Thus for $(t_1, t_2, t_3) = (52, 35, 43)$, $(c_1, c_2) = (40, 21)$, and $\theta = 5$, as above, the value of (t_1', t_2', t_3'), (c_1', c_2') corresponding to the observed division is $[(t_1 - \theta,\ t_2 - \theta,\ t_3 - \theta), (c_1,\ c_2)] = [(47,\ 30,\ 38), (40, 21)]$. The ranks $(R_{t_1'}, R_{t_2'}, R_{t_3'})$, $(R_{c_1'}, R_{c_2'})$ of these, relative to all five numbers, are (5, 2, 3), (4, 1), and the mean ranks are $\bar{R}_{t'} = 10/3 = 3.33$ and $\bar{R}_{c'} = 5/2 = 2.50$. The absolute value of the difference of these means is $f_2 = |\bar{R}_{t'} - \bar{R}_{c'}| = |3.33 - 2.50| = .83$. For the other nine divisions the corresponding calculations are shown in Table 3.4.

Table 3.4

	(t_1', t_2', t_3')	(c_1', c_2')	$(R_{t_1'}, R_{t_2'}, R_{t_3'})$	$(R_{c_1'}, R_{c_2'})$	$\bar{R}_{t'} - \bar{R}_{c'}$	$\|\bar{R}_{t'} - \bar{R}_{c'}\| = f_2$
→①	(47, 30, 38)	(40, 21)	(5, 2, 3)	(4, 1)	.83	.83
②	(47, 30, 40)	(38, 21)	(5, 2, 4)	(3, 1)	1.67	1.67
③	(47, 40, 38)	(30, 21)	(5, 4, 3)	(2, 1)	2.50	2.50
④	(40, 30, 38)	(47, 21)	(4, 2, 3)	(5, 1)	0	0
⑤	(47, 30, 21)	(38, 40)	(5, 2, 1)	(3, 4)	−.83	.83
⑥	(47, 21, 38)	(30, 40)	(5, 1, 3)	(2, 4)	0	0
⑦	(21, 30, 38)	(47, 40)	(1, 2, 3)	(5, 4)	−2.50	2.50
⑧	(47, 40, 21)	(30, 38)	(5, 4, 1)	(2, 3)	.83	.83
⑨	(40, 30, 21)	(47, 38)	(4, 2, 1)	(5, 3)	−1.67	1.67
⑩	(40, 21, 38)	(47, 30)	(4, 1, 3)	(5, 2)	−.83	.83

The ordering f_2, given by $f_2 = |\bar{R}_{t'} - \bar{R}_{c'}|$, is

f_2: ⑥ = ④ < ⑧ = ⑩ = ⑤ = ① < ② = ⑨ < ⑦ = ③.
↑

This ordering is very much like f_1, the only difference here being the greater number of equalities in f_2 than in f_1. It can be said that $f_1 = |\bar{t}' - \bar{c}'|$ has given a finer ordering to these divisions than has $f_2 = |\bar{R}_{t'} - \bar{R}_{c'}|$, or that f_1 is more sensitive to the exact values of the observations than is f_2. Because of the equalities in f_2, for these observations $A_{f_2}(5)$ is 8/10, since ⑧, ⑩, and ⑤ are now also as far to the right as ①.

A third example of an ordering can be given by comparing, for each division, the number above and below the median. (To find the median of a set of numbers, arrange them in order. The median will be the one in the middle if there is one. If not, the median is the average of the two in the middle.) If $n_{t'}^+$ and $n_{t'}^-$ denote the number of $(t_1', \ldots, t_n')$ above and below the median of $(t_1', \ldots, t_n', c_1', \ldots, c_m')$ and n_c^+ and n_c^- correspondingly for $(c_1', \ldots, c_m')$, a function f_3 will be defined by

$$f_3 = \left| \frac{n_{t'}^+ - n_{t'}^-}{n} - \frac{n_{c'}^+ - n_{c'}^-}{m} \right|.$$

Thus for $(t_1, t_2, t_3) = (52, 35, 43)$, $(c_1, c_2) = (40, 21)$, and $\theta = 5$, $[(t_1', t_2', t_3'), (c_1', c_2')] = [(47, 30, 38), (40, 21)]$. The median M of these last five numbers is 38. Since, of (t_1', t_2', t_3'), 47 is above 38, $n_{t'}^+ = 1$. Similarly, $n_{t'}^- = 1$, $n_{c'}^+ = 1$, and $n_{c'}^- = 1$. The value of f_3 is then

$$f_3 = \left| \frac{1 - 1}{3} - \frac{1 - 1}{2} \right| = 0.$$

For the other nine divisions, the computation of f_3 is given in Table 3.5.

Table 3.5

	(t_1', t_2', t_3')	(c_1', c_2')	M	$n_{t'}^+$	$n_{t'}^-$	$n_{c'}^+$	$n_{c'}^-$	$\left\lvert \frac{n_{t'}^+ - n_{t'}^-}{3} - \frac{n_{c'}^+ - n_{c'}^-}{2} \right\rvert$
→ ①	(47, 30, 38)	(40, 21)	38	1	1	1	1	0
②	(47, 30, 40)	(38, 21)	38	2	1	0	1	.83
③	(47, 40, 38)	(30, 21)	38	2	0	0	2	1.67
④	(40, 30, 38)	(47, 21)	38	1	1	1	1	0
⑤	(47, 30, 21)	(38, 40)	38	1	2	1	0	.83
⑥	(47, 21, 38)	(30, 40)	38	1	1	1	1	0
⑦	(21, 30, 38)	(47, 40)	38	0	2	2	0	1.67
⑧	(47, 40, 21)	(30, 38)	38	2	1	0	1	.83
⑨	(40, 30, 21)	(47, 38)	38	1	2	1	0	.83
⑩	(40, 21, 38)	(47, 30)	38	1	1	1	1	0

The ordering f_3, given by

$$f_3 = \left| \frac{n_{t'}^+ - n_{t'}^-}{n} - \frac{n_{c'}^+ - n_{c'}^-}{m} \right|,$$

is

$$f_3\colon ⑥ = ④ = ⑩ = ① < ⑧ = ⑤ = ② = ⑨ < ⑦ = ③.$$
$$\uparrow$$

In the sense that there are more equals, this ordering is less sensitive to these observations than is either f_1 or f_2. There are also some changes: ① precedes ⑧ rather than being equal to ⑧ as in f_2, or following ⑧ as in f_1. The value of $A_{f_3}(5)$ is 10/10.

In general, among f_1, f_2, and f_3, f_1 will give an ordering with the fewest equalities and f_3 with the most, and there will usually be some inversions between any two of them. It will by no means always be true that $A_{f_1}(\theta)$, $A_{f_2}(\theta)$, and $A_{f_3}(\theta)$ will be in increasing order, as here. However, the statement that f_1 is the most sensitive to the observations while f_3 is the least is intuitively clear from the realization that f_1 depends upon the numerical values of $(t_1', \ldots, t_n')$, $(c_1', \ldots, c_m')$ while f_2 depends on their order relations, that is, the comparisons within each possible pair (see Exercise 3.3). f_3 depends only upon the comparison of each with the median.

Whether sensitivity to the observations is desirable or not depends largely upon what weight, in an analysis, is to be given to the extreme observations, particularly when there is a preponderance of extremes on one side of one group. If it were known that the extremes were "typical" of observations of the sort being studied, they would be given due weight. If it were known that they were "atypical," they would simply be thrown out. However, in most cases it is not known whether extremes are typical or not. The use of ranks offers a way to give extremes (some of which are possibly atypical) weight somewhere between the possibly excessive extra weight of f_1 and the no extra weight of f_3.

There is another advantage that f_2 or f_3 offers over f_1. The set of values of f_1 depend upon the scores $(t_1', \ldots, t_n')$ and $(c_1', \ldots, c_m')$. If there are no ties among $(t_1', \ldots, t_n', c_1', \ldots, c_m')$, the possible values of f_2 or f_3 depend only upon the fact that there are n in one group and m in the other. Hence the last two columns in Tables 3.4 and 3.5 can be used for any observations (t_1', t_2', t_3'), (c_1', c_2') and it is not necessary to make the computations of these tables for another value of θ or for another experiment. For any observations (t_1, t_2, t_3), (c_1, c_2) and any value of θ, $A_{f_2}(\theta)$ can be found by referring the value of f_2 for $(t_1 - \theta, t_2 - \theta, t_3 - \theta), (c_1, c_2)$ to the last column of Table 3.4. $A_{f_3}(\theta)$ can be found, in the same manner, from the last column of Table 3.5.

Since both f_2 and f_3 have this last property and $f_2 = |\bar{R}_{t'} - \bar{R}_{c'}|$ is generally more sensitive to the observations than is f_3, there is a purely arithmetic basis for preferring f_2 among these three functions. Many theoretical investigations support this preference, although there are circumstances in which f_1 or f_3 (or some other f) would be preferable. The recognition of these circumstances requires both considerable experience with experiments similar to the one being studied as well as some theoretical background. In Chapters 11 and 13 brief suggestions of the nature of these circumstances are given.

EXERCISES

3.1. For the Example 1 in this chapter, that is, $(t_1, t_2) = (25, 27), (c_1) = (31)$, and $\theta = 5$ (see Figure 3.1), find the orderings for $f_2 = |\bar{R}_{t'} - \bar{R}_{c'}|$ and for

$$f_3 = \left|\frac{n_{t'}^+ - n_{t'}^-}{n} - \frac{n_{c'}^+ - n_{c'}^-}{m}\right|.$$

3.2. a. For Example 1 of Chapter 1, that is, $(t_1, t_2, t_3) = (52, 35, 43), (c_1, c_2) = (40, 21)$, find, for $\theta = 30$, each of the three orderings given by $f_1 = |\bar{t}' - \bar{c}'|$, $f_2 = |\bar{R}_{t'} - \bar{R}_{c'}|$, and

$$f_3 = \left|\frac{n_{t'}^+ - n_{t'}^-}{n} - \frac{n_{c'}^+ - n_{c'}^-}{m}\right|.$$

b. Compute $A_{f_1}(30)$, $A_{f_2}(30)$, and $A_{f_3}(30)$.

3.3. For the ten divisions of Table 3.4, show that the function f_4 described below is equivalent to $f_2 = |\bar{R}_{t'} - \bar{R}_{c'}|$. To define f_4, let

$$U_1 = \text{number of pairs, } (t_i', c_j') \text{ with } t_i' > c_j',$$
$$U_2 = \text{number of pairs, } (t_i', c_j') \text{ with } t_i' < c_j'.$$

Then $f_4 = |U_1 - U_2|$. For example, if $(t_1', t_2') = (3, 7)$, $(c_1', c_2') = (4, 9)$, there are four $(= m \cdot n)$ possible pairs (t_i', c_j'): (3, 4), (3, 9), (7, 4), and (7, 9). Of these, only the third has $t' > c'$, so $U_1 = 1$. The other three have $t' < c'$, so that $U_2 = 3$. Therefore, $f_4 = |U_1 - U_2| = |1 - 3| = 2$.

CHAPTER 4

A_f WITH $f = |\bar{t} - \bar{c}|$

A SIMPLE EXAMPLE

The number $A_f(\theta)$, described in Chapter 3, was called there the agreement, relative to the class of additive models, between the model corresponding to θ and the observations $(t_1, \ldots, t_n)$, $(c_1, \ldots, c_m)$. As already pointed out, the meaning of *agreement* is entirely dependent upon the function, or corresponding ordering, f, defined on the set of possible no-treatment observations implied by the assumption that θ is the treatment effect. If this ordering expresses how much more these implied no-treatment observations suggest some nonzero treatment effect than they suggest zero treatment effect, the meaning of "agreement" will have accord with its everyday meaning.

It will be helpful toward establishing the meaning of agreement to see the uses which can be made of the numbers $A_f(\theta)$. Some discussion of the descriptive use of these numbers, as well as of details of their computation, will be given in these three chapters. For the present, f will be taken as $|\bar{t} - \bar{c}|$. In the following tables $A_f(\theta)$ will be computed for several values of θ for the example $(t_1) = (20)$, $(c_1, c_2) = (0, 10)$.

If it is assumed that the treatment effect is $\theta = 15$, then, without treatment $(t_1 - \theta) = (20 - 15) = (5)$ would have been observed, in a no-treatment experiment, for the subject assigned to the treatment group. $(c_1, c_2) = (0, 10)$ would have been observed for the subjects assigned to the control group. The other two assignments of subjects, with these implied no-treatment scores, to two such groups are $(t_1') = (0)$, $(c_1', c_2') = (5, 10)$, and $(t_1') = (10)$, $(c_1', c_2') = (0, 5)$. These, together with the computation of f, are shown in Table 4.1.

$A_f(15)$ is 1, since the ordering given by f is $[(5), (0, 10)] < [(0), (5, 10)] = [(10), (0, 5)]$, and, since $[(5), (0, 10)]$ corresponds to what was observed, all three implied possible no-treatment outcomes are at least as far to the right in the ordering.

For $\theta = 14$, the corresponding calculations are given in Table 4.2.

Table 4.1

For $\theta = 15$, $(t_1 - \theta) = (5)$, $(c_1, c_2) = (0, 10)$

(t_1') (c_1', c_2')	$\bar{t}' - \bar{c}'$	$f = \lvert\bar{t}' - \bar{c}'\rvert$
→ (5) (0, 10)	5 − 5 = 0	0
(0) (5, 10)	0 − 7.5 = −7.5	7.5
(10) (0, 5)	10 − 2.5 = 7.5	7.5
	$A_f(15) = 3/3 = 1$	

$A_f(14)$ is the same as $A_f(15)$ and each is 1. These observations make no distinction between the assumptions "$\theta = 15$" and "$\theta = 14$." They are each, as measured by $|\bar{t} - \bar{c}|$, in agreement with the data. It is clear here that the fact that $A_f(\theta) = 1$ does not "prove" that θ is the treatment effect. If it did, then it would have been "proved" by these observations that $\theta = 15$ and that $\theta = 14$.

Table 4.2

For $\theta = 14$, $(t_1 - \theta) = (6)$, $(c_1, c_2) = (0, 10)$

(t_1') (c_1', c_2')	$\bar{t}' - \bar{c}'$	$f = \lvert\bar{t}' - \bar{c}'\rvert$
→ (6) (0, 10)	6 − 5 = 1	1
(0) (6, 10)	0 − 8 = −8	8
(10) (0, 6)	10 − 3 = 7	7
	$A_f(14) = 3/3 = 1$	

To see the descriptive use of A_f, it will be helpful to compute it for some more values of θ. The following tables show the computation for $\theta = -5$, 5, 25, and 35. The first row in the column headed $[(t_1'), (c_1', c_2')]$ will be the observed division, that is, will be $[(t_1 - \theta), (c_1, c_2)]$.

For $\theta = -5$

(t_1')	(c_1', c_2')	$\bar{t}' - \bar{c}'$	$f = \lvert\bar{t}' - \bar{c}'\rvert$
→(25)	(0, 10)	25 − 5 = 20	20
(0)	(25, 10)	0 − 17.5 = −17.5	17.5
(10)	(0, 25)	10 − 12.5 = −2.5	2.5
		$A_f(-5) = 1/3$	

For $\theta = 5$

(t_1')	(c_1', c_2')	$\bar{t}' - \bar{c}'$	$f = \lvert\bar{t}' - \bar{c}'\rvert$
→(15)	(0, 10)	$15 - 5 = 10$	10
(0)	(15, 10)	$0 - 12.5 = -12.5$	12.5
(10)	(0, 15)	$10 - 7.5 = 2.5$	2.5

$A_f(5) = 2/3$

For $\theta = 25$

(t_1')	(c_1', c_2')	$\bar{t}' - \bar{c}'$	$\lvert\bar{t}' - \bar{c}'\rvert$
→(−5)	(0, 10)	$-5 - 5 = -10$	10
(0)	(10, −5)	$0 - 2.5 = -2.5$	2.5
(10)	(0, −5)	$10 + 2.5 = 12.5$	12.5

$A_f(25) = 2/3$

For $\theta = 35$

(t_1')	(c_1', c_2')	$\bar{t}' - \bar{c}'$	$\lvert\bar{t}' - \bar{c}'\rvert$
→(−15)	(0, 10)	$-15 - 5 = -20$	20
(0)	(−15, 10)	$0 + 2.5 = 2.5$	2.5
(10)	(0, −15)	$10 + 7.5 = 17.5$	17.5

$A_f(35) = 1/3$

θ	A_f
−5	$\frac{1}{3}$
5	$\frac{2}{3}$
15	1
25	$\frac{2}{3}$
35	$\frac{1}{3}$

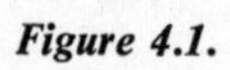

Figure 4.1.

In summary, these values of A_f are given, together with their graph, in Figure 4.1.

A finer graph can be constructed by computing for intervening values of θ. In this example a little trial and error gives the complete graph as shown in Figure 4.2.

The symmetry, even spacing, and location of the jumps at multiples of 10 are due to the small, and very artificial, example used here. As will be seen, graphs of A_f will, in general, have many more jump points, which will be spaced quite unevenly. For descriptive purposes the exact location of the jump points is not of great importance, and a reasonable picture of the

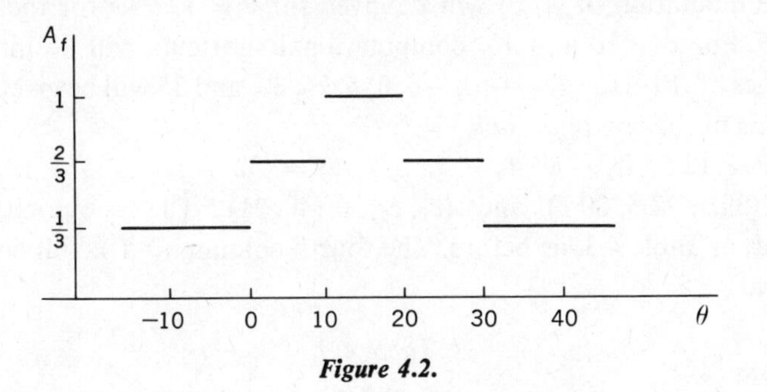

Figure 4.2.

graph can be obtained by computing A_f at evenly spaced values of θ. Some indications of where to start and how finely to space will be given later.

As a description, the graph shows that the treatment effects with θ between 10 and 20 are the additive treatment models most in agreement with these observations. Those for which θ is above 30, or for those for which θ is below 0, are the models least in agreement with these observations.

ANOTHER EXAMPLE

For further illustration, a curve A_f will be computed for Example 1 in Chapter 1. This will be done for $f = |\bar{t}' - \bar{c}'|$, as above. θ will be the parameter of additive models, $h(c) = c + \theta$.

The observations of Example 1 of Chapter 1 are $(t_1, t_2, t_3) = (52, 35, 43)$ and $(c_1, c_2) = (40, 21)$. Here

$$\bar{t} = \frac{52 + 35 + 43}{3} = \frac{130}{3} = 43.3 \quad \text{and} \quad \bar{c} = \frac{40 + 21}{2} = \frac{61}{2} = 30.5,$$

so that $\bar{t} - \bar{c} = 43.3 - 30.5 = 12.8$. This suggests choosing a starting point near $\theta = 12.8$, say, $\theta = 12.5$, and working in both directions from the starting point in some convenient steps to obtain an idea of the shape of the curve, A_f. The choice of the steps is not critical; should they be too large, the values of A_f can later be found at some intervening points. The steps here will be $\theta = 12.5$, then $\theta = 10, 15, 5, 20$, etc., to find $A_f(\theta)$ for $\theta = -10, -5, 0, 5, 10, 12.5, 15, 20, 25, 30$, and 35. The choice of the distance, 5, for the steps is arbitrary; in general, steps of 1/6 to 1/4 of the ranges in the two sets $(t_1, \ldots, t_n)$, $(c_1, \ldots, c_m)$ will give a reasonable picture of A_f. Here the range of (t_1, t_2, t_3) is $52 - 35 = 17$, of (c_1, c_2) is $40 - 21 = 19$, and 1/4 of 20 is 5. The first two steps were taken to be small to have a little more detail near $\theta = \bar{t} - \bar{c} = 12.8$.

The computation of $A_f(\theta)$ will be given for $\theta = 12.5$ as for the previous example. For $\theta = 10$ and 15, computational shortcuts will be introduced. The values of $A_f(\theta)$ for $\theta = -10, -5, 0, 5, 25, 30$, and 35 will be given without the details of the computations.

For $\theta = 12.5$, $(t_1 - \theta,\ t_2 - \theta,\ t_3 - \theta) = (52 - 12.5,\ 35 - 12.5,\ 43 - 12.5) = (39.5, 22.5, 30.5)$ and $(c_1, c_2) = (40, 21)$. The computations are arranged, in Table 4.3, as before. The fourth column, $(\sum t')$, will be referred to below.

Table 4.3

$\theta = 12.5$

(t_1', t_2', t_3')	(c_1', c_2')	$\bar{t}' - \bar{c}'$	$\lvert\bar{t}' - \bar{c}'\rvert$	$(\sum t')$
→(39.5, 22.5, 30.5)	(40, 21)	30.83 − 30.50 = 0.33	.33	92.5
(39.5, 22.5, 40)	(30.5, 21)	34.00 − 25.75 = 8.25	8.25	102.0
(39.5, 22.5, 21)	(40, 30.5)	27.67 − 35.25 = −7.58	7.58	83.0
(39.5, 40, 30.5)	(22.5, 21)	36.67 − 21.75 = 14.92	14.92	110.0
(39.5, 21, 30.5)	(40, 22.5)	30.33 − 31.25 = −.92	.92	91.0
(40, 22.5, 30.5)	(39.5, 21)	31.00 − 30.25 = .75	.75	93.0
(21, 22.5, 30.5)	(40, 39.5)	24.67 − 39.75 = −15.08	15.08	74.0
(39.5, 40, 21)	(22.5, 30.5)	33.50 − 26.50 = 7.00	7.00	100.5
(40, 22.5, 21)	(39.5, 30.5)	27.83 − 35.00 = −7.17	7.17	83.5
(40, 21, 30.5)	(39.5, 22.5)	30.50 − 31.00 = −.50	.50	91.5

Since each of the divisions of the implied no-treatment scores leads to a value of $|\bar{t}' - \bar{c}'|$ as high or higher than that corresponding to the division of the experiment actually conducted, it follows that $A_f(\theta) = 1.00$ for $\theta = 12.5$ and $f = |\bar{t}' - \bar{c}'|$. That is to say, the assumption that the treatment effect is 12.5 is, within the class of additive models, in agreement with the observations.

Before finding A_f for other values of θ, it will be helpful to shorten the computations. It is sufficient to consider, instead of $\bar{t}' - \bar{c}'$, only the sum of the t' (written $\sum t'$). Note that $\bar{t}' = (1/n) \sum t'$ and $\bar{c}' = (1/m) \sum c'$, so that

$$\begin{aligned}
\bar{t}' - \bar{c}' &= \frac{1}{n} \sum t' - \frac{1}{m} \sum c' \\
&= \frac{1}{n} \sum t' - \frac{1}{m} (\sum c' + \sum t' - \sum t') \\
&= \left(\frac{1}{n} + \frac{1}{m}\right) \sum t' - \frac{1}{m} (\sum c' + \sum t'), \\
\frac{nm}{n+m} (\bar{t}' - \bar{c}') &= \sum t' - \frac{nm}{n+m} \frac{1}{m} (\sum c' + \sum t') \\
&= \sum t' - \frac{n}{n+m} (\sum c' + \sum t').
\end{aligned}$$

This means that, instead of asking how many divisions give a value of $\bar{t}' - \bar{c}'$ farther from zero than the observed, it is the same to ask how many divisions give a value of $\sum t'$ more distant from $[n/(n + m)](\sum c' + \sum t')$ than the observed. Since $[n/(n + m)](\sum c' + \sum t')$ is fixed, for a given θ, the computation will be considerably shortened. For example, for $\theta = 12.5$, $(\sum c' + \sum t') = 40 + 21 + 39.5 + 22.5 + 30.5 = 153.5$, and $[n/(n + m)] \times (\sum c' + \sum t') = [3/(3 + 2)](153.5) = 92.1$. Starting with the last column of Table 4.3 gives

$\sum t'$	$\sum t' - \frac{n}{n+m} (\sum c' + \sum t')$
→92.5	.4
102.0	9.9
83.0	−9.1
110.0	17.9
91.0	−1.1
93.0	.9
74.0	−18.1
100.5	8.4
83.5	−8.6
91.5	−.6

and, as before, all the divisions give a higher absolute value than that corresponding to the observed.

Using this same shortcut, the values of $A_f(\theta)$ are found for $\theta = 10$ in Table 4.4. For $\theta = 10$, $(t_1 - \theta,\ t_2 - \theta,\ t_3 - \theta) = (52 - 10,\ 35 - 10,\ 43 - 10) = (42, 25, 33)$ and $(c_1, c_2) = (40, 21)$. Hence $\sum t' + \sum c' = (42 + 25 + 33) + (40 + 21) = 161$ and $[n/(n + m)](\sum t' + \sum c') = \frac{3}{5}(161) = 96.6$.

Table 4.4

(t_1', t_2', t_3')	(c_1, c_2)	$\sum t'$	$\sum t' - 96.6$
→(42, 25, 33)	(40, 21)	100	3.4
(42, 25, 40)	(33, 21)	107	10.4
(42, 25, 21)	(40, 33)	88	−8.6
(42, 40, 33)	(25, 21)	115	18.4
(42, 21, 33)	(40, 25)	96	−.6
(40, 25, 33)	(42, 21)	98	1.4
(21, 25, 33)	(40, 42)	79	−17.6
(42, 40, 21)	(25, 33)	103	6.4
(40, 25, 21)	(42, 33)	86	−10.6
(40, 21, 33)	(42, 25)	94	−2.6

All the divisions in the table except the fifth, sixth, and tenth lead to a higher absolute value for $\sum t' - [n/(n + m)](\sum t' + \sum c')$ than that (3.4) for the observed. The same is true for $\bar{t}' - \bar{c}'$ and so, for $\theta = 10$, $A_f(\theta)$ is 7/10.

For $\theta = 15$ a slightly shorter method of calculation will be used. The comparison of $\sum c'$ with $[m/(n + m)](\sum c' + \sum t')$ is equivalent to the comparison

Table 4.5

(t_1', t_2', t_3')	(c_1', c_2')	$\sum c'$	$\sum c' - 58.4$
→(37, 20, 28)	(40, 21)	61	2.6
	(28, 21)	49	−9.4
	(20, 21)	41	−17.4
	(37, 21)	58	−.4
	(28, 40)	68	9.6
	(20, 40)	60	1.6
	(37, 40)	77	18.6
	(20, 28)	48	−10.4
	(37, 28)	65	6.6
	(37, 20)	57	−1.4

of $\sum t'$ with $[n/(n + m)](\sum c' + \sum t')$. Further, it is necessary to only write (c_1', c_2') of (t_1', t_2', t_3'), (c_1', c_2'). Using these facts, the computation of A_f for $\theta = 15$ is given in Table 4.5. If $\theta = 15$, $(t_1', t_2', t_3') = (52 - 15, 35 - 15, 43 - 15) = (37, 20, 28)$ and $(c_1', c_2') = (40, 21)$ for the experiment conducted and $[m/(m + n)](\sum c' + \sum t') = \frac{2}{5}(146) = 58.4$.

Seven of the possible values of $|\sum c' - 58.4|$ in the table are as large or larger than the value corresponding to the observed experiment, so that $A_f(15) = 7/10$. So far, $A_f(\theta)$, for $f = |\bar{t}' - \bar{c}'|$, has been found for $\theta = 12.5$, 10, and 15. The results are given in Table 4.6.

Table 4.6

θ	$A_f(\theta)$
10	.7
12.5	1.0
15	.7

Using the method of computation shown in Table 4.5, it is a simple matter to continue to find $A_f(\theta)$ for other values of θ. This has been done to give Table 4.7. A graph of these values is given in Figure 4.3.

Table 4.7

θ	$A_f(\theta)$
−10	.1
−5	.3
0	.4
5	.5
10	.7
12.5	1.0
15	.7
20	.5
25	.4
30	.3
35	.1

The interpretation of Figure 4.3 is that values of θ near 12.5 are most in agreement with the observations and that values of θ beyond -10, or

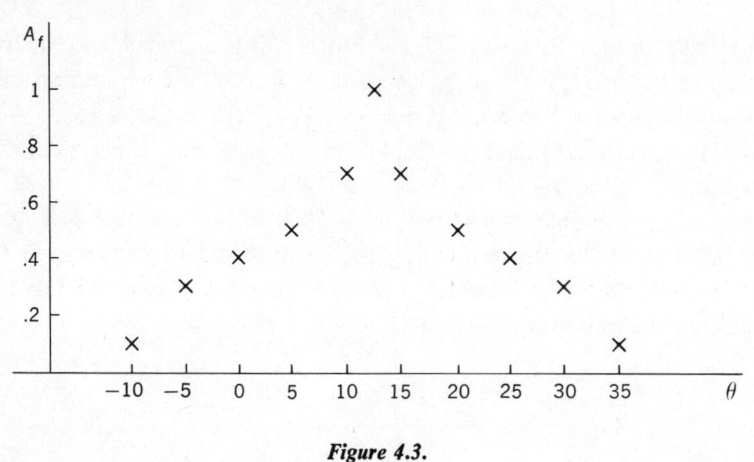

Figure 4.3.

beyond 35, are least in agreement with the observations (see Exercise 4.6). More exactly, the implied no-treatment observations, corresponding to assumptions that θ is near 12.5, suggest that there was no treatment effect more than do any of the other implied no-treatment outcomes which could have been observed with these subjects. The implied no-treatment observations corresponding to assumptions that θ is beyond $\theta = -10$, or $\theta = 35$, suggest that there was some nonzero treatment effect more than do any of the other implied no-treatment outcomes possible with these subjects. This can be stated: "In view of the observations $(t_1, \ldots, t_n)$, $(c_1, \ldots, c_m)$, assumptions that θ is the treatment effect are most reasonable for values of θ near 12.5 and least reasonable for values of θ beyond -10 or 35." However, this brief statement, when fully qualified, becomes the following two paragraphs.

For each θ it is asked whether it is reasonable to assume that θ is the treatment effect. If so, $(t_1 - \theta, \ldots, t_n - \theta)$, $(c_1, \ldots, c_m)$ should look like a reasonable no-treatment outcome. To determine whether it does, some background of experience with the sort of outcomes that are possible with subjects like these is needed. This background is needed for no-treatment experiments and for experiments in which there was some treatment effect. Without introducing any more structure than the fact that there was a group of n treatment subjects and a group of m control subjects and the assumption that θ was the (additive) treatment effect, the only possible background is the set of the no-treatment outcomes which could have been observed for each way these subjects could have been divided into two such groups. This provides a background for no-treatment outcomes. The background for treatment outcomes is provided by the knowledge that the presence of a nonzero (additive) treatment effect will tend to shift the scores for the treatment group relative to the control group.

Consequently, if $(t_1 - \theta, \ldots, t_n - \theta), (c_1, \ldots, c_m)$ more strongly suggests such a shift than do most of the possible rearrangements of $(t_1 - \theta, \ldots, t_n - \theta, c_1, \ldots, c_m)$, it is not reasonable to suppose that $(t_1 - \theta, \ldots, t_n - \theta), (c_1, \ldots, c_m)$ looks like a no-treatment outcome. In other words, "undoing" the effect, θ, did not produce a reasonable-looking no-treatment outcome and θ is not a reasonable assumption.

$A_f(\theta)$ is a refinement of the last two sentences in that it expresses (relatively) how reasonable θ is as an assumption in terms of how many of the possible outomes more strongly suggest, as measured by f, some shift than does $(t_1 - \theta, \ldots, t_n - \theta), (c_1, \ldots, c_m)$.

With this refinement, and its qualifications, the statement in quotations above could include the sentence "Assumptions that θ is the treatment effect become somewhat steadily less reasonable as θ is changed from 12.5 to -10 or 35."

EXERCISES

4.1. Without referring to the text

a. Write a description of how to compute $A_f(\theta)$ for observations $(t_1), (c_1, c_2)$.

b. Apply your description to compute $A_f(7)$ for $(t_1) = (20), (c_1, c_2) = (0, 10)$, and $f = |\bar{t} - \bar{c}|$.

If you have difficulty, refer to Tables 4.1 and 4.2. If you still have difficulty, refer to pages 17–19.

4.2. Find, by trial and error, the end points of the interval where $A_f(\theta) = 1$ for $(t_1) = (22), (c_1, c_2) = (31, 26)$, and $f = |\bar{t} - \bar{c}|$.

4.3. Compute, with $f = |\bar{t}' - \bar{c}'|$, the values of $A_f(\theta)$ for Example 2 of Chapter 1 for $\theta = 500$.

4.4. As in Exercise 4.3, compute $A_f(\theta)$ for some other multiple of 100 in the range $\theta = -200$ to 1300. (If each of the multiples of 100 is assigned to at least one student, a fairly complete graph can be constructed in class.)

4.5. Compute, with $f = |\bar{t}' - \bar{c}'|$, the values of $A_f(\theta)$ for Example 3 of Chapter 1 for $\theta = 1, -5$, and 16.

4.6. Why, for the example of Figure 4.3, will $A_f(\theta)$ be equal to .1 for all $\theta < -10$? Where, between $\theta = -5$ and -10, does A_f jump from .1 to its next higher value?

CHAPTER 5

A_f BASED ON RANKS

As will be seen, it is possible to use other functions, f, to construct a descriptive curve $A_f(\theta)$. The function used here will be $|\bar{R}_{t'} - \bar{R}_{c'}|$, where $\bar{R}$ denotes the average rank. There are several advantages to this choice, one of them being a saving in computation. The computations given in the last chapter for $A_f(\theta)$ with $f = |\bar{t}' - \bar{c}'|$ would be impractical if there were many more subjects in the treatment and control groups. For example, with five treatment and five control subjects, there are 252 divisions of the 10 scores into two sets of five. This is still possible, although tedious, and a program for a high-speed computer would be helpful. Beyond the capacity of computers, an approximation is available which will be discussed in Chapter 14. At present, for Example 1 of Chapter 1 the details of the computation of a curve $A_f(\theta)$ based on the ranks follow.

Starting again with $(t_1, t_2, t_3) = (35, 43, 52)$, $(c_1, c_2) = (21, 40)$, and $\theta = 12.5$, the implied no-treatment scores are $(t_1 - \theta, t_2 - \theta, t_3 - \theta) = (22.5, 30.5, 39.5)$ and $(c_1, c_2) = (21, 40)$. Replacing these by their ranks gives $(R_{t_1 - \theta}, R_{t_2 - \theta}, R_{t_3 - \theta}) = (2, 3, 4)$, and $(R_{c_1}, R_{c_2}) = (1, 5)$. The mean ranks are

$$\bar{R}_{t-\theta} = \frac{2 + 3 + 4}{3} = 3 \quad \text{and} \quad \bar{R}_c = \frac{1 + 5}{2} = 3,$$

so that f is 0 for $\theta = 12.5$. To find A_f, the values of $f = |\bar{R}_{t'} - \bar{R}_{c'}|$ are listed in Table 5.1 for each of the divisions of $(t_1 - \theta, t_2 - \theta, t_3 - \theta, c_1, c_2)$ into sets of three and two numbers. The last column, $\sum R_{c'}$, will be referred to below.

Since all the divisions into two sets lead to a value of $f = |\bar{R}_{t'} - \bar{R}_{c'}|$ as high or higher than the value 0 corresponding to the original division, $A_f(\theta) = 10/10 = 1$ for $\theta = 12.5$. The interpretation is, as before, that the assumption "$\theta = 12.5$" and the observations are as much in agreement as possible within the class of additive models.

Table 5.1

(t_1', t_2', t_3')	(c_1, c_2)	*Ranks*	$\lvert\bar{R}_{t'} - \bar{R}_{c'}\rvert$	$\sum R_{c'}$
(22.5, 30.5, 39.5)	(21, 40)	(2, 3, 4) (1, 5)	$\lvert 9/3 - 6/2\rvert = 0$	6
(22.5, 30.5, 21)	(39.5, 40)	(2, 3, 1) (4, 5)	$\lvert 6/3 - 9/2\rvert = 15/6$	9
(22.5, 30.5, 40)	(21, 39.5)	(2, 3, 5) (1, 4)	$\lvert 10/3 - 5/2\rvert = 5/6$	5
(22.5, 21, 39.5)	(30.5, 40)	(2, 1, 4) (3, 5)	$\lvert 7/3 - 8/2\rvert = 10/6$	8
(22.5, 40, 39.5)	(21, 30.5)	(2, 5, 4) (1, 3)	$\lvert 11/3 - 4/2\rvert = 10/6$	4
(21, 30.5, 39.5)	(22.5, 40)	(1, 3, 4) (2, 5)	$\lvert 8/3 - 7/2\rvert = 5/6$	7
(40, 30.5, 39.5)	(21, 22.5)	(5, 3, 4) (1, 2)	$\lvert 12/3 - 3/2\rvert = 15/6$	3
(22.5, 21, 40)	(30.5, 39.5)	(2, 1, 5) (3, 4)	$\lvert 8/3 - 7/2\rvert = 5/6$	7
(21, 30.5, 40)	(22.5, 39.5)	(1, 3, 5) (2, 4)	$\lvert 9/3 - 6/2\rvert = 0$	6
(21, 40, 39.5)	(22.5, 30.5)	(1, 5, 4) (2, 3)	$\lvert 10/3 - 5/2\rvert = 5/6$	5

The saving in calculation, given by the use of ranks, results from the fact that for any θ the set of possible values of $|\bar{R}_{t'} - \bar{R}_{c'}|$ will be the same as in the fourth column of Table 5.1. Thus there is no need to write down all the divisions of $(t_1', t_2', t_3', c_1', c_2')$ into two groups each time a different value of θ is considered. The set of values in column four will always be the same, so that once it is recorded it can be used for all θ (and for all experiments with the subjects divided into sets of two subjects and of three subjects).

However, it is still simpler to record the values of $\sum R_{c'}$ since, as for $\bar{t}' - \bar{c}'$, it does not matter whether it is asked "How far is $|\bar{R}_{t'} - \bar{R}_{c'}|$ from zero?" or whether it is asked "How far is $\sum R_{c'}$ from $[m/(m + n)]\,[\sum R_{c'} + \sum R_{t'}]$?" For the example here, $\sum R_{c'}$ is 6, so that its distance from $\frac{2}{5}(1 + 2 + 3 + 4 + 5) = 6$ is 0. Since, for every division, the distance of the corresponding sum from 6 is at least 0, $A_f(12.5) = 10/10$, as above.

Table 5.2

$\sum R_{c'}$	*No. of divisions*
3	1
4	1
5	2
6	2
7	2
8	1
9	1

Before computing $A_f(\theta)$ for other θ, it will be convenient to arrange the values of $\sum R_{c'}$ in a table as in Table 5.2. [Similar tables for other values of (m, n) appear in Table B.] Then, for each value of θ, it will be sufficient to refer the sum of the control ranks, in the ranking of $(t_1 - \theta, t_2 - \theta, t_3 - \theta, c_1, c_2)$, to this table to obtain $A_f(\theta)$. Thus for $\theta = 10$, $(t_1 - \theta, t_2 - \theta, t_3 - \theta) = (35 - 10, 43 - 10, 52 - 10) = (25, 33, 42)$ and $(c_1, c_2) = (21, 40)$. The corresponding ranks are (2, 3, 5) and (1, 4), so that $\sum R_c = 5$. From Table 5.2 it is clear that eight of the possible values of $\sum R_{c'}$ are as far or farther from 6 as is 5. Hence $A_f(10) = 8/10$.

The computations for $\theta = -10, -5, 0, 5, 10, 12.5, 15, 20, 25, 30$, and 35 appear in Table 5.3, where, in each row, the computations just made are carried out.

Table 5.3

θ	$(t_1 - \theta, t_2 - \theta, t_3 - \theta)$	(c_1, c_2)	(R_{c_1}, R_{c_2})	$\sum R_c$	$A_f(\theta)$
−10	(45, 53, 62)	(21, 40)	(1, 2)	3	2/10
−5	(40, 48, 57)	(21, 40)	(1, 2.5)*	3.5*	3/10*
0	(35, 43, 52)	(21, 40)	(1, 3)	4	4/10
5	(30, 38, 47)	(21, 40)	(1, 4)	5	8/10
10	(25, 33, 42)	(21, 40)	(1, 4)	5	8/10
12.5	(22.5, 30.5, 39.5)	(21, 40)	(1, 5)	6	10/10
15	(20, 28, 37)	(21, 40)	(2, 5)	7	8/10
20	(15, 23, 32)	(21, 40)	(2, 5)	7	8/10
25	(10, 18, 27)	(21, 40)	(3, 5)	8	4/10
30	(5, 13, 22)	(21, 40)	(3, 5)	8	4/10
35	(0, 8, 17)	(21, 40)	(4, 5)	9	2/10

* See Exercise 5.8 for computation when there are ties.

The graph of these values of A_f is shown in Figure 5.1. An interpretation of the graph can be given in the same way as for one constructed with $f = |\bar{t}' - \bar{c}'|$. The additive models corresponding to values of θ near 12.5 are the most in agreement with the observations (here, as measured by $|\bar{R}_{t'} - \bar{R}_{c'}|$), while those corresponding to θ outside the range, say, from 0 to 25, show considerably less agreement with such an assumption.

For comparison, the graph of A_f, with $f = |\bar{t}' - \bar{c}'|$, is reproduced in Figure 5.2. In each graph the exact values of A_f are given for θ between 10 and 15.

The most striking difference is that the curve based on the ranks drops off at a lower rate than does the curve based on the means. For this reason the

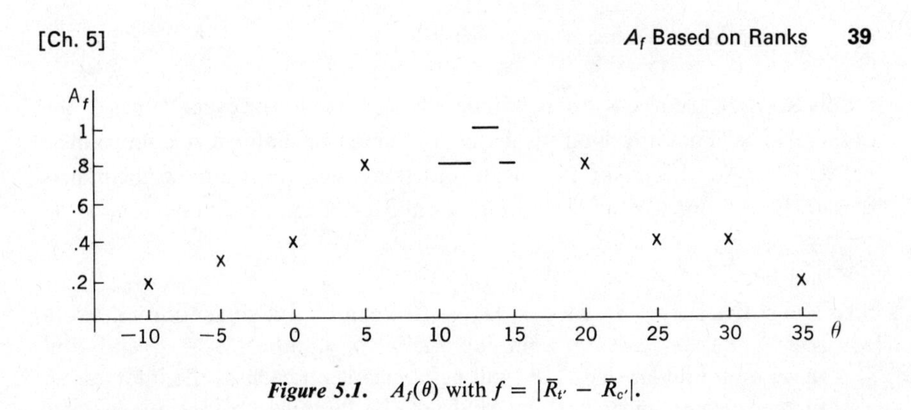

Figure 5.1. $A_f(\theta)$ with $f = |\bar{R}_{t'} - \bar{R}_{c'}|$.

analysis based on ranks makes the experiment seem less precise than does the analysis based on means. It is, however, also possible that for different sets of scores, this comparison could be reversed; that is, the analysis based on means would appear less precise than that based on ranks. In terms of fixed subjects, it would be difficult to describe when one analysis would be more precise than the other. When the subjects can be regarded as having come from a population of subjects, there is a basis for choice among various functions f for analysis. Some mention of this basis appears in Chapter 13.

For computational simplicity the method based on the ranks is certainly preferable. There are other considerations that indicate the method based on the ranks has advantages. One, mentioned earlier, is the sensitivity of the mean to aberrant observations. An extreme observation will make greater differences to the shape of a curve computed with $|\bar{t}' - c'|$ than to that of a curve computed with $|\bar{R}_{t'} - \bar{R}_{c'}|$. The sensitivity of the mean to the exact value of the observations is also reflected in the details of the curves for θ between 10 and 15. Completely subjectively, that is, without any criterion for how much "smoothing" is desirable, it can be said that the details of the curve in Figure 5.2 based on $|\bar{t}' - \bar{c}'|$ overstate the accuracy of the observations. An analysis based on the median will be given in Chapter 6. For these

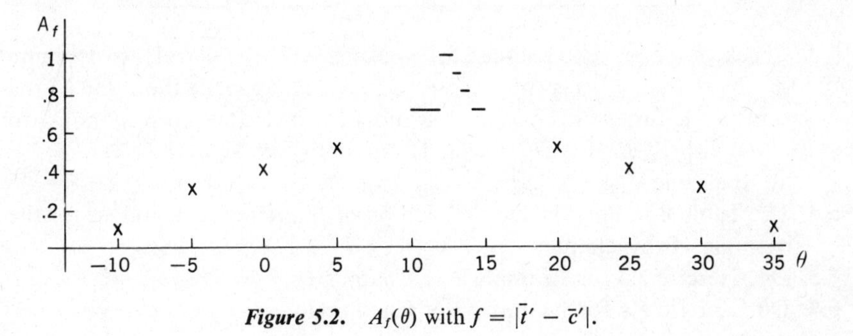

Figure 5.2. $A_f(\theta)$ with $f = |\bar{t}' - \bar{c}'|$.

observations, the curve A_f there will be less sensitive to the exact values of the observations. That the analysis based on ranks can afford a compromise between the sensitivity of the mean and the insensitivity of the median is one of the reasons for the increasing popularity of rank methods.

EXERCISES

5.1. The entire curve, A_f, for $f = |\bar{R}_t - \bar{R}_c|$, can be drawn as follows. From $(t_1, \ldots, t_n)$, $(c_1, \ldots, c_m)$ compute the $n \cdot m$ numbers $t_i - c_j$ and plot these on a line labeled θ. A_f will be constant on each of the intervals so formed. Hence the graph can be drawn by finding $A_f(\theta)$ for a value of θ in each interval and drawing a horizontal line at height $A_f(\theta)$ over the interval containing θ. (For the value of A_f at the end points of these intervals, see Exercise 5.8.)

For $(t_1) = (20)$, $(c_1, c_2) = (0, 10)$ find $A_f(\theta)$ for $f = |\bar{R}_t - \bar{R}_c|$ in this manner. Compare your graph with Figure 4.2.

5.2. From the set of integers (1, 2, 3, 4, 5, 6, 7), list the 35 possible choices of three different integers together with their sums. That is, complete Table a. Also complete Table b, in which are counted how many times each sum occurs in Table a. Compare Table b with the corresponding entry in Table B in Part III.

Table a

Choice	*Sum*
1 2 3	6
1 2 4	7
1 2 5	8
1 2 6	9
1 2 7	10
1 3 4	8

Table b

Sum	*No. of times*	*No. of times/35*
6	1	.0286
7	1	.0286
8	2	.0572

5.3. Check your answer to Exercise 5.1 by using Table B in Part III to compute A_f. Note that $A_f(\theta)$ is twice the P-value listed opposite the value of the sum of the ranks of the smaller group. (The orderings corresponding to $|\bar{R}_t - \bar{R}_c|$, $|\sum R_t - [n(n + m + 1)/2]|$, and $|\sum R_c - [m(n + m + 1)/2]|$ are the same.)

5.4. Use Table B in Part III and the method of Exercise 5.1 to find A_f for the example of this chapter.

5.5. Do Exercise 5.4 for Example 2 of Chapter 1.

5.6. Do Exercise 5.4 for Example 3 of Chapter 1.

5.7. When there are ties among the observations, the ranks are defined as follows. Arrange the observations in a nondecreasing order and assign ranks as though there were no ties. Then, within each tie, replace the ranks by their mean. Thus the ranks for (3, 6, 5, 3) would be (1.5, 4, 3, 1.5), since

$$\begin{array}{cccc} 3 \leq & 3 < & 5 < & 6 \\ \underline{1} & \underline{2} & 3 & 4 \\ 1.5 & 1.5 & 3 & 4 \end{array}$$

Similarly, the ranks for (172, 186, 172, 208, 186, 172) are (2, 4.5, 2, 6, 4.5, 2), since

$$\begin{array}{cccccc} 172 \leq & 172 \leq & 172 < & 186 \leq & 186 < & 208 \\ \underline{1} & \underline{2} & \underline{3} & \underline{4} & \underline{5} & 6 \\ 2 & 2 & 2 & 4.5 & 4.5 & 6 \end{array}$$

Suppose $(t_1, t_2, t_3, t_4) = (1.8, 1.6, 1.8, 2.1)$ and $(c_1, c_2, c_3) = (0.1, 1.8, 1.6)$. Find the ranks $(R_{t_1}, R_{t_2}, R_{t_3}, R_{t_4})$ of (t_1, t_2, t_3, t_4) in the combined set $(t_1, t_2, t_3, t_4, c_1, c_2, c_3)$. What is the difference, $\bar{R}_t - \bar{R}_c$, in the mean ranks of the two sets?

5.8. When a value of θ is chosen so that there are ties in the observations, the computation of $A_f(\theta)$ is basically the same. Recall that the motivation for considering the regroupings of $(t_1 - \theta, \ldots, t_n - \theta, c_1, \ldots, c_m)$ was the possible assignments of the $m + n$ subjects to two groups of sizes n and m and that the scores are for subjects. Hence, what is required is to keep track of subjects, as well as scores, when listing these arrangements.

For $(t_1, t_2, t_3) = (35, 43, 52)$, $(c_1, c_2) = (21, 40)$, and $\theta = -5$, the scores $(t_1 - \theta, t_2 - \theta, t_3 - \theta, c_1, c_2)$ are $(40_1, 48, 57, 21, 40_2)$, where the subscripts point out that the two 40's correspond to two different subjects. The ranks for these five numbers are (see Exercise 5.7) $(2.5_1, 4, 5, 1, 2.5_2)$, so that $\sum R_{c'} = 3.5$.

What is needed now is the set of all possible values for $\sum R_{c'}$. List the 10 possible subsets of 2 from $(2.5_1, 4, 5, 1, 2.5_2)$ and compute the value of $\sum R_{c'}$ for each. Thus verify that the value of $A_f(\theta)$ for $\theta = -5$ in Table 5.3 is as shown.

5.9. The following graphical method of computing $A_f(\theta)$ is sometimes useful. Plot the scores $(t_1, t_2, \ldots, t_n)$ on one scale, and the scores $(c_1, c_2, \ldots, c_m)$ on another scale on a separate sheet. If the scales are placed parallel to each other, the ranks of either set of numbers is apparent. The value of θ for the model $h(c) = c + \theta$ can be found as the difference between a point on the t scale and the point just below it on the c scale. For example, if $(c_1, c_2) = (0, 10)$ and $(t_1) = (20)$ it is clear from the graph

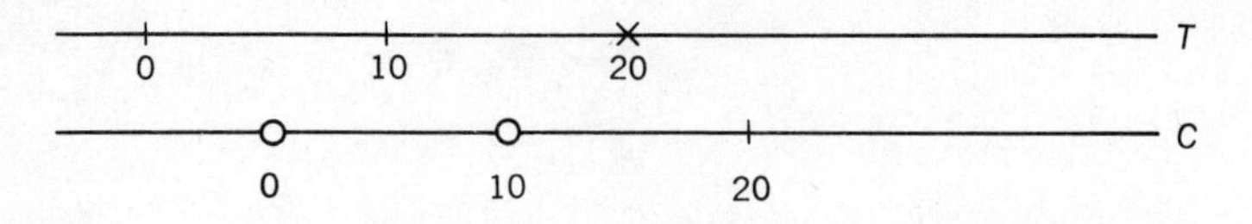

that for $\theta = 0$, $\bar{R}_t = 30$, $\bar{R}_c = 1.5$, and from the graph

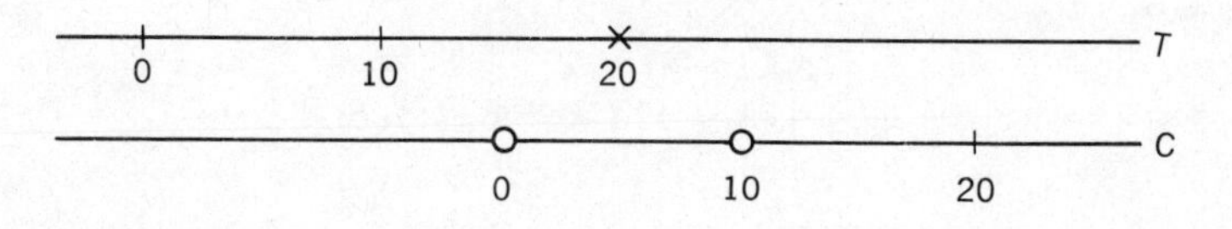

that for $\theta = 15$, $\bar{R}_t = 2$ and $\bar{R}_c = 2$. It is also clear that, for θ between 10 and 20, $\bar{R}_t = 2$ and $\bar{R}_c = 2$.

a. Use this graphical method to find all the values of θ, so that $\bar{R}_t = \bar{R}_c$ for each of the three examples of Chapter 1.

b. Find the values of $A_f(\theta)$ for $\theta = 20, 25, 30$, and 35 in Table 5.3 by this method.

CHAPTER 6

A_f BASED ON THE MEDIAN

In this chapter an answer to the question, for a given θ, "Is the assumption that θ is the treatment effect in agreement with the observations?" will be given by considering the median. In particular, for each division of $(t_1 - \theta, t_2 - \theta, t_3 - \theta, c_1, c_2)$ into two sets (t_1', t_2', t_3'), (c_1', c_2') let $n_{t'}^+$ and $n_{t'}^-$ be the numbers of (t_1', t_2', t_3') above and below the median M of $(t_1', t_2', t_3', c_1', c_2')$. Let $n_{c'}^+$ and $n_{c'}^-$ be the corresponding two numbers for (c_1, c_2). The function f, for A_f, will be taken as

$$\left|\frac{n_{t'}^+ - n_{t'}^-}{n} - \frac{n_{c'}^+ - n_{c'}^-}{m}\right|.$$

That is, A_f will be the proportion of divisions with f at least as large as for the observed division. Consider $(t_1, t_2, t_3) = (35, 43, 52)$, $(c_1, c_2) = (21, 40)$, and $\theta = 12.5$, and $(t_1', t_2', t_3') = (22.5, 30.5, 39.5)$ and $(c_1', c_2') = (21, 40)$. The median M of all five numbers is 30.5, so that $n_{t'}^+ = 1$, $n_{t'}^- = 1$, $n_{c'}^+ = 1$, $n_{c'}^- = 1$, and

$$f = \left|\frac{1-1}{3} - \frac{1-1}{2}\right| = 0.$$

Since f is always at least 0, $A_f(12.5) = 1$. In this chapter A_f will be computed as described here. Other conventions are possible (see Exercises 6.1 and 6.2).

Before computing A_f for other values of θ, it is convenient to note two things. The first is that, just as for the means, or the mean ranks, it is easier to compute $n^+ - n^-$ for only one group. Here, comparing distances of f from zero is equivalent, for this example, with comparing distances of $n^+ - n^-$ (for either group) with zero. The second is that, as for the ranks, the possible values of $n^+ - n^-$ do not depend upon the values of $(t_1', t_2', t_3', c_1', c_2')$ and so the use of a table of them can replace the listing of all the divisions into two sets. However, to find this table, one listing has to be made and the one for $\theta = 12.5$ will be done to confirm that $A_f(12.5) = 1$. This calculation is in Table 6.1.

Table 6.1

(t_1', t_2', t_3')	(c_1', c_2')	M	$n_{c'}^+ - n_{c'}^-$	$\lvert n_{c'}^+ - n_{c'}^- \rvert$
(22.5, 30.5, 39.5)	(21, 40)	30.5	$1 - 1 = 0$	0
	(39.5, 40)		$2 - 0 = 2$	2
	(21, 39.5)		$1 - 1 = 0$	0
	(30.5, 40)		$1 - 0 = 1$	1
	(21, 30.5)		$0 - 1 = -1$	1
	(22.5, 40)		$1 - 1 = 0$	0
	(21, 22.5)		$0 - 2 = -2$	2
	(30.5, 39.5)		$1 - 0 = 1$	1
	(22.5, 39.5)		$1 - 1 = 0$	0
	(22.5, 30.5)		$0 - 1 = -1$	1

From Table 6.1 it is clear that $A_f(12.5) = 1$. Also the set of possible values of $n_c^+ - n_c^-$ is seen to be

$n_c^+ - n_c^-$	*No. of divisions*
−2	1
−1	2
0	4
1	2
2	1

which will be used to find $A_f(\theta)$ for $\theta = -10, -5, 0, 5, 10, 12.5, 15, 20, 25, 30$, and 35. This computation is given in Table 6.2, with $(t_1, t_2, t_3) = (35, 43, 52)$, $(c_1, c_2) = (21, 40)$.

These values of $A_f(\theta)$ are graphed in Figure 6.1. The graph is more spread out than that for the ranks. This slower rate of decrease to its minimum value than either that for the ranks or that for the mean will often, but not always, be the case for analyses based on the median.

For comparative purposes all three curves $A_f(\theta)$, for $f = |\bar{t}' - \bar{c}'|$ (the difference in arithmetic means), for $f = |\bar{R}_{t'} - \bar{R}_{c'}|$ (the difference in mean ranks), and for

$$f = \left| \frac{n_{t'}^+ - n_{t'}^-}{n} - \frac{n_c^+ - n_{c'}^-}{m} \right|$$

Table 6.2

θ	$(t_1 - \theta, t_2 - \theta, t_3 - \theta)$	(c_1, c_2)	M	$n_{c'}^{+} - n_{c'}^{-}$	$A_f(\theta)$
−10	(45, 53, 62)	(21, 40)	45	$0 - 2 = -2$	2/10
−5	(40, 48, 57)	(21, 40)	40	$0 - 1 = -1$	3/10*
0	(35, 43, 52)	(21, 40)	40	$0 - 1 = -1$	6/10
5	(30, 38, 47)	(21, 40)	38	$1 - 1 = 0$	10/10
10	(25, 33, 42)	(21, 40)	33	$1 - 1 = 0$	10/10
12.5	(22.5, 30.5, 39.5)	(21, 40)	30.5	$1 - 1 = 0$	10/10
15	(20, 28, 37)	(21, 40)	28	$1 - 1 = 0$	10/10
20	(15, 23, 32)	(21, 40)	23	$1 - 1 = 0$	10/10
25	(10, 18, 27)	(21, 40)	21	$1 - 0 = 1$	6/10
30	(5, 13, 22)	(21, 40)	21	$1 - 0 = 1$	6/10
35	(0, 8, 17)	(21, 40)	17	$2 - 0 = 2$	2/10

* See Exercise 6.1 for the computation with ties.

(the difference in the mean number of observations above and below the common median), appear in Figure 6.2.

The most striking difference among the three curves is the difference in their spread. This difference suggests that analyses based on means are more precise than those based on ranks and that those based on ranks are more precise than those on medians. This suggestion is reinforced by the reflection that the sensitivity of means, ranks, and medians to the observations are in the same order. For much of the data that is encountered in practice the above suggestion of a decreasing order in precision will be realized.

There are data for which the comparisons can be reversed. That is, it is possible that the subjects and model could be such that the analysis based on ranks, or that based on medians, would give the tightest curve. Assumptions about the source of the subjects can give conditions under which certain

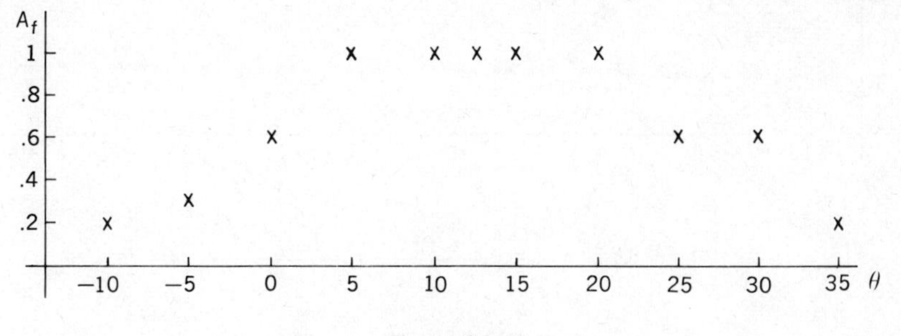

Figure 6.1.

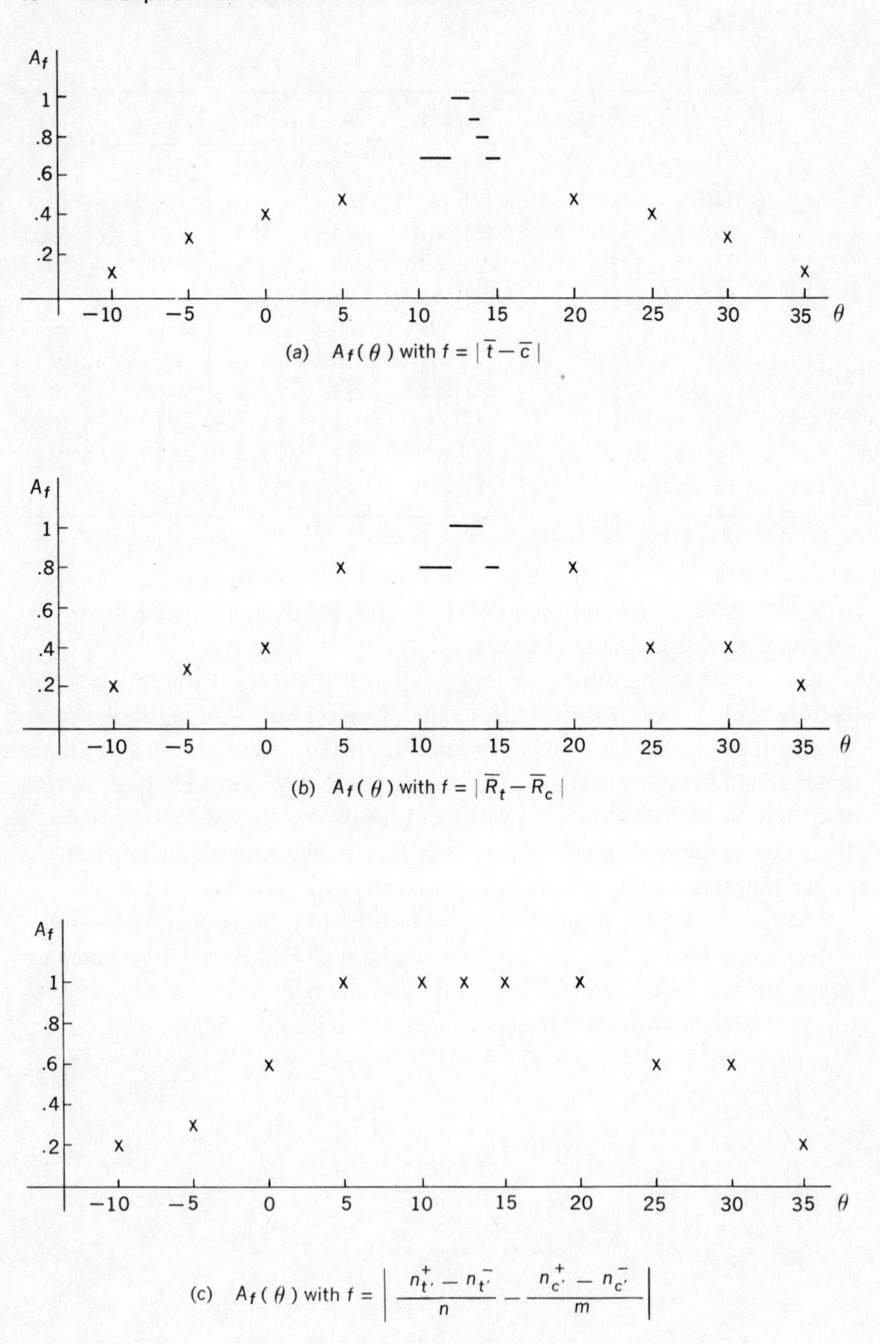

(a) $A_f(\theta)$ with $f = |\bar{t} - \bar{c}|$

(b) $A_f(\theta)$ with $f = |\bar{R}_t - \bar{R}_c|$

(c) $A_f(\theta)$ with $f = \left| \dfrac{n_{t\cdot}^{+} - n_{t\cdot}^{-}}{n} - \dfrac{n_{c\cdot}^{+} - n_{c\cdot}^{-}}{m} \right|$

Figure 6.2.

analyses will be best in this respect. Some more will be said about these later. If it should be difficult to judge which of these theoretical assumptions would be applicable to a given sort of experiment, it is always possible to base a choice of analysis, for future experiments, on comparisons among analyses made on past experiments. The distinction just made between future and past experiments is very important. The choice of a single analysis, from among several made on a present experiment, for describing the same present experiment will always leave open the possibility that the analysis was selected to force the experiment to yield certain conclusions. However, the performance and presentation of several analyses on the same experimental outcome can be valuable, if it is remembered that those that more strongly "show" something are not to be singled out, except perhaps as suggestions for future analyses.

It should also be noted that sensitivity of the functions f is not always desirable. When there is a possibility that some experiments include atypical subjects, called outliers or contaminations, the use of analyses sensitive to extreme observations can result in atypical conclusions. The usual case is that an investigator cannot recognize an extreme observation as atypical. (If he can, from consideration of the subject and/or the conditions under which the observation was taken, he should discard it.) The use of a relatively insensitive analysis will decrease the effect upon the description of unclassifiable extreme observations without ignoring the extreme observations.

EXERCISES

6.1. For θ fixed, the computation of

$$f = \left| \frac{n_{t-\theta}^{+} - n_{t-\theta}^{-}}{n} - \frac{n_c{}^{+} - n_c{}^{-}}{m} \right|$$

is often made from the table below (where the right and bottom marginals are totals).

	$t - \theta$	c	
Above M	$n_{t-\theta}^{+}$	$n_c{}^{+}$	A
Equal to M	$n_{t-\theta}^{0}$	$n_c{}^{0}$	E
Below M	$n_{t-\theta}^{-}$	$n_c{}^{-}$	B
	n	m	N

The orderings by f above and by $|(n_{t-\theta}^+ - n_{t-\theta}^-) - (n/N)(A - B)|$ are equivalent. Verify this for $\theta = -5$ and the observations of the example of this chapter. [Note that, in listing the implied no-treatment outcomes for $\theta = -5$, the tied scores are to be labeled and treated as two scores (see Exercise 5.8).]

6.2. Primarily because it is easier to make tables for the proportions of divisions that lead to the various values of f, the table in Exercise 6.1 is usually abridged to

	$t - \theta$	c	
Above	$n_{t-\theta}^+$	n_c^+	A
Below	$n_{t-\theta}^-$	n_c^-	B
	n'	m'	N'

by ignoring those equal to the median. With f defined from this table as $f = |n_{t-\theta}^+ - (n'A/N')|$, compute $A_f(\theta)$ for the same values of θ as in Table 6.2. [Note that, for each (n', m'), a table corresponding to Table 6.2 is needed.] (For larger sample sizes and only a few observations equal to the median, there is not much difference between A_f based on the two methods.)

6.3. The value of $A_f(\theta)$ is the same if any one of the functions

$$\left|n_{t-\theta}^+ - \frac{n'A}{N'}\right|, \quad \left|n_{t-\theta}^- - \frac{n'B}{N'}\right|, \quad \left|n_c^+ - \frac{m'A}{N'}\right|, \quad \left|n_c^- - \frac{m'B}{N'}\right|$$

is used. Verify this for $\theta = 35$ for the example of Table 6.2.

6.4. Because of the equivalence of Exercise 6.3, tables of the proportion of divisions that lead to the various values of f (as defined in Exercise 6.2) are made only for values of N', p = smaller of (n', m'), and q = smaller of (A, B). Use Table K to compute $A_f(35)$ as in Exercise 6.3. (Read the introduction to Table K.)

6.5. The simplest way to construct the graph of $A_f(\theta)$ is to find the $n \cdot m$ numbers $t_i - c_j$ and plot them on a line labeled θ. A_f will be constant on the intervals so defined and the curve may be drawn by finding A_f for one point in each interval. Use Table K (ignore observations equal to the median) and this method to construct the curve A_f for Example 3 of Chapter 1.

CHAPTER 7

RANDOMIZATION

A set of subjects available for a treatment and control experiment will have their no-treatment scores, if observed, spread across some range. Just what this range is and how they will be distributed will not generally be known. There is an appeal to wanting the subjects who will be control subjects and those who will be treatment subjects to have their no-treatment scores as equally distributed across this (unknown) range as possible. Since these scores are unknown, there is no way to assure such an equal distribution for any particular experiment. The manner and sense with which randomization can be used to "usually" achieve this equal distribution will be explored now.

Suppose four subjects are identified with the labels A, B, C, and D. If two are to be assigned to treatment and two to control, there are six possible experiments which could be carried out with these subjects. They are the following.

Treatment		*Control*	
A	B	C	D
A	C	B	D
A	D	B	C
B	C	A	D
B	D	A	C
C	D	A	B

There are means of selecting one of these six experiments (see Exercises 7.3 and 7.4 for several such means of randomization), so that each of the six has the same chance of being the one selected. When such a means of randomization is used, it is said that the probability is 1/6 that each of the six possible experiments is carried out. If it is supposed that the no-treatment scores of the four subjects are 10, 12, 15, and 19 for *A*, *B*, *C*, and *D*, respectively, random selection would imply that each of the six possible experimental outcomes in Figure 7.1 would be observed with probability 1/6.

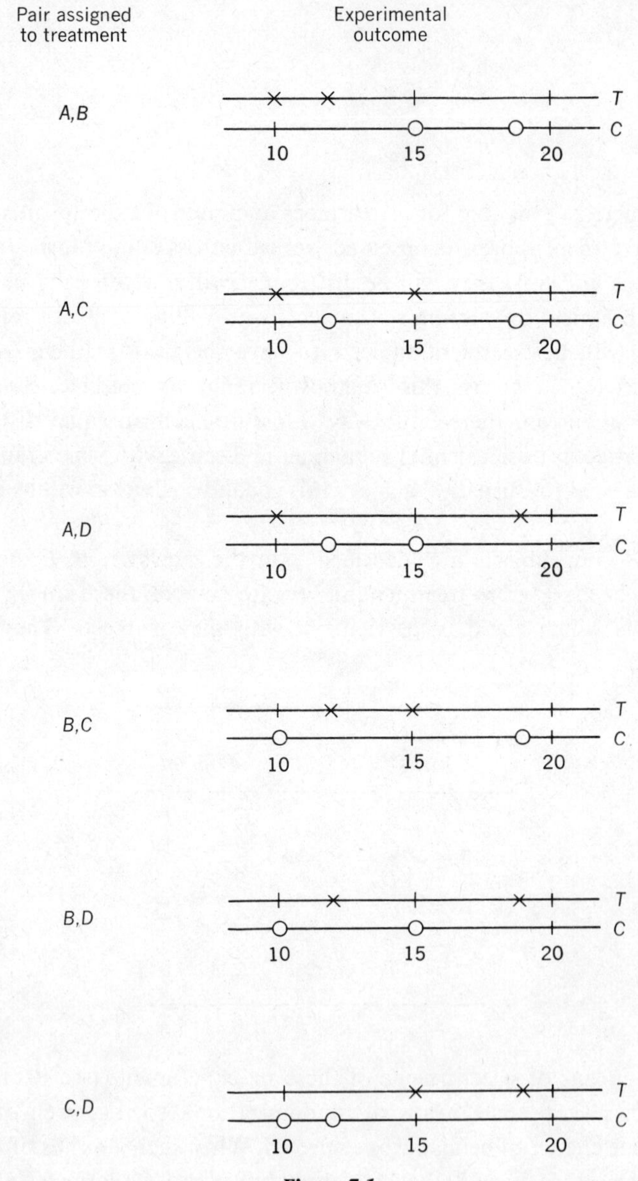

Figure 7.1.

From inspection of the six possible experiments graphed in Figure 7.1, an idea of the effect of randomization, when there is no treatment effect, can be gained. The experiment with (A, B) assigned to treatment gives a strong impression that there is a negative treatment effect, while the experiment with (C, D) assigned to treatment gives a strong impression of a positive treatment effect. Similarly, the experiments corresponding to (A, C) and (B, D) give some impression of a negative effect and a positive effect, respectively. The two corresponding to (A, D) and (B, C) give almost no impression of a treatment effect.

Since, with randomization, the six experiments are equally likely, it can be said that in some average sense there is no impression given of the presence of a treatment effect. While this "on the average" absence of an impression of a treatment effect does not give any assurance for any single experiment, it is clearly a desirable property for a large set of experiments.

Randomization has another property that is not so apparent here, where there are only four subjects and six possible experiments: With a larger set of fairly homogeneous subjects most of the possible experiments will not be grossly misleading. Or, stated another way, the probability of a grossly misleading experiment will be small. To be entirely meaningful, the foregoing statements require precise definitions of when an experimental outcome is misleading. This in turn will require precise definitions of the manner in which conclusions are based on the observed outcomes. Before considering some of these, it will be of interest to observe how a curve, $A_f(\theta)$, describes each of the six no-treatment experiments of Figure 7.1. These curves have been constructed, for $f = |\bar{R}_t - \bar{R}_c|$, for each of the six experiments and are shown in Figure 7.2.

The corresponding descriptive statements would be like the one following, for the experiment (A, B). The additive models most in agreement with these observations are those for which θ is between -7 and -5 while the models for which θ is less than -9 or for which θ is greater than -3 are the least in agreement with the observations. For each of the other experiments there would be an analogous descriptive statement and the effect of the randomization is to select one of these descriptions with probability 1/6.

It is known here that there is no treatment effect and the ideal descriptive statement would be that the only appropriate additive model is that for $\theta = 0$. The curve corresponding to this statement is shown in Figure 7.3 as having the value 1 only at $\theta = 0$ and having the value 0 for all other θ.

Each of the curves in Figure 7.2, which were based on the observations, is an approximation to this ideal curve; how good the approximation is

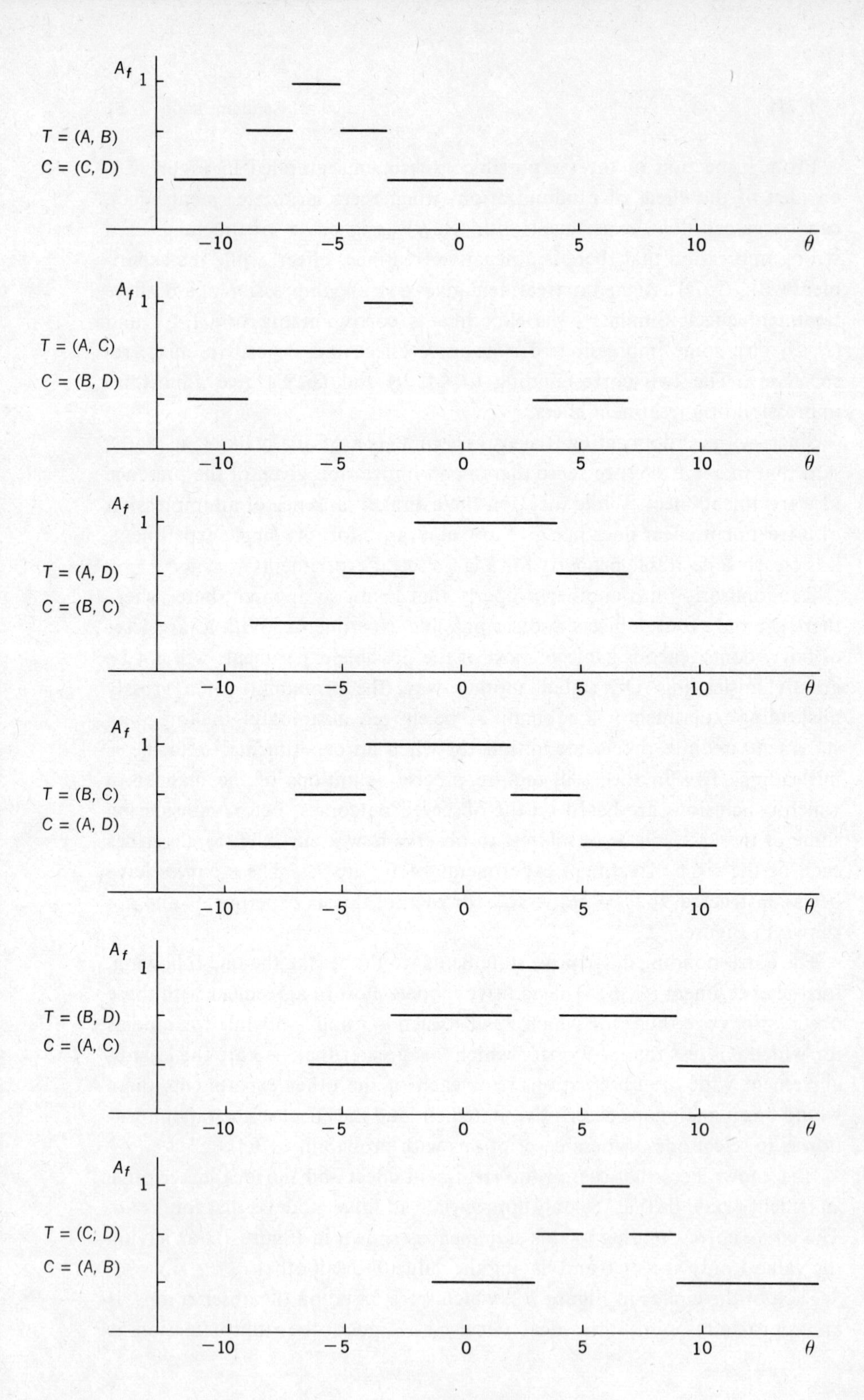

A_f
1
T = (A, B)
C = (C, D)
−10
−5
0
5
10
θ
A_f
1
T = (A, C)
C = (B, D)
−10
−5
0
5
10
θ
A_f
1
T = (A, D)
C = (B, C)
−10
−5
0
5
10
θ
A_f
1
T = (B, C)
C = (A, D)
−10
−5
0
5
10
θ
A_f
1
T = (B, D)
C = (A, C)
−10
−5
0
5
10
θ
A_f
1
T = (C, D)
C = (A, B)
−10
−5
0
5
10
θ

Figure 7.2.

depends upon the size of the experiment, the heterogeneity of the subjects, and the particular assignment of subjects to the treatment group realized by the randomization. Another way to describe, for these subjects, the effect of randomization and the construction of A_f is to say that one of the curves in Figure 7.2 is selected at random and used as an approximation to the ideal curve in Figure 7.3— an approximation in two senses: first, in that each curve is not "centered" at $\theta = 0$ since the "centers" of the curves are scattered about $\theta = 0$, and, second, in that each curve is not concentrated closely around its central value. The approximations would be better if the subjects had had no-treatment scores which were less heterogeneous or, if with subjects about as heterogeneous as these, there were more subjects in the two groups.

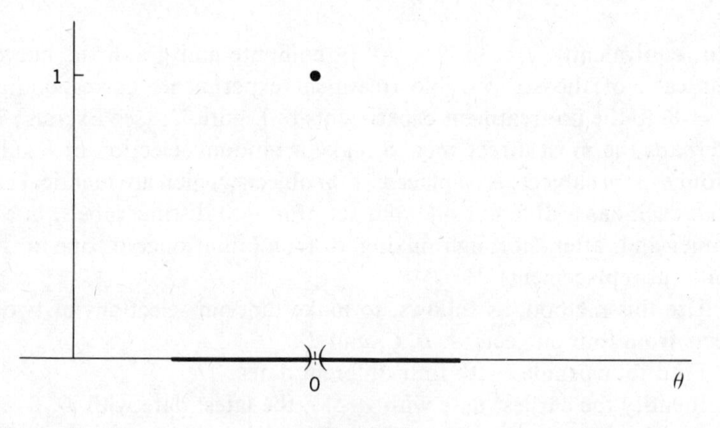

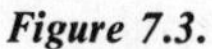

Figure 7.3.

The approximation will also depend on the choice of the function f, in fact, so heavily that it is necessary to choose the function f without regard to the observed outcome in order that the random properties of the curve A_f be realized. The simplest way to guarantee that the choice of f does not depend upon the outcome of the experiment is to specify the choice before the experiment is performed.

There is an important point here. There is no reason why, with or without randomization, an experimenter should not compute, for exploratory purposes, as many curves $A_f(\theta)$ for different functions f and different classes of models as he should choose. It is even desirable to do so as a check upon whether the indications of the experiment are sensitive to the choice of the class of models and to the particular analysis used. However, without random assignment of subjects to treatment and control, or without the specification of f before the experiment it is usually impossible to describe the probabilistic properties of A_f.

EXERCISES

7.1. a. Compute, for the experiment corresponding to the assignment of subjects (A, B) to treatment, the first curve, A_f, of Figure 7.2.

b. If the treatment effect is $\theta = 8$, the scores that would be observed for the two treatment subjects, (A, B), will be $(10 + \theta, 12 + \theta) = (18, 20)$. Compute A_f for the corresponding observed outcome $(t_1, t_2) = (18, 20)$, $(c_1, c_2) = (15, 19)$.

7.2. Using

$$f = \left|\frac{\text{No. of } t' > M}{n} - \frac{\text{No. of } t' < M}{n}\right|$$

(or, equivalently, $f = |n_{t'}{}^{+} - n_{t'}{}^{-}|$), compute and graph the curves A_f for each of the six possible treatment experiments corresponding, if $\theta = 8$, to the no-treatment experiments of Figure 7.1 (see Exercise 7.1b).

7.3. Perhaps the most direct way to make a random selection of n subjects from $n + m$ subjects is to place $n + m$ objects, which are identical except that each has a different one of a set of $n + m$ distinct labels, in a container and, after thorough mixing, draw n (all at once or one at a time without replacement).

Use this method, as follows, to make random selections of two subjects from four subjects A, B, C, and D.

Find four pennies with four different dates.

Identify the earliest date with $A, \ldots,$ the latest date with D.

Put the four pennies in a container which is large enough to permit thorough mixing (a tin can, a large dice cup, a paper bag, etc.).

After thorough shaking, draw two of the pennies and record the corresponding names.

Use this method to make 100 selections of two out of four subjects and count the number of times that each of the six possible pairs were selected.

7.4. Tables of random digits have been made. These are constructed so that each digit in the table is essentially a random selection of one from the digits $(0, 1, \ldots, 9)$ [and, each pair of digits is a random selection of one pair from the set $(00, 01, \ldots, 99)$ of 100 pairs; each triple is a random selection of one triple from the 1000 possible triples, etc.].

A section of one such table (Rand's 1,000,000 random digits) is reproduced in Table A in Part III. To use this to select two objects from a set of four objects labeled A, B, C, and D, proceed as follows.

Without regard to the entries in the table, select (1) a starting point, that is, a page number, a row number, and a column number; and (2) select also a direction of reading (that is, from left to right as usual, or down columns and advancing to the right, etc.). Then, reading from the starting point in the specified direction, if the first digit encountered is a 1, select A; if a 2, select B; if a 3, select C; if a 4, select D. If it is anything but a 1, 2, 3, or 4, skip it and go on. For the next digit encountered, which is different from the first, select a second subject from the remaining three subjects.

Use this method to make 100 selections of two subjects from A, B, C, and D. (It is not necessary to select 100 starting points. After two subjects have been selected, start again with the next digit in the specified direction of reading.)

7.5. Note that in Exercise 7.4, time can be saved by also identifying 5, 6, 7, and 8 with A, B, C, and D, respectively, and skipping only the 0's and 9's. What would be the effect on the selection if, further, 0 were identified with A, and 9 with B, in an attempt to use all the digits?

7.6. Write instructions for the use of Table A in Part III to select 40 subjects from a set of 100. Also write instructions to select 40 subjects from a list of 80.

CHAPTER 8

BASING DECISIONS ON EXPERIMENTS

In this chapter there are to be described three sorts of decisions which are often based on experiments. For each of the three, it is assumed that the class of models, here the additive class, is fixed. The decisions can be given the form of assertions concerning which model in the class is the true model, that is, which actually obtained or was operative during the experiment. For such assertions to be true it is necessary that the true model be in the class and it is assumed that this is the case. The procedure for making the decisions will have certain probabilistic properties, if subjects have been randomly assigned to treatment and control and if the true model is in the class of models used. If the true model is not in the class, it can only be hoped that the fixed class of models is large enough so that it contains a model close enough to the true model so that the asserted probabilistic properties will be closely approximated in practice.

The three sorts of decisions to be considered are almost universally referred to as (1) confidence intervals, (2) tests of hypotheses, and (3) estimates.

An experimenter who is using his observed outcome to produce a confidence interval would end his analysis with a statement such as "The treatment effect, θ, is between 16.3 and 27.1." The end points, $a = 16.3$, $b = 27.1$, would have been computed, in a certain way, from the observations.

An experimenter who is using his observations to test the hypothesis, say, $\theta = 10$, would end his analysis with a statement such as "The treatment effect, θ, is not 10." A selection of one of two statements, "θ is 10," "θ is not 10," would have been based on the observations.

An experimenter who is using his observations to estimate would end his analysis with a statement such as "The estimated value of the treatment effect, θ, is 7." The estimated value would have been computed from the observations.

In testing hypotheses the two statements between which a choice is made are sometimes of the form, "θ is in a set A," "θ is not in a set A," where A is a fixed set. If the set A is that of the single point, θ_0, the simple case above is realized. Only this simple case will be considered until Chapter 12. Also, in the present discussion there is a simplifying feature introduced by the restriction to a simple class (the additive) of models: The models in the class are identified with the value of a single parameter θ so that the decisions to be taken can be identified or described in terms of intervals (or subsets) of the line whose points are θ. Examples for larger classes of models and for which subsets of more complicated spaces are appropriate will be given in Chapter 16.

Before proceeding to a more detailed description of each of the procedures, confidence intervals, tests of hypotheses, and estimates it should be remarked that the testing of hypotheses and estimation have each been developed within somewhat independent theories and have had a development subsumed within decision theory. The development of theory for confidence intervals has, largely, relied upon that for testing hypotheses. The approach here will be to describe each of the three procedures as it relates to the descriptive curve A_f. The reason for the choice of this approach is simply that a curve A_f is descriptive and has a natural relationship to confidence intervals, to tests, and to estimates. None of the latter three is (primarily) intended to be descriptive and, when so used, it is by virtue of the inclusion of the method of computation and the method's properties, the underlying assumptions, and the data or some summary of the data.

As will be seen, it is simpler to compute a confidence interval than it is to compute an entire curve A_f, and it is simpler to test a hypothesis, or to compute an estimate, than it is to compute an entire curve A_f. However, the computational aids of tables and approximations and of high-speed calculators (these last are not described in this text) render the computation of the curves A_f quite feasible. (Somewhat paradoxically, high-speed calculators also make feasible the collection of such vast amounts of data that the recommendation above to include the observations in a description is not always possible.)

Because of the greater simplicity of computation for arriving at the particular, for the observations, decisions of confidence intervals, tests, or estimates, it is only reasonable to recommend that no more be computed in any instance where no description of a relationship between the observations and a class of models is desired.

CONFIDENCE INTERVALS

To introduce confidence intervals, a curve A_f which is slightly different from the ones encountered so far will be considered. There are analyses which yield continuous curves, that is, curves that have no jumps. One possible such curve is shown in Figure 8.1. In the figure a horizontal line has been drawn, at height α, which intersects the curve in two points. There are two values, θ_1 and θ_2, of θ which correspond to these points of intersection. These two points determine an interval (θ_1, θ_2) of the values of θ between θ_1 and θ_2. This interval will be used to make a statement about the unknown value of θ. The statement will assert that θ is between θ_1 and θ_2.

Thus, for a given number α, a given class of models, and a given analysis, a particular experimental outcome will lead to a curve A_f and, by the construction above, an interval and a statement.

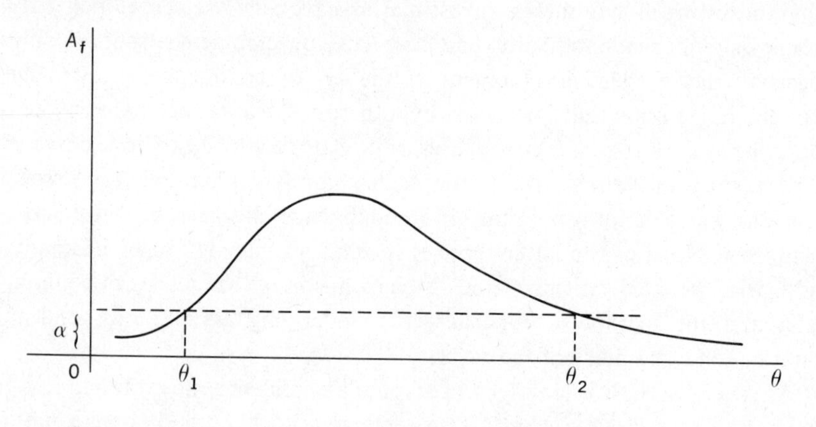

Figure 8.1. A continuous curve A_f.

For some experimental outcomes the resulting statements will be true; for other outcomes they will be false. Since the value of θ is not known, there is no way to know whether the statement resulting from a particular experiment is true or false. However, the method of construction and randomization will determine that the probability of a true statement is at least $1 - \alpha$. In practice this means that, of a large number of independent experiments, approximately $100(1 - \alpha)$ per cent will result in statements which are correct.

If the curve, A_f, is not continuous but has jumps, the construction of the interval is essentially the same; the confidence interval will consist of those values of θ for which $A_f(\theta)$ is above α. Thus in Figure 8.2 the interval corresponding to $1 - \alpha = .75$ consists of those θ between 4 and 25, since A_f is greater than .25 for those θ. The interval might also contain one or both end points; to determine whether an end point is included, A_f can be calculated for the end point. It is included if A_f is larger than α; otherwise it is not included. In practice it is usually well to include the end points. The interval won't be any longer and it will still be true, with randomization, that the probability that the interval contains the true value of θ is at least $1 - \alpha$. However, for the correspondence between confidence intervals and tests of hypotheses, to be given in the next section, the confidence set needs to be defined as the set of values of θ for which $A_f(\theta)$ is larger than α.

If $1 - \alpha$ were .50, the interval from Figure 8.2 would consist of those θ between 7 and 19, because A_f is above $\alpha = .50$ for those θ. Similarly, if $1 - \alpha$ were .25, the interval of those θ for which A_f is above $\alpha(=.75)$ would be that from 12 to 16.

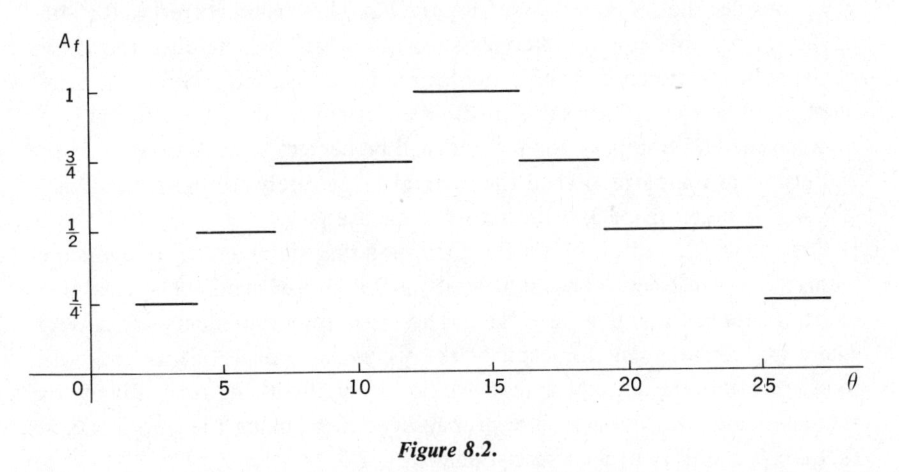

Figure 8.2.

When the curve A_f is not known for all θ but has been found only for some values of θ, it is not possible to find the end points exactly from the graph, although they can be found by trial and error with values of θ near an approximation that can be read directly from the graph. The approximation consists of those values of θ in an interval $[a, b]$, where the end points a and b are found as follows. Find some points θ' with $A_f(\theta')$ above α. Then a is the largest value of θ which is to the left of θ' and for which $A_f(\theta)$ is equal to or below α; b is the smallest value of θ which is to the right of θ' and for which $A_f(\theta)$ is equal to or below α. Clearly this approximation requires that there is only a single interval for which A_f is above α. For most reasonable functions f this will be the case; if not, the modification is obvious. Also, it is clear that this approximation will, in most cases, give too long an interval. However, if the exact construction would give probability at least $1 - \alpha$ that θ is in the interval, the probability for the approximation will also be at least $1 - \alpha$.

If it is known that the set of points θ for which $A_f(\theta)$ is larger than α is an interval, the confidence interval can be found by locating only the end points of the interval. That is, to find the interval there is no need to compute all of A_f.

From the graph of Figure 4.3, the approximate interval for $1 - \alpha = .8(\alpha = .2)$ is $-10 \leq \theta \leq 35$, while that for $1 - \alpha = .6(\alpha = .4)$ is $0 \leq \theta \leq 25$.

To illustrate how, with randomization, the probability is at least $1 - \alpha$ that the interval of θ for which $A_f(\theta)$ is above α will contain the true value of θ, consider the six curves A_f of Figure 7.2. These each correspond to one of the six possible equally likely experiments which can be observed if two of the subjects are chosen from the four subjects available. Since the treatment effect was $\theta = 0$ for these possible experiments, the statement that θ is between the end points of the interval will be correct when 0 is between the end points and incorrect when the interval lies entirely to one side of zero. If $1 - \alpha$ is taken to be 2/3, the six intervals are $[-9, -3]$, $[-9, 3]$, $[-5, 7]$, $[-7, 5]$, $[-3, 9]$, and $[3, 9]$. Of the corresponding statements, the two statements "The treatment effect is between -9 and -3" and "The treatment effect is between 3 and 9" are false. The other four statements are correct. There is one statement for each of the six possible experiments and, with randomization, the six experiments would be equally likely. Accordingly, the six statements each would have probability 1/6 of being the one made, so that the probability of a correct statement is 2/3.

It is well to recall the conditions which will ensure that confidence intervals constructed in the above manner will have probability at least $1 - \alpha$ of leading to correct statements.

The first is that the treatment subjects be selected from the $n + m$ subjects, at random, so that each possible experiment be equally likely.

A second condition is that the analysis, that is, the function f used to construct the curve A_f, as well as α, be fixed without regard to the observed outcome. The best way to guarantee this is to decide upon them before observing the outcome.

A third condition is that the family of models used be relevant, that is, that they contain the true model. Here this would require that the treatment effect is, in fact, additive. If the treatment effect is not additive, it is difficult to know what the statement "The additive treatment effect is between a and b" means and hence curious to ask whether it is true or false. This is one of the disadvantages of working with small classes of models and emphasizes why a precise statement of the assumptions underlying the analysis be included with a report of the analysis.

In general, it might seem desirable to take α quite small ($1 - \alpha$ very large), so that the probability of a correct statement will be almost 1. However, the average length of the confidence interval will increase as α decreases. One must make a choice between making precise statements about θ which have a low probability of being correct and making imprecise statements which have a high probability of being correct.

With $1 - \alpha$ fixed, the properties of confidence intervals also depend upon the choice of the analysis f. In some cases there is a basis for choosing f so that certain optimum properties will result for the intervals. A discussion of these bases and the sort of optimality will not be undertaken here, although some indication of their nature is given in Chapter 13. The analyses presented here are each optimum under certain circumstances and can, in general, be expected to be reasonable.

Of course, if an experimenter were to discover during the course of a sequence of similar experiments that a certain function f gave better analyses than another, he would certainly be justified in using that f for future analyses.

TESTS OF HYPOTHESES

When an experimenter is faced with a choice between two actions and with the necessity to base this choice of actions on the outcome of a particular experiment, and he makes this choice with a prescribed rule, he is said to be testing a hypothesis. The rule is called the *test of the hypothesis*.

Suppose, for example, the experimenter with the diet supplement had to choose between conducting further experiments with the supplement and not conducting further experiments. One conceivable rule on which he could have based his choice is the following. If the experimental rats all gain more or all gain less than any of the control rats, more experiments will be conducted. Otherwise, no more experiments will be conducted.

It is clear here that conducting no more experiments is the appropriate action if, in fact, there is no treatment effect. It is also clear that an experimenter would use this rule only if he regarded it as equally appropriate to continue experimentation if the effect of treatment were to either increase or decrease weight gains.

If, as we have assumed, the treatment effect is additive, the statements above can be made in terms of the additive parameter θ. If θ is zero, the appropriate action is to discontinue experimentation; if θ is not zero, the appropriate action is to continue experimentation. A rule for basing a choice between the actions on the observed outcome is called a *test of the null hypothesis*, $\theta = 0$, against the alternative hypothesis, $\theta \neq 0$.

A test of such a null hypothesis, that is, a rule to decide whether to accept or reject the null hypothesis, $\theta = 0$, can be based on a curve A_f, as follows, for any given number α: If $A_f(0) > \alpha$, accept $\theta = 0$; if $A_f(0) \leq \alpha$ reject $\theta = 0$.

For illustration, suppose this rule, with $\alpha = 1/3$, is applied to each of the possible experiments of Figure 7.2. For the first, $A_f(0) = 1/3$, so that the hypothesis, $\theta = 0$, would be rejected. For the second, $A_f(0) = 2/3$, so that the hypothesis, $\theta = 0$, would be accepted. Similarly, the hypothesis $\theta = 0$ would be accepted for the third, fourth, and fifth, and rejected for the sixth. Accordingly, for the first experiment it would have been decided to continue experimentation; for the second, third, fourth, and fifth, it would have been decided to discontinue experimentation, and for the sixth it would have been decided to continue. In practice, of course, only one of these six possible experiments would have been observed and one action chosen.

If there were randomization for the selection of the treatment and control subjects, each of the possible experiments, and hence each of the decisions above, would have probability 1/6. Since the action appropriate to $\theta = 0$ (here discontinue experimentation) is to be taken if $A_f(0) \leq \alpha$, and since we know, for these experiments, that θ is zero, the probability of the error "Continue experimentation when there is no treatment effect" is 1/3.

There is also a relation between tests of such null hypotheses and confidence intervals that makes it possible to describe tests in terms of the intervals. Suppose that, for a given α, it is desired to test the null hypothesis $\theta = \theta_0$. Suppose the probability that a confidence interval covers the parameter θ is at least $1 - \alpha$ [as it will be if constructed from a curve $A_f(\theta)$ as the points for which $A_f(\theta)$ is above α, and the subjects were assigned at random to the two groups]. Then, if the action appropriate to $\theta \neq \theta_0$ for some fixed null hypothesis θ_0 is to be taken whenever the confidence interval fails to cover θ_0, the probability of wrongly adopting this action (that is, adopting this action when $\theta = \theta_0$) is at most α.

If it is only desired to select the action, with no description of the relation between the observations and the family of models, there is no need to compute the entire curve A_f or even to compute the confidence interval. It is enough to determine whether $A_f(\theta_0)$ is above α or not.

When, for a given experiment, $A_f(\theta_0)$ is less than or equal to α, it is often said that the null hypothesis is rejected at the level α. When $A_f(\theta_0)$ is greater than α, it is often said that the null hypothesis θ_0 is accepted at level α. It is often not clear when these statements are intended as statements descriptive of the experimental outcome or as statements descriptive of the experimenter's choice of action. As statements descriptive of the experimental outcome, they can, of course, be read as statements that $A_f(\theta_0) \leq \alpha$ (if θ_0 is rejected), or that $A_f(\theta_0) > \alpha$ (if θ_0 is accepted).

The exact value of $A_f(\theta_0)$ is called the *observed level of significance*. Hence the curve $A_f(\theta)$ could be described as the curve of observed levels of significance. However, in the theory of testing hypotheses, the term "level of significance" is used solely in connection with a null hypothesis which is prescribed.

The functions f presented in the first few chapters are well known and the tests based on them have names. These names are often those of persons who are among those who first proposed them as tests or studied their properties as tests. Tests based on $|\bar{t} - \bar{c}|$ are named *Fisher-Pitman tests*; those based on $|\bar{R}_t - \bar{R}_c|$ are named *Wilcoxon, Mann-Whitney tests*; and those based on $|n_t^+ - n_t^-|$ are called *median tests*. The estimation described below has been developed by Hodges and Lehmann.

ESTIMATION

It is sometimes desired to choose, on the basis of an experiment, a single model as the model, in a class, which is most appropriate. If the class of models is the additive class, each model is identified by a value of the additive parameter θ, and the choice, based on the experiment, of a value of θ is called an *estimate* of θ.

If, for a given analysis f, a curve $A_f(\theta)$ has already been constructed, the value of θ which seems "most consistent" with the experimental outcome is that corresponding to the "center" of the curve $A_f(\theta)$. This "center" will be taken as the midpoint of the interval for which $A_f(\theta)$ is equal to 1.

From Figure 5.2 the value of θ so obtained is $\theta = 12.5$, and this can be taken as an estimated value of the treatment effect based on the observations and an analysis with $f = |\bar{t}' - \bar{c}'|$. The dependence upon the analysis can be noted by selecting the corresponding value of θ from the graph of Figure 5.1. This value is $\theta = 13$ and is an estimate based on the observations and the analysis with $f = |\bar{R}_{t'} - \bar{R}_{c'}|$.

For a single experiment there is no answer to which of the estimates is better. Presumably it would be the estimate closer to the "true" value of θ, but this true value is not known. Generally speaking, a better method of estimation is that which "on the average" produces estimates which are closer to the (unknown) true value of θ. The average in question can be computed over the randomization for a fixed set of subjects. However, almost always the subjects are different for different experiments and the average is computed for a population of subjects.

As an example of the effect of randomization upon the estimated value of θ, consider the six curves A_f of Figure 7.2. For these, the analysis was with $f = |\bar{R}_t - \bar{R}_c|$, and it was known that $\theta = 0$. The estimated values of θ are $\theta = -6, -3, 1, -1, 3$, and 6. With randomization, each of these values would have been observed with probability 1/6. Because of the small number of subjects and the magnitude of the differences of no-treatment scores among the subjects, these estimated values are not clustered tightly around zero. Their average is zero.

As for confidence intervals and tests of hypotheses, it is not necessary to compute the entire curve $A_f(\theta)$ to find the estimated value. It is sufficient to find the extremes of the interval where A_f is 1. These extremes can usually be easily located by trial and error. In many cases the center of the interval can be approximated by considering the functions f. For example, if $f = |\bar{t}' - \bar{c}'|$, the value $\theta = \bar{t} - \bar{c}$ for the randomization observed can be taken as the estimated value. Similarly, the difference between the medians for the observed experiment will give a value of θ close to the center of the interval, $A_f(\theta) = 1$, for $f = |n_t^+ - n_t^-|$. For $f = |\bar{R}_t - \bar{R}_c|$, a method for approximating this midpoint is given in Exercise 8.8.

DECISIONS, ASSERTIONS, AND DESCRIPTIONS

In this chapter, decisions have been described as assertions primarily as a convenience. Within decision theory, a decision is regarded as a choice among possible acts, acts whose adoption will have consequences for those making the decision. This meaning is the intention here. Thus, the assertion, from a confidence interval, that θ is between 10 and 20 is regarded as the decision to act as though θ were between 10 and 20. The action might be an assertion; for instance, an experimenter might attend a meeting in which a decision was to be chosen and refuse to support a choice which would be appropriate if θ were zero.

A clear distinction between a choice of an action and a description is not easily made. The following rough classification of experiments will help to give some insight into the distinctions which arise.

Decision Experiments

To choose an action, an experiment is designed and carried out. The design includes the specifications of the methods of measurement, a family of models, the possible decisions, the method of randomization, the null hypothesis (if any), the analysis, and the level of significance (if any). After the experiment is carried out, the action is adopted in accordance with the prespecifications.

Exploratory Experiment

It is thought that a difference in conditions will produce a noticeable effect in a response. The method of measurement, a family of models, the method of randomization, and the analysis are set in advance. However, no particular set of actions is known in advance; the experiment is being conducted to "see."

Nonexperiment

Data, relevant to a question, are available. They could have been collected at some other time, with or without randomization, for some other purpose. They could be easily obtainable, from a present experiment, with little cost and with no effect on the purpose of the present experiment. The division of subjects for the present purpose might have no relation to the original division.

This classification is neither exhaustive nor mutually exclusive. A decision experiment can be regarded as an exploratory experiment. Either of the first two can be regarded as a nonexperiment.

When statistical analyses are described as having probabilistic properties, it is assumed that a decision experiment, or sometimes an exploratory experiment, is to be conducted. Exceptions from their prescriptions are delicate (or trivial) and will not be discussed here. The curves A_f seem particularly appropriate for the description of an exploratory experiment. That their descriptions have the relation which they do to the rules for basing certain decisions on an experiment is not necessary. However, description by stating how one would act is well known and often effective. Also, the probabilistic properties of rules for basing decisions on experiments have been extensively studied for a great variety of functions f, as well as for a great variety of underlying assumptions concerning the randomness of the observations. The results of these studies are applicable for the determination of the properties of A_f as a random approximation to a curve which singles out the true model in a class of models.

For a nonexperiment, the random properties of A_f, if any exist, are unknown. It can still be a useful description of the relation between the observations and a class of models. As an example, suppose an experimenter plans to conduct an exploratory experiment and publish the resulting curve A_f. When he sees the observations, there is one that is atypical, but there is no apparent difference between the subject from which the observation came and the other subjects in the same group. He can, with or without a rule, discard the observation and construct A_f with the remaining ones. This change would amount to a selection of the analysis on the basis of the observations and, effectively, change the experiment from an exploratory experiment to a nonexperiment. That is, the experimenter has some data available, relevant to his question, which was collected for another purpose. (It is possible to prescribe analyses, f, which anticipate outliers and what is to be done with them. It is assumed here that the experimenter did not anticipate outliers.) In most such cases it would be foolish not to describe the experimental outcome, and a description based on all the observations might be extremely atypical. It goes without saying that if the suspect observation is excluded, the fact should be included with the description. If space permits, the inclusion of curves A_f, both with and without the atypical observation, can be useful.

If A_f is constructed from a nonexperiment, it can be asked why it should be constructed with equal weights for the possible divisions of the subjects into two groups. The answer is that the use of any weights is what is called an *interpolatory procedure* when there is no reasonably objective basis for the choice of weights. Strictly speaking, any analysis of data is an interpolatory procedure—no one can "prove" that a random-digit source produces equally likely groups of digits, although it is reasonable to assume that some sources (including Rand's, after their smoothing) do produce such digits. In Chapter 10 some examples in which the assignment of equal weights is truly interpolatory are given. The use of equal weights is recommended, because of its simplicity, when no other basis exists for a choice of weights. In Chapter 12 a curve A_f will be described whose construction can be thought as that with a different set of weights (on a different set of possible experiments).

EXERCISES

8.1. For each of the six possible experiments of Exercise 7.2, find the confidence interval based on $f = |n_t^+ - n_t^-|$ (discarding observations equal to the median) for $\alpha = 1/6$. Verify that five out of the six intervals contain $\theta = 8$. That is, with randomization, the probability would be 5/6 that the statement based on the interval will be true.

8.2. If there had been randomization, what would be the 80 per cent confidence interval ($\alpha = .2$) for Example 2 of Chapter 1? Base the interval on $f = |n_t^+ - n_t^-|$ (discarding observations equal to the median).

8.3. For the gain scores in Example 3 of Chapter 1, what would the 90 per cent confidence interval be, based on $|\bar{R}_t - \bar{R}_c|$, if there had been randomization?

8.4. The students, in class, can arrange themselves in pairs. Within each pair, A is to write five different numbers without telling B what the numbers are. From these five numbers, A is to select two at random and give the remaining three to B as the scores of three control subjects. To the two selected at random, A is to add the same number, θ, and give only the two results (not θ) to B as the scores of two treatment subjects.

Repeat with A and B interchanged.

Then (perhaps before the next meeting) each student is to compute a 60 per cent ($\alpha = .4$) confidence interval based on the difference in mean ranks. If the number of students whose intervals contain the value of θ is counted, this number will be approximately 60 per cent of the number of students.

8.5. A small experiment was carried out to decide whether to conduct a series of experiments to distinguish between two methods of teaching or to regard the two methods as equivalent. Twenty students were randomly divided into two classes of 10 students each. The gains [(score on a posttest) − (score on a pretest)] were

Method 1 (15, 8, 10, 17, 12, 16, 14, 11, 18, 21),
Method 2 (7, 4, 3, 6, −2, 13, 5, 1, 9, 2).

If the additive treatment effect θ is zero, no further experiments are to be done. If θ is not zero, more experiments are to be made. Suppose that it has been decided that the probability of continuing with experiments if there is no difference should be no more than .1, and that it has been decided to use $f = |\bar{R}_t - \bar{R}_c|$. Which action is taken?

8.6. Suppose that the experiment in Exercise 8.5 had been conducted with six students for one method and four for the other, and that

$$f = |n_t^+ - n_t^-|$$

is to be used for testing that $\theta = 0$. If the scores were

Method 1 (13, 10, 18, 16, 12, 23),
Method 2 (2, 6, 3, 1),

and α were .01, what decision would be taken?

8.7. Find, within the class of additive models, the estimated value of θ for each of the three examples of Chapter 1. Use, in each example, each of the three functions $f = |\bar{t} - \bar{c}|$, $f = |\bar{R}_t - \bar{R}_c|$, and $f = |n_t^+ - n_t^-|$ and compare the estimates.

8.8. For a two-sample experiment, the midpoint of the interval, $A_f(\theta) = 1$, for $f = |\bar{R}_t - \bar{R}_c|$, can be approximated as follows. For the original observations, $(t_1, \ldots, t_n)$ and $(c_1, \ldots, c_m)$, compute the $n \cdot m$ differences

$t_i - c_j$, $i = 1, \ldots, n$, $j = 1, \ldots, m$. The median M of these differences will be, approximately, the center of the interval.

Example. For the experiment (A, B) of Figure 7.1, $(t_1, t_2) = (10, 12)$, $(c_1, c_2) = (15, 19)$, so that the four differences are

$$t_1 - c_1 = -5,\ t_1 - c_2 = -9,\ t_2 - c_1 = -3,\ t_2 - c_2 = -7$$

The median of these is -6. See the graph of Figure 7.2.

Compute the three estimates of Exercise 8.7, based on $|\bar{R}_t - \bar{R}_c|$, in this manner.

CHAPTER 9

A DIFFERENT DESIGN

The analyses described above were based on the fact that a set of $n + m$ subjects had been divided into two groups, one for treatment and one for control or for a second treatment. Experiments of this sort are referred to as *two-sample experiments.* In this chapter another method of dividing subjects into two groups is to be considered. Experiments which use this method are referred to as *paired comparison experiments.* The method depends upon a basis for matching, before the assignment of treatments, the subjects into pairs so that the two subjects within each pair can be expected to have no-treatment scores which would be, if observable, approximately the same.

As a typical example in which this design is utilized, consider an agronomist who wishes to compare two varieties of wheat. Suppose he has available a field in which to grow the two varieties and can divide the field into n sections. Suppose, also, that he can divide each of these sections into a pair of equal adjacent plots so that the two plots within each pair can be expected to produce about the same yield when planted to the same variety.

Within each pair, variety A is raised on one of the plots and variety B on the other. If n were four, a possible experimental outcome would be the following set of yields, in pounds per plot.

Var. *A* 92	Var. *B* 76
Var. *B* 75	Var. *A* 95
Var. *A* 67	Var. *B* 78
Var. *B* 57	Var. *A* 64

These, and the differences, can be displayed in a table or in a graph as in Figure 9.1. Analyses will be given of the differences (d_1, d_2, d_3, d_4) within each pair. The purpose of an analysis will again be to establish a descriptive relationship between the observations and a class of models. The class of models will be the additive models; that is, if a yield c would be observed for variety B on a given plot, then the yield $t = c + \theta$ would have been observed if variety A had been planted on that plot instead. Hence for any given model θ, where θ is the value of the treatment effect (or treatment difference), and for observations $(t_1, c_1), (t_2, c_2), \ldots, (t_n, c_n)$, the corresponding hypothetical no-treatment observations are $(t_1 - \theta, c_1), (t_2 - \theta, c_2), \ldots, (t_n - \theta, c_n)$. The corresponding no-treatment differences are $(d_1 - \theta, d_2 - \theta, \ldots, d_n - \theta)$.

Var. A	Var. B	Diff.(d)
92	76	16
95	75	20
67	78	−11
64	57	7

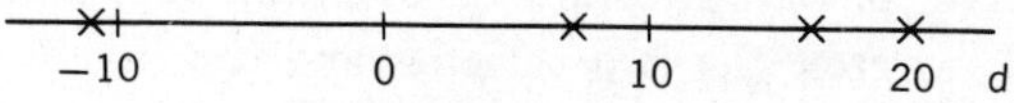

Figure 9.1.

Relationships between the observations and the class of models will be given by curves A_f for suitably chosen functions f. $A_f(\theta)$ will be, for each θ, the proportion of experiments which could have been conducted with these subjects and which lead to a value of f as high as or higher than the value of f for $(d_1 - \theta, \ldots, d_n - \theta)$. However, the set of possible experiments depends upon the design, so that a different set is to be taken here.

This set corresponds to the 2^n different assignments of the subjects to the treatments which are possible within the pairs. The corresponding set of (no-treatment) differences in yields is that obtained by the 2^n possible assignments of + and − signs to the observed differences, $(d_1 - \theta, d_2 - \theta, \ldots, d_n - \theta)$. For a given function, f, and for each θ, each of these assignments of signs will lead to a value of f. By definition, $A_f(\theta)$ is the proportion of these values which are at least as great as the value of f for $(d_1 - \theta, \ldots, d_n - \theta)$.

For illustration, the value of $A_f(\theta)$ is computed for $f = |\bar{d} - \theta|$, or, equivalently, with $f = |\sum d'|$. The computation, for $\theta = 10$, proceeds as follows. The differences, as observed, are (16, 20, −11, 7). If θ is 10, the corresponding differences for the no-treatment (or single variety) experiment are (6, 10, −21, −3). To keep track of the sign changes it is easier to start with all + signs, as in Table 9.1. The set of differences corresponding to the observations and $\theta = 10$ is marked. From Table 9.1, $A_f(10) = 14/16$, since only two of the assignments of signs lead to smaller values of $|\sum d'|$ than 8.

Table 9.1

	d_1'	d_2'	d_3'	d_4'	$\sum d'$
	6	10	21	3	40
	6	10	21	−3	34
	6	10	−21	3	−2
→	6	10	−21	−3	−8
	6	−10	21	3	20
	6	−10	21	−3	14
	6	−10	−21	3	−22
	6	−10	−21	−3	−28
	−6	10	21	3	28
	−6	10	21	−3	22
	−6	10	−21	3	−14
	−6	10	−21	−3	−20
	−6	−10	21	−3	8
	−6	−10	21	−3	2
	−6	−10	−21	3	−34
	−6	−10	−21	−3	−40

For $\theta = 0$, the computation of $A_f(0)$ is given in Table 9.2, where the observed differences are marked. Because six of these sums are at least as large, in absolute value, as 32, the value of $A_f(0)$ is 6/16. The interpretation of these two values of A_f is as before: Within the class of additive models, the model corresponding to $\theta = 10$ (that is, to a higher yield of 10 pounds per plot for variety A) is more in agreement with the observations than the model corresponding to $\theta = 0$.

Proceeding as in Tables 9.1 and 9.2, values of A_f can be found for as many values of θ as desired, and the curve, or its approximation, graphed. Although somewhat laborious, some shortcuts are available (see Exercise 9.1) which can be used for experiments with a small number of observations. In Chapter 15 an approximation will be given for experiments with many observations.

Table 9.2

d_1'	d_2'	d_3'	d_4'	$\sum d'$
16	20	11	7	54
16	20	11	−7	40
→16	20	−11	7	32
16	20	−11	−7	18
16	−20	11	7	14
16	−20	11	−7	0
16	−20	−11	7	−8
16	−20	−11	−7	−22
−16	20	11	7	22
−16	20	11	−7	8
−16	20	−11	7	0
−16	20	−11	−7	−14
−16	−20	11	7	−18
−16	−20	11	−7	−32
−16	−20	−11	7	−40
−16	−20	−11	−7	−54

There is an analysis based on ranks which is used for paired comparison experiments. The basis of the analysis is the comparison of the sum of the ranks of the positive differences with the sum of the ranks of the negative differences, where the ranks are those of the absolute values of all the differences. This corresponding function, f, can be written as

$$f = |\sum R^+_{|d-\theta|} - \sum R^-_{|d-\theta|}|,$$

where $R^+_{|d-\theta|}$ denotes the rank of $|d - \theta|$ for a positive value of $d - \theta$ and $R^-_{|d-\theta|}$ denotes that for a negative value of $d - \theta$. The advantages of using ranks are the same as for the two-sample problem. The use of ranks provides a compromise, in sensitivity to observations, between analyses based on means and analyses based on medians. Further, the computation of A_f from ranks requires only one computation of the table of possible values of f for each n (Table C). For $n = 4$, these possible values are in the fourth column of Table 9.3. The value of f can be found, simply, from a graph for moderate sample sizes (see Exercise 9.4).

In Table 9.3 $A_f(0)$ is computed directly for the differences (16, 20, −11, 7). It is equivalent to use f as $|\sum R^+_{|d'|} - \sum R^-_{|d'|}|$ or as $|\sum R^+_{|d'|} - [n(n+1)/4]|$. Note that for $\theta = 0$ there are no zeros among the differences $(d_1 - \theta, \ldots,$

Table 9.3

d_1'	d_2'	d_3'	d_4'	*Ranks of positive d'*	$\sum R^+_{\|d'\|}$
16	20	11	7	1 2 3 4	10
16	20	11	−7	2 3 4	9
→16	20	−11	7	1 3 4	8
16	20	−11	−7	3 4	7
16	−20	11	7	1 2 3	6
16	−20	11	−7	2 3	5
16	−20	−11	7	1 3	4
16	−20	−11	−7	3	3
−16	20	11	7	1 2 4	7
−16	20	11	−7	2 4	6
−16	20	−11	7	1 4	5
−16	20	−11	−7	4	4
−16	−20	11	7	1 2	3
−16	−20	11	−7	2	2
−16	−20	−11	7	1	1
−16	−20	−11	−7	—	0

$d_n - \theta$). When there are zeros, n should be replaced by n' = [the number of $(d_1 - \theta, \ldots, d_n - \theta)$ not equal to zero] when Table C is used.

For $f = |\sum R^+_{|d'|} - [n(n+1)/4]|$ (or for $f = |\sum R^+_{|d'|} - \sum R^-_{|d'|}|$), the value of $A_f(0)$ is 6/16. That is, 6 of the 16 possible assignments of signs lead to values of $\sum R^+_{|d'|}$ which are as far or farther from $n(n+1)/4 = 5$, as is the value 8.

When computed for all values of θ (except at the jumps), the curve A_f appears as in Figure 9.2 (see Exercise 9.5). Descriptively, the curve indicates that the evidence in the present observations is that variety *A* yields more than variety *B*. More specifically, if it is assumed that the difference in yield between the varieties is a constant θ for all plots, then values of θ between 7 and $11\frac{1}{2}$ are most in agreement with the observations and values of θ below −11 or above 20 are least in agreement with the observations.

Randomization for paired comparison experiments is to be recommended, as for two-sample experiments. It will provide, in an average sense, a balanced assignment of treatments to the more favorable and the less favorable subjects (plots) within each pair. Randomization will also preclude the possibility that the experimenter will introduce any bias he might have into the process of subject selection.

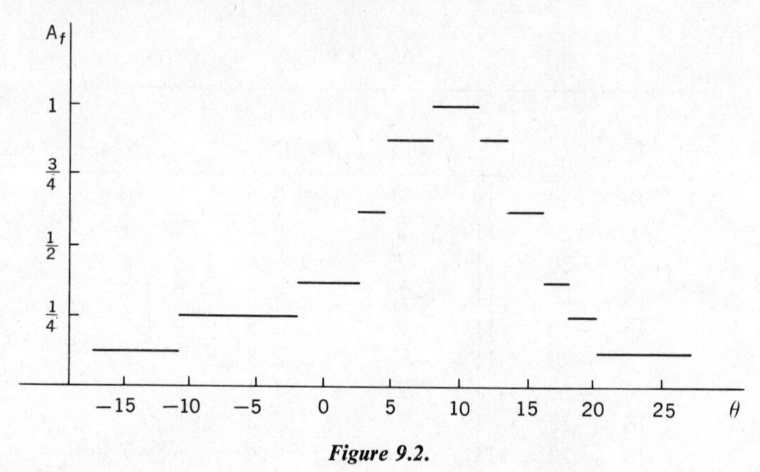

Figure 9.2.

The simplest method of randomly assigning the treatments to subjects is by tossing a coin. If the subjects within a pair are identified as 1 and 2, for instance, and the treatments as A and B, the outcome heads on the coin can determine the assignment $1A$ and $2B$, while tails can determine $1B$ and $2A$. A table of random digits can be used instead of the coin with odd and even replacing heads and tails.

If there has been randomization, the relation of the three sorts of decision making to the curve A_f is as described in Chapter 8. That is, for a number α and a function f, which are fixed before the experiment is observed, the set of values of θ for which A_f is greater than α will be a $1 - \alpha$ confidence set for θ. Likewise, the fixed null hypothesis θ_0 can be tested by rejecting θ_0 if $A_f(\theta_0)$ is no greater than α and accepting θ_0 if $A_f(\theta_0)$ is greater than α. The center of the interval where $A_f = 1$ can be used as an estimate of θ. For the probabilistic properties of these decision procedures, as well as for those of A_f as a description, to obtain, it is necessary that the class of models contain the model which was effective during the experiment. That is, for the present example, it is necessary that the difference, in yield, between the varieties be constant for the several plots.

EXERCISES

9.1. For a given θ, the set of values of $f = |\sum d'|$ for the 2^n assignments of signs to $|d_1 - \theta|, |d_2 - \theta|, \ldots, |d_n - \theta|$ can be written as follows. Starting with the first, $|d_1 - \theta|$, form two numbers by adding and subtracting the second, $|d_2 - \theta|$. Then, from each of these, form two more numbers by adding and subtracting the third, $|d_3 - \theta|$. Continue, forming two numbers from each by adding and subtracting the next, until the nth, at which time there will be 2^{n-1} numbers. These are one half of the possible values of $\sum d'$. The other half are the negatives of the first half.

Thus, for Table 9.1, where the observed differences are (16, 20, −11, 7) and $\theta = 10$, start with $|16 - 10| = 6$, $|20 - 10| = 10$, $|-11 - 10| = 21$, and $|7 - 10| = 3$,

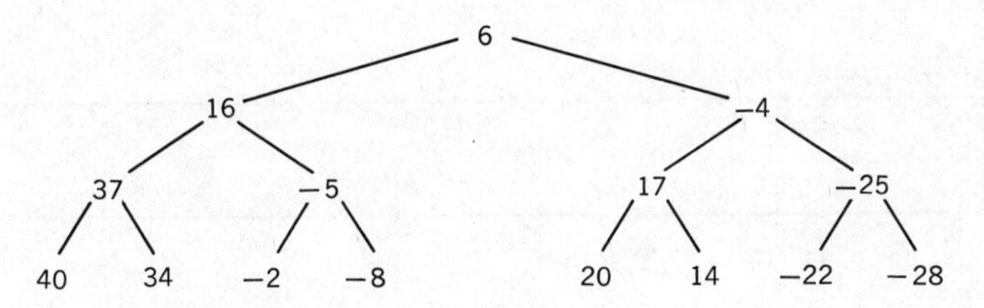

so that the set of possible values of $\sum d'$ is

$$\begin{Bmatrix} 40, & 34, & -2, & -8, & 20, & 14, & -22, & -28 \\ -40, & -34, & 2, & 8, & -20, & -14, & 22, & 28 \end{Bmatrix}.$$

Use this device to find, for the same observed differences, the values of $A_f(\theta)$ for $\theta = -5, 0, 5, 10, 15, 20, 25$, and graph the approximation to A_f.

9.2. Verify, by enumeration, that the value of $A_f(4)$ is 5/8 for $f = |\sum R^+_{|d'|} - [n(n+1)/4]|$ for the example used for Figure 9.2.

9.3. Enumerate the 32 possible assignments of + and − signs to the integers (1, 2, 3, 4, 5). For each of these compute the sum of those with the + signs. Then collect the possible values of this sum in a table together with the number of times it occurs. That is, complete Tables a and b.

Table a

Assignments of signs	*Sum of +'s*
1 2 3 4 5	15
1 2 3 4 −5	10
1 2 3 −4 5	11
1 2 3 −4 −5	6

Table b

Sum	*No. of times*	*No. of times/32*
15	1	.03125
14		

Compare Table b with the corresponding entry in Table C in Part III.

9.4. A simple graphical method for finding $\sum R^+_{|d-\theta|}$ is the following. Plot the differences on each of two lines, one line labeled from left to right, the other from right to left, with uniform scales. Place the two lines so that the values of θ on each scale are in alignment and then, reading only to the right of θ, total the ranks (positions) of the points on the left to right scale among the points on both scales. For $\theta = 10$ this method is illustrated in the figure below. There the value of $\sum R^+_{|d-10|}$ is 5. Use this

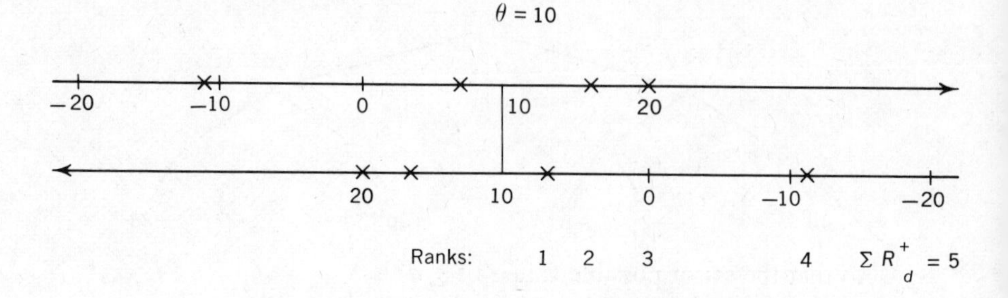

method to find $\sum R^+_{|d-\theta|}$ for $\theta = -6$, 2, and 6 1/2 for the observations $[(t_1, c_1), (t_2, c_2), (t_3, c_3)] = [(20, 25), (33, 27), (29, 21)]$ from a paired comparison experiment.

9.5. For $f = |\sum R^+_{|d-\theta|} - [n(n+1)/4]|$, the curve $A_f(\theta)$ can be constructed easily, as follows. From the observations $(d_1, \ldots, d_n)$, form the $n(n+1)/2$ averages $(d_i + d_j)/2$, $i \leq j$. If these are plotted on a line labeled θ, $A_f(\theta)$ will be constant on the intervals so defined, so that it need be computed for only one point in the interval. Use this method to find $A_f(\theta)$ for the observations $[(t_1, c_1), (t_2, c_2), (t_3, c_3)] = [(20, 25), (33, 27), (29, 21)]$ from a paired comparison experiment.

9.6. When there are ties among $(|d_1 - \theta|, \ldots, |d_n - \theta|)$, the convention for defining ranks is the same as in the two-sample problem (see Exercise 5.7). The set of possible values of f is found in the same manner as in Table 9.3, with the replacement of the integers by the observed tied ranks. For the same observations, $(d_1, d_2, d_3, d_4) = (16, 20, -11, 7)$, as in Table 9.3, find $A_f(\theta)$ for $\theta = -2$ and 18.

9.7. Another function that is sometimes used for the analysis of differences from paired comparison experiments is the absolute value of the difference between the number of + signs and the number of − signs or, equivalently, $f = |\text{no. of +'s} - n'/2|$, ($n'$ = no. of nonzero d'). For the observed differences (16, 20, −11, 7), the value of f is $|3 - 2| = 1$. a. Find the set of all possible values of f for the 16 possible assignments of signs to (16, 20, 11, 7) and thus find $A_f(0)$. b. Find $A_f(\theta)$, for all θ, for $f = |[\text{no. of +'s among } (d_1 - \theta, \ldots, d_n - \theta)] - (n'/2)|$ for the differences (16, 20, −11, 7). Note that A_f is constant on the intervals defined by the points $(d_1, \ldots, d_n)$.

CHAPTER **10**

POPULATIONS

BASIC PROPERTIES

The word *population*, as used in statistics, occurs in two different, but related, senses. The first sense, related to the origin of the word statistics, is that of a body of individuals identified in some manner. The populations consisting of the taxpayers of a given state, of automobiles in Canada, of marketable white pine in a certain forest, of high school graduates, are all self-explanatory. They are not necessarily well defined. If a population is to be studied, one of the first steps is to give a more precise, and operational, definition of exactly which individuals are in the population. Depending upon the purpose of the study, a taxpayer in a given state might be further defined as anyone who filed a state income tax form for a given year, or, as a resident who filed a federal form for a given year. A high school graduate might be further defined as anyone who so described himself in the last census or as anyone completing the last year in an accredited high school since 1927.

The second sense in which population is used arises when a method of sampling from a population is given. A set of possible outcomes for the application of the method can be described. This list of outcomes, together with a corresponding list of numbers called *probabilities*, is also called a population. In this sense, a population is a model for the method of sampling from the set of individuals (the "population"). As an example, suppose the set of individuals in question is the adult fish in a given lake, and the method of sampling is to catch a certain number n in a prescribed manner. A possible set of outcomes is {pike, bass, minnow, other}. This list of outcomes, together with probabilities as in Table 10.1, is also called a population and is a model for the method of sampling. As a model for the method of sampling the fish in the lake, it is not necessarily directly relevant to the population of fish in the lake. For any of a number of reasons, for instance, if minnows were less apt to be caught than bass by the method of sampling, the probabilities for Table 10.1 could be considerably different than if bass were less apt to be caught than minnows. It is also possible that there are some fish (nonrespondents) in the lake which cannot be caught by the prescribed manner.

The word "population" will be used here in this second sense—as a model for the performance of a trial. A population will consist of an exhaustive list of possible outcomes for the trial together with a probability for each outcome. The trial need not involve sampling from a collection of individuals; that is, there may be no "population" in the first sense which is related to a given population in the second sense.

Table 10.1

Outcomes	*Probability*
Pike	.2
Bass	.3
Minnow	.1
Other	.4
	1

The trials for which populations are models are often described as random. The word "random" is used to denote haphazardness, irregularity, or unpredictability. However, in some contexts the word has acquired a more limited meaning. A sequence of trials is described as random when it is impossible to predict the outcome of any given trial and when it is possible to predict, for a large number of trials, the frequencies of occurrence of each of the possible outcomes of the trial.

An example with which almost everyone has had some experience is the issuance of insurance policies. A company issuing policies covering, for a year, single-family dwellings against loss from fire certainly does not know on which particular policies it will have to make a given payment. However, to set premiums, it is necessary that they know, approximately, the proportion of policies for which they will have to make each given payment. That is, if a sequence T_1, T_2, $T_3, \ldots$ of policies were issued, there is no way, at the time of issue, to predict that the corresponding sequence of payments would be \$0, \$1000, \$0, \$0, \$5000, ... However, from past experience it could be known for what proportion of the policies each possible payment would be made. A risk table summarizing these proportions might, if no policy had a face value of more than \$5000, be as shown in Table 10.2.

Table 10.2

Loss, $	*Probabilities*
0	.981
1000	.010
2000	.003
3000	.002
4000	.001
5000	.003

This set of possible losses and probabilities is called a population, and knowledge of it is considered as complete knowledge of a sequence of trials to which it is relevant. Insurance companies spend considerable effort to determine for which sequences of trials particular tables, or populations, are relevant. For different circumstances, different tables are required, hence their interest, for fire insurance, in factors such as type of construction and heating and availability of fire protection.

An even more well-known example of a population is the following:

Outcomes	*Probabilities*
H	1/2
T	1/2

This population is relevant to the sequence of outcomes produced by most, but not all, methods of coin tossing. It is a matter of common belief that, of a large number of tosses, approximately one half will result in heads and one half will result in tails and that the outcome of a particular toss is unpredictable. For some particular methods of tossing, the relevance of this population to the corresponding sequence of trials has been experimentally verified. One method for which they are relevant is the usual method of placing a coin on the thumb and bent forefinger and flipping it vigorously upward. A method for which the two probabilities are not equal is the following. If a Jefferson nickel is held on edge, lightly under one finger, on a smooth table top and spun, it will show a slight bias in a long sequence of tosses.

The digits in a random-number table can be regarded as a sequence of trials from the population

Outcomes	0	1	2	3	4	5	6	7	8	9
Probabilities	.1	.1	.1	.1	.1	.1	.1	.1	.1	.1

These tables are (essentially) constructed from a random source whose trials can be regarded as successive tosses of a symmetric 10-sided die or as successive draws, with replacement and thorough mixing after each draw, from an urn containing 10 objects distinguished only by the labels 0, 1, 2, . . ., 9.

A population is a list of possible outcomes and the associated probabilities. A population is relevant to a sequence of trials if, for the actual performance of a very long sequence of such trials, it can be expected that the observed proportion of each outcome will be approximately the corresponding probability of the population. The outcome of a trial to which a population is relevant is called an *observation* from the population.

The observed proportions in a particular sequence of trials are called *relative frequencies*. A coin was tossed 10 times, in the usual manner described above, and resulted in H, T, T, H, T, T, T, T, H, T. For this sequence the relative frequency of H is 3/10 and the relative frequency of tails is 7/10. Clearly, for a very short sequence of trials, the relative frequencies do not closely approximate the probabilities of a relevant population. This is even more obvious if a single trial is considered; the only possible relative frequencies are zero and 1.

For a very long sequence of trials it is still possible that the relative frequencies will not closely approximate the probabilities. However, this possibility becomes increasingly remote as the length of the sequence increases, and it can be expected that the relative frequencies will approximate the probabilities of the population. The tendency, as the number of trials increases, of the relative frequency to approximate the probability can be seen by tossing a coin 100 times and recording the cumulative relative frequency every 5 or 10 tosses. These numbers will (usually) become closer and closer to $P(\mathrm{H})$. The output of random-number generators is "tested" by recording the relative frequencies for single digits, pairs, triples, "poker hands" in groups of five, etc. If, in a long table, these relative frequencies are not close to their probabilities, the table, or some portion of it, is discarded, and more digits are generated. Insurance companies realize a large number of trials, and better agreement between relative frequencies (actual payments) and probabilities (risk tables) by issuing a large number of policies and by the practice of reinsuring.

A population has been defined as a list of possible outcomes, for a trial, together with a probability corresponding to each outcome in the list. It is convenient to start with a list of outcomes with the property that exactly one of the outcomes will occur for a single performance of the trial. For example, for the trial "toss two coins," either of the lists {HH, HT, TH, TT} or {(first coin is H), (first coin is T)} has this property. Since it ignores the outcome of the second coin, the second list above would not ordinarily be taken. The list of outcomes, {(first coin is H), (second coin is H)}, does not have the property in question, since, on a single toss of two coins, both coins could be heads or neither coin could be heads.

When the list of outcomes is such that, for a single performance of the trial, exactly one outcome will occur, it is clear that for a sequence of performances of the trial, the relative frequencies of the outcomes will each be nonnegative and that their sum will be 1. The probabilities corresponding to the outcomes are a model for the relative frequencies and are taken so that they are nonnegative and add to 1.

Any collection of outcomes in the list is called an *event*. An event is said to occur if any one of its outcomes occurs. Again, because it will be true of any relative frequencies obtained from a sequence of performances of the trial, the probability of an event is defined to be the sum of the probabilities of its outcomes.

As an example, consider again the trial "toss two coins." A population for this trial is

Outcomes	*Probability*
HH	1/4
HT	1/4
TH	1/4
TT	1/4

For the event (first coin is H), the probability is $1/4 + 1/4 = 1/2$, since (first coin is H) = (HT, HH) and $P(\text{HT}) = 1/4$, $P(\text{HH}) = 1/4$. Similarly, $P(\text{at least one H}) = P(\text{HH, HT, TH}) = 3/4$ and $P(\text{exactly one H}) = P(\text{HT, TH}) = 1/2$.

This population is not the only conceivable population for the trial "toss two coins." Another population is

Outcomes	*Probability*
HH	4/10
HT	1/10
TH	1/10
TT	4/10

For this population, P(first coin is H) = 1/2, P(at least one H) = 6/10, and P(exactly one H) = 2/10.

In general, any four nonnegative numbers, which total 1, give a population for this trial (with this list of outcomes). If the population is

Outcomes	*Probability*
HH	p_1
HT	p_2
TH	p_3
TT	p_4

then P(first coin is H) $= p_1 + p_2$, P(at least one H) $= p_1 + p_2 + p_3$, and P(exactly one H) $= p_2 + p_3$.

Which of these populations is relevant to a particular manner of tossing two coins is a matter for experimental verification. Experience with the usual manner of tossing supports the first example in which the four probabilities are equal.

If a function f is defined on the set of outcomes, then events can be defined in terms of the values of f. As an example, let f = (number of heads) be defined (in the obvious manner) on {HH, HT, TH, TT}. Then the events $\{f = 2\}$, $\{f = 1\}$, and $\{f = 0\}$ are, respectively, {HH}, {HT, TH}, and {TT}. Similarly, the events, $\{f < 2\}$, $\{f \leq 2\}$, $\{0 \leq f < 1\}$, and $\{|f - 1| < 1/2\}$ are {TT, TH, HT}, {HH, HT, TH, TT}, {TT}, and {HT, TH}.

Events defined in this manner have already been encountered. If the trial consists of dividing five no-treatment scores (47, 30, 38, 40, 21) into a set (t_1', t_2', t_3') and (c_1', c_2'), the outcomes, together with the values of $f = \sum R_c$ = the sum of the ranks of c_1', c_2', are listed in Table 10.3.

The event $\{f = 5\}$ is {A, F}, and the event $\{f \geq 5\}$ is {A, C, E, F, G, H, I, J}. The event $\{|\sum R_c - [m(n + m + 1)/2]| \geq 2\} = \{|\sum R_c - (2 \cdot 6/2)| \geq 2\}$

Table 10.3

	Outcomes		
	(t_1', t_2', t_3')	(c_1', c_2')	$f = \sum R_c$
A	(47, 30, 38)	(40, 21)	5
B	(47, 30, 40)	(38, 21)	4
C	(47, 30, 21)	(38, 40)	7
D	(47, 38, 40)	(30, 21)	3
E	(47, 38, 21)	(30, 40)	6
F	(47, 40, 21)	(30, 38)	5
G	(30, 38, 40)	(47, 21)	6
H	(30, 38, 21)	(47, 40)	9
I	(30, 40, 21)	(47, 38)	8
J	(38, 40, 21)	(47, 30)	7

is {B, D, H, I}. $A_{|\sum R_c - [m(n+m+1)/2]|}$, by definition, is the number of outcomes in the event

$$\left\{\left|\sum R_c - \frac{m(n+m+1)}{2}\right| \geq \left|\sum R_c^0 - \frac{m(n+m+1)}{2}\right|\right\},$$

where $\sum R_c^0$ is the sum of the ranks for the no-treatment scores implied by the observations and the assumption of θ. If the observed outcome were obtained in a randomized experiment, the relevant probabilities for the table would each be 1/10 and A_f would be the probability of a value of $|\sum R_c - [m(m+n+1)/2]|$ as high or higher than that obtained from the present experiment. Without a randomization, for which the probabilities are known, there would be be no way to infer the relevant probabilities for Table 10.3. Hence the probabilistic properties of decisions, or descriptions, based on A_f could not be known.

Note that the descriptive properties of a curve A_f do not depend upon whether there was randomization. It would be impossible to maintain that, if two experimenters obtained the same observations, the one who had randomized would be in any different position with respect to describing a relationship between his observations and a given family of models than would the one who did not randomize.

The one who did randomize could, with known risks, base a decision on his experiment provided the manner in which he did so was prescribed before the experiment. Even if there were no decisions to be based on the experiments, the advantages of randomization are as described in Chapters 1 and 8, and randomization is to be recommended. However, neither the absence of randomization nor the fact that a decision has been properly based on a randomized experiment need preclude the making of any descriptive statements for which no probabilistic properties are claimed. In this connection it is to be emphasized that if one "digs" long enough, a class of models and an analysis f can almost always be found so that a given set of observations singles out certain models in the class. Hence, careful substantiation both from other experiments and from comparisons with other models and experiments for the same, or similar, phenomena are necessary for the establishment of the models indicated by any one experiment.

THE MEAN AND STANDARD DEVIATION OF A DISTRIBUTION

A *distribution* is a particular kind of population, one for which the possible outcomes are describable by a number. A population is a set of outcomes and corresponding probabilities; a distribution is a set of numbers and a probability associated with each number in the set. Two of the important features of a distribution are its mean and its standard deviation. The mean, μ, of a distribution is a measure of where the distribution is centered. The standard deviation, σ, of a distribution is a measure of the average distance that the values x of the distribution are dispersed around this center.

The simplest type of distribution has all its probability concentrated on a single point, say, x_0.

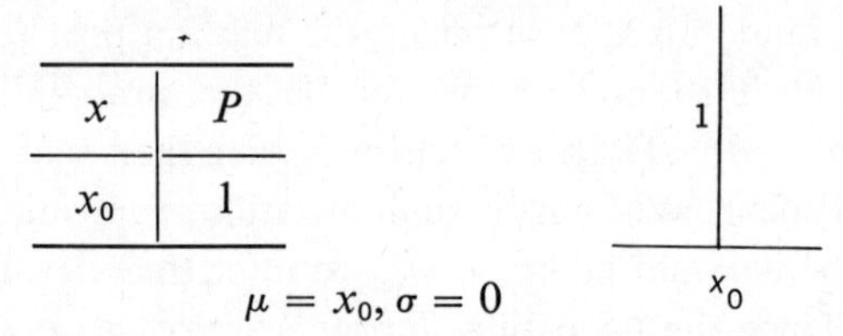

x	P
x_0	1

$$\mu = x_0, \sigma = 0$$

For this distribution the mean is the point x_0, where the probability is concentrated. The standard deviation is 0, since there is no dispersion around x_0.

The next most simple type of distribution is the symmetric distribution on two points. If these two points are −1 and 1, as

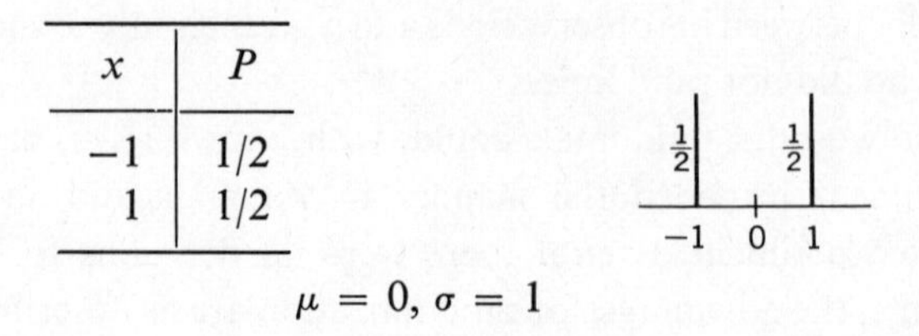

x	P
−1	1/2
1	1/2

$$\mu = 0, \sigma = 1$$

the mean μ is 0, since the distribution is centered on 0, and the standard deviation σ is 1, since each possible value of x is at a distance 1 from the mean.

Measurements are often transformed by changing the point from which the measurements are made (the origin) and changing the units in which the measurements are made (the scale). The effect of such changes on the mean and standard deviation can be seen by considering the following simple example. Suppose a trial consists of tossing a coin to select and measure the height of one of two persons whose heights are 72 and 68 inches. The population is any one of the following.

x	P
68	1/2
72	1/2

for measurement, in inches, from the floor.

$x - 60$	P
8	1/2
12	1/2

for measurements, in inches, from a 5-foot table.

$\frac{x-60}{12}$	P
2/3	1/2
1	1/2

for measurements, in feet, from a 5-foot table.

$\frac{x-84}{12}$	P
−4/3	1/2
−1	1/2

for measurements, in feet, from a 7-foot ceiling.

The means and standard deviations of these distributions are, with their graphs,

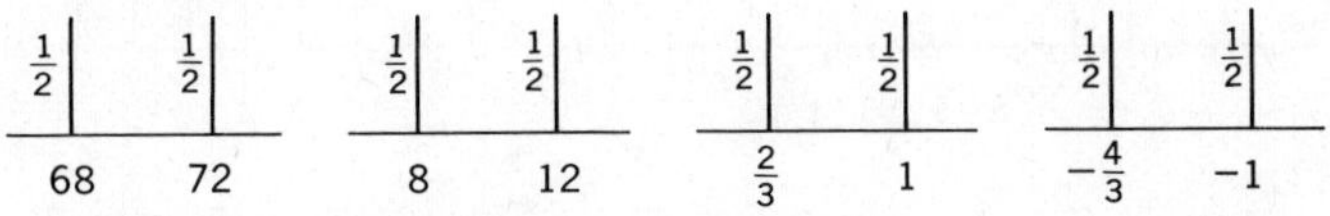

Graph (bar heights)	Values	Mean	Standard deviation
$\frac{1}{2}$, $\frac{1}{2}$	68, 72	$\mu = 70$	$\sigma = 2$
$\frac{1}{2}$, $\frac{1}{2}$	8, 12	$\mu = 10$	$\sigma = 2$
$\frac{1}{2}$, $\frac{1}{2}$	$\frac{2}{3}$, 1	$\mu = 5/6$	$\sigma = 1/6$
$\frac{1}{2}$, $\frac{1}{2}$	$-\frac{4}{3}$, -1	$\mu = -7/6$	$\sigma = 1/6$

The mean changes with either a change in origin or a change in scale. The standard deviation changes only with a change in scale. In general, if x is measured in certain units from zero, then the same measurements from a different origin in different units are $(x - a)/b$, where a is the distance from zero (in the original units) and b is the number of the original units for each of the new units. If a population has mean μ_x, and standard deviation σ_x, then the population of values of $(x - a)/b$, with the probabilities corresponding to values of x, will have mean and standard deviation given by

$$\mu_{(x-a)/b} = \frac{\mu_x - a}{b},$$

$$\sigma_{(x-a)/b} = \frac{\sigma_x}{b}.$$

It is often convenient to take, for a given distribution, the mean μ as origin and the standard deviation σ as the unit of measurement. A distribution transformed in this manner is called a *standard*, or *unit distribution* and has

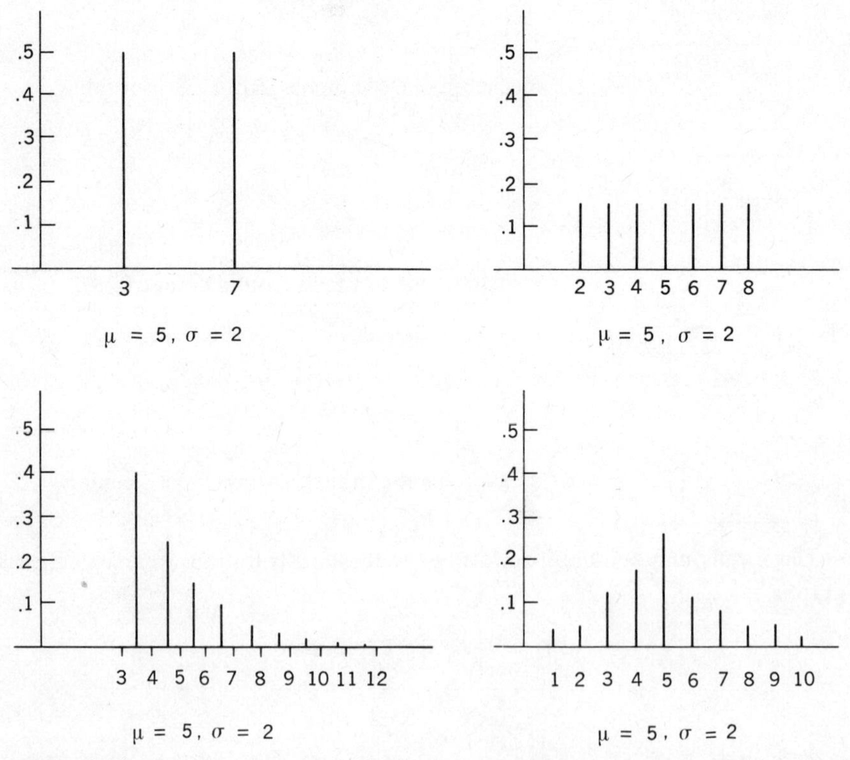

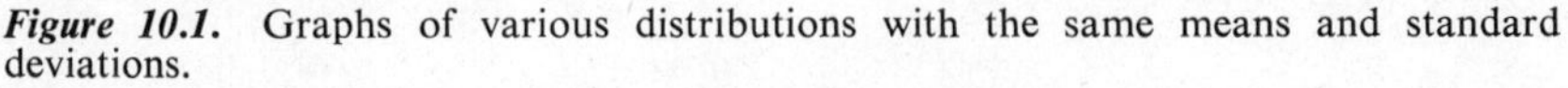

Figure 10.1. Graphs of various distributions with the same means and standard deviations.

mean zero and standard deviation 1. The unit symmetric two-point distribution is

x	P
-1	$1/2$
1	$1/2$

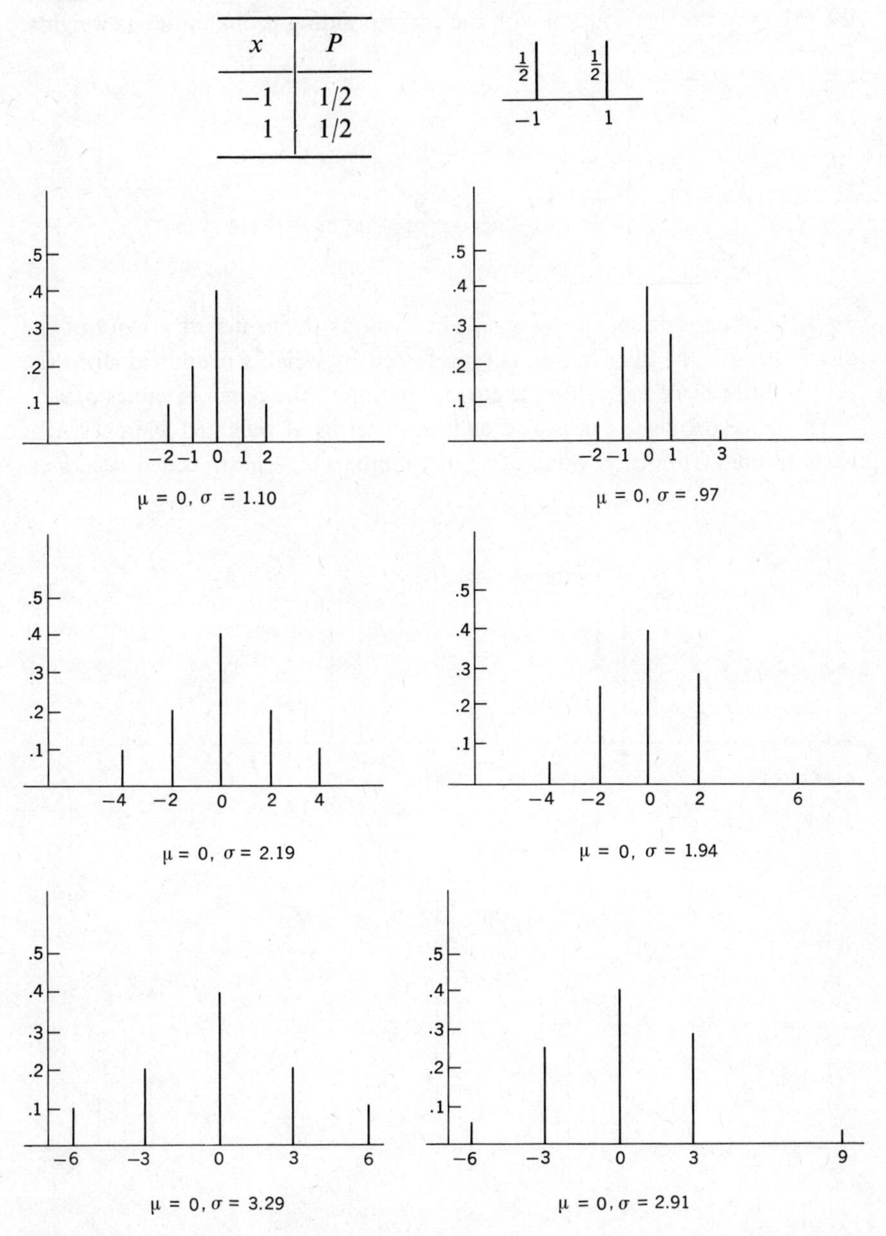

Figure 10.2. Graphs of various distributions with the same means and different standard deviations.

For a general discrete distribution the mean and standard deviation are defined in terms of weighted averages. The mean is the weighted average of the values in the distribution with the corresponding probabilities as weights. For

x	P
x_1	p_1
x_2	p_2
$\vdots$	$\vdots$
x_n	p_n

$$\mu = x_1p_1 + x_2p_2 + \cdots + x_np_n$$

or, as is often written, $\mu = \sum x_ip_i$. The mean is the center of gravity of the distribution if the distribution is represented by weights proportional to the probabilities placed at distances corresponding to the possible values of x.

The standard deviation is also defined in terms of weighted averages. If μ is subtracted from each value of x, the numbers $x - \mu$ are called *deviations*

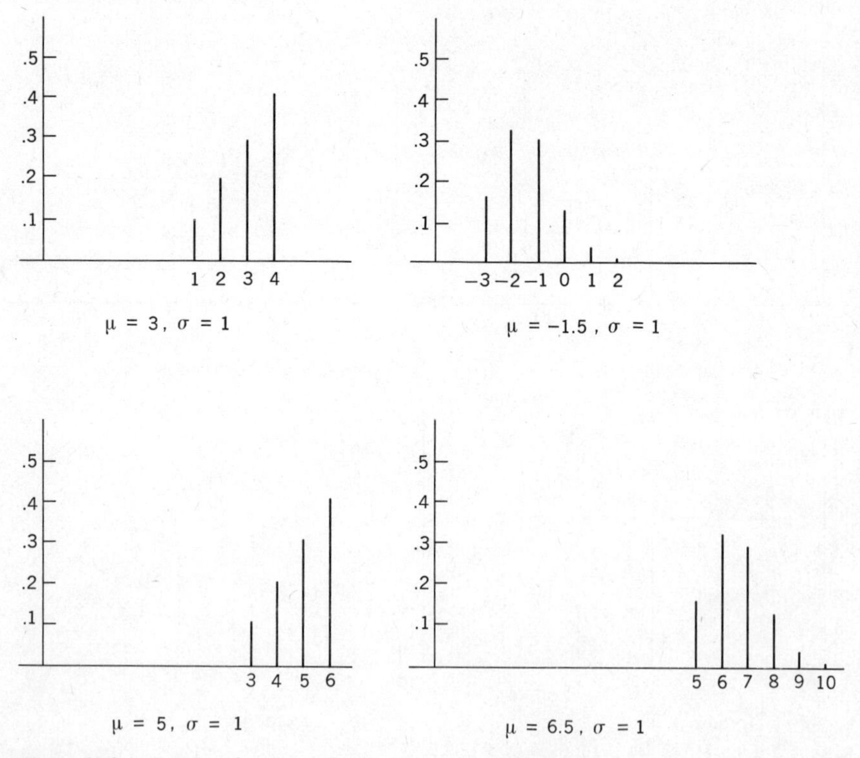

Figure 10.3. Graphs of various distributions with different means and the same standard deviations.

and the numbers $(x - \mu)^2$ are called *squared deviations*. The standard deviation is the square root of the weighted average of these squared deviations:

$$\sigma = \sqrt{(x_1 - \mu)^2 p_1 + (x_2 - \mu)^2 p_2 + \cdots + (x_n - \mu)^2 p_n}$$

or

$$\sigma = \sqrt{\sum (x_i - \mu)^2 p_i}.$$

The weighted average of the squared deviations is called the *variance*, σ^2. It is computationally simpler to note that $\sigma^2 = \sum (x_i - \mu)^2 p_i = (\sum x_i^2 p_i) - \mu^2$, that is, the variance σ^2 can be computed as the difference between the mean of x^2, μ_{x^2}, and the squared mean of x, $(\mu_x)^2$. The computation of the mean, the variance, and the standard deviation can be conveniently carried out in a table as follows.

x	P	$x \cdot P$	$x^2 \cdot P$
x_1	p_1	$x_1 p_1$	$x_1^2 p_1$
x_2	p_2	$x_2 p_2$	$x_2^2 p_2$
$\vdots$	$\vdots$	$\vdots$	$\vdots$
x_n	p_n	$x_n p_n$	$x_n^2 p_n$
	1	μ_x	μ_x^2

$$\sigma^2 = \mu_{x^2} - (\mu_x)^2, \qquad \sigma = \sqrt{\mu_{x^2} - (\mu_x)^2}$$

The computations, for two numerical examples, are

x	P	xP	x^2P
−1	1/2	−1/2	1/2
1	1/2	1/2	1/2
	1	0	1

$$\mu_x = 0, \qquad \sigma_x^2 = 1 - (0)^2 = 1, \qquad \sigma_x = 1$$

x	$P \cdot 5$	$x \cdot P \cdot 5$	$x^2 \cdot P \cdot 5$
0	1	0	0
1	1	1	1
2	1	2	4
3	1	3	9
4	1	4	16
	5	10	30

$$\mu_x = \frac{10}{5} = 2, \qquad \sigma_x^2 = \frac{30}{5} - (2)^2 = 2,$$
$$\sigma_x = \sqrt{2} = 1.414$$

where, in the second example, the divisions by 5 were made to account for the fact that the weights, $P \cdot 5$, did not add to 1.

In Figures 10.1, 10.2, and 10.3 on preceding pages 86-88, various distributions are drawn. Those in Figure 10.1 all have the same mean and standard deviation, although they differ in "shape." Those in Figure 10.2 have the same mean; the standard deviation changes as the scale changes within a column. In Figure 10.3 the standard deviation is the same in each column; the means are different.

SAMPLES WITHOUT REPLACEMENT FROM POPULATIONS

The simplest model for sampling from a population, that is, a set of individuals, is to suppose that the population consists of N individuals, $I_1, I_2, \ldots, I_N$, and that some n of these are to be selected as the sample. It can either be that all n are to be taken at once or that the n are to be taken one at a time. A distinction must be made between these two methods if the order in which individuals are drawn is important.

Sampling from a set of individuals in this manner defines a set of outcomes, the set of all possible samples. This set of outcomes is the set of all possible ordered subsets of n individuals that can be formed from the N individuals.

For example, if $N = 5$ and $n = 2$, the possible outcomes to drawing a sample of two individuals from the population $\{I_1, I_2, I_3, I_4, I_5\}$ are

$$\begin{array}{ccccc}
 & (I_1, I_2) & (I_1, I_3) & (I_1, I_4) & (I_1, I_5) \\
(I_2, I_1) & & (I_2, I_3) & (I_2, I_4) & (I_2, I_5) \\
(I_3, I_1) & (I_3, I_2) & & (I_3, I_4) & (I_3, I_5) \\
(I_4, I_1) & (I_4, I_2) & (I_4, I_3) & & (I_4, I_5) \\
(I_5, I_1) & (I_5, I_2) & (I_5, I_3) & (I_5, I_4) &
\end{array}$$

The diagonal has been omitted because, without replacement, the same individual cannot occur twice in the sample. These outcomes, with a probability for each, define a "population" of possible samples of size 2 from the original set of individuals, $\{I_1, I_2, \ldots, I_5\}$.

The simplest probability for this population of samples is that which assigns the same probability to each. Sampling so that this population of samples is relevant [that is, so that, in a long sequence of repetitions of taking a subset of 2 from $\{I_1, I_2, I_3, I_4, I_5\}$, each of the possible samples above would occur approximately equally often] is called *simple random sampling*.

Methods of sampling, to which this probabilistic assumption is relevant, exist. One, which has already been mentioned, is to establish a correspondence between each individual and the numbers from 1 through N and to select the n individuals for the sample with a table of random digits. Other methods depend upon some form of thorough mixing of the individuals in the population. Although there are both theoretical and empirical reasons to believe that thorough mixing will result in the drawing of samples so that equal probabilities for the samples are relevant, most sets of individuals do not lend themselves readily to such mixing. Fish in a lake are a good example. The fish, or the lake, can hardly be stirred and, even if the capture is carried out at various locations and depths, and by several means, it is difficult to imagine that some sorts of fish would not be more easily captured than others or even to imagine some sorts would not evade capture altogether. An assumption, for such a difficult sampling problem, that all possible samples are equally likely is usually a rather crude approximation. Crude, perhaps, but necessary, since it would be impossible to establish a correspondence between the fish in the lake and the integers $1, \ldots, N$ and use a random number table to achieve simple random sampling.

The same practical impossibility of thorough mixing, or use of a random-number table, exists for samples of pieces of coal from a carload of coal. An approximation to simple random sampling is attained by drilling cores at randomly selected points on the surface of the load and then using a randomly selected "slice" from the core. If the coal in the car is not uniform in size, it is possible that, during shipping, it has become stratified. In this case the sampling is often also "stratified"; that is, the selection of slices of the cores is (randomly) made so that given proportions of them occur from each of several depths.

For many populations, a correspondence between the individuals and the integers $1, \ldots, N$ is already established for purposes other than the sampling. For example, lists of registered voters, births, insurance policies, vehicles, and publications are routinely kept for various purposes. The problem of selecting a random sample from such a list is, in principle, easily solved by use of a random-number table. However, it is sometimes so difficult to locate, in the file, each item selected by the table that an approximation is utilized. From randomly selected starting points, items are taken at uniform spacings between starting points. How well a scheme of "random starts" approximates equiprobability for samples clearly depends upon the (local) "mix" in the files.

For the problems considered so far in this text, the sets of individuals from which the sample is to be drawn have been relatively small. If a sample is to be taken from a set of, say, 50 individuals, there is no problem in identifying them with the integers from 1 to 50 and selecting the sample with the aid of a table of random digits. Without random digits, some form of thorough mixing can be substituted. An identification of each individual can be recorded on 1 of 50 very similar objects and these objects mixed or shuffled before n are selected. Pieces of paper, with the identifications, can be folded, or turned upside down on a table top, and then mixed, or the identifications recorded on each card of a deck of 50 cards and, after shuffling, n cards dealt. The only caution is that thorough mixing takes a while; two or three "shuffles" or "riffles" between hands in card playing, for instance, do not constitute thorough mixing.

Some elementary properties of sampling are to be considered now. It will be sufficient to suppose that each individual in the population is identified by a number or a "score" and to describe the sample by the scores of the individuals in the sample. If more than one individual has the same score, they are to be distinguished by subscripts, as $12_1, 12_2, \ldots$. Thus, if a set of $N = 5$ individuals have scores $\{1_1, 6_1, 2, 6_2, 1_2\}$, the "population" of equally likely samples of size $n = 2$ is in the first two columns of Table 10.4.

Table 10.4

Possible samples			
(X_1, X_2)	(X_2, X_1)	P	f
$(1_1, 6_1)$	$(6_1, 1_1)$	1/10	6
$(1_1, 2)$	$(2, 1_1)$	1/10	2
$(1_1, 6_2)$	$(6_2, 1_1)$	1/10	6
$(1_1, 1_2)$	$(1_2, 1_1)$	1/10	1
$(6_1, 2)$	$(2, 6_1)$	1/10	12
$(6_1, 6_2)$	$(6_2, 6_1)$	1/10	36
$(6_1, 1_2)$	$(1_2, 6_1)$	1/10	6
$(2, 6_2)$	$(6_2, 2)$	1/10	12
$(2, 1_2)$	$(1_2, 2)$	1/10	2
$(6_2, 1_2)$	$(1_2, 6_2)$	1/10	6

In the third column are the values of a function f defined for the possible samples by the product X_1X_2 of the observations (X_1, X_2) in the sample. In Table 10.4 the two samples (X_1, X_2) and (X_2, X_1) have been "grouped," since the value of f does not depend upon the order in which the individuals in a sample are drawn.

The distribution consisting of the possible values of f and the probabilities implied by the assumption that the possible samples are equally likely is called the *sampling distribution* of f. It is obtained from Table 10.4 as

$f = X_1X_2$	P
1	1/10
2	2/10
6	4/10
12	2/10
36	1/10
	1

Any function defined for the possible samples has a sampling distribution implied by the scores in the population from which the sample is drawn and the probabilities for the "population" of possible samples. There is an extensive theory of sampling distributions of functions f. However, almost all the functions considered in detail here are describable as sums. A few of the basic properties of the sampling distributions of functions which can be described as sums are to be discussed now.

If f is defined as $X_1 + X_2$, the sampling distribution of $f = X_1 + X_2$ is, from Table 10.4, easily seen to be

$f = X_1 + X_2$	P
2	1/10
3	2/10
7	4/10
8	2/10
12	1/10

The mean μ_f of this distribution is 6.4 and the variance is $\sigma_f^2 = \mu_{f^2} - (\mu_f)^2 = 49 - 40.96 = 8.04$. However, these can be found without enumerating all the possible samples of size 2 and then finding the distribution of f. It is sufficient to know the mean and variance of the scores in the population $\{1_1, 6_1, 2, 6_2, 1_2\}$, the sample size, and that the sampling was simple random (without replacement). The distribution of scores in the population (more exactly, the "population" of samples of size 1) is

X	P
1	2/5
2	1/5
6	2/5

so that the population mean μ_X and the population variance are given by $\mu_X = 3.2$, $\sigma_X{}^2 = \mu_{X^2} - (\mu_X)^2 = 78/5 - (3.2)^2 = 15.6 - 10.24 = 5.36$.

The mean and variance of $f = X_1 + \cdots + X_n$ for simple random samples of size n, without replacement, from a population of N in which the scores X are distributed with mean μ_X and variance $\sigma_X{}^2$ are given by

$$\mu_f = n\mu_X,$$

$$\sigma_f{}^2 = n\sigma_X{}^2 \frac{N-n}{N-1}.$$

For the present example, $N = 5$, $n = 2$, $\mu_X = 3.2$, and $\sigma_X{}^2 = 5.36$. Therefore,

$$\mu_f = 2(3.2) = 6.4,$$

$$\sigma_f{}^2 = 2(5.36)\frac{5-2}{5-1} = \frac{6}{4}(5.36) = 8.04,$$

in agreement with the values found above after enumeration of the possible samples of size 2 and tabulation of the sampling distribution of f.

As a second example, consider the population of scores {52, 35, 43, 40, 21} which appeared in Example 1 of Chapter 1. The mean μ_X and variance $\sigma_X{}^2$ of these scores are found in Table 10.5.

Table 10.5

X	X^2
21	441
35	1225
40	1600
43	1849
52	2704
191	7819

$$\mu_X = \frac{191}{5} = 38.2, \qquad \sigma_X{}^2 = \frac{7819}{5} - (38.2)^2 = 104.56$$

Hence, if 3 of the 5 subjects with the scores {52, 35, 43, 40, 21} are selected, at random, for the treatment group and there is no treatment effect, the mean μ_f and variance σ_f^2 of the sum f of the scores for the treatment group are given by

$$\mu_f = 3 \cdot \mu_X = 3(38.2) = 114.6,$$

$$\sigma_f^2 = 3\sigma_X^2 \frac{5-3}{5-1} = \frac{6}{4}(104.56) = 156.84.$$

The mean and variance of the sum f' of the scores for the control group are given by

$$\mu_{f'} = 2 \cdot \mu_X = 2(38.2) = 76.4,$$

$$\sigma_X^2 = 2\sigma_X^2 \frac{5-2}{5-1} = \frac{6}{4}(104.56) = 156.84.$$

Since $f + f'$ is, for any division into groups of three and two, equal to a constant (the sum T of the five numbers) $f' = T - f$, so that (see page 86) the relations $\mu_{f'} = T - \mu_f$ and $\sigma_{f'}^2 = \sigma_f^2$ hold.

If the observations {52, 35, 43, 40, 21} are replaced by their ranks and the equally likely divisions into groups of three and two are considered, the same relationships obtain between the means and variances. For the ranks {5, 2, 4, 3, 1}, the mean is $\mu_X = 3$ and the variance is

$$\sigma_X^2 = \frac{(5-3)^2 + (2-3)^2 + (4-3)^2 + (3-3)^2 + (1-3)^2}{5}$$

$$= \frac{4 + 1 + 1 + 0 + 4}{5} = 2.$$

Consequently, the sum f of the ranks for the treatment group, if there is no treatment effect, has, as its mean and variance,

$$\mu_f = 3\mu_X = 3 \cdot 3 = 9,$$

$$\sigma_f^2 = 3\sigma_X^2 \frac{5-3}{5-1} = \frac{6}{4} \cdot 2 = 3.$$

Since for f', the sum of the ranks in the control group, $f' + f = 1 + 2 + 3 + 4 + 5 = 15$, it follows that $\mu_{f'} = 15 - \mu_f = 6$ and $\sigma_{f'}^2 = \sigma_f^2 = 3$.

No matter what the scores $\{x_1, \ldots, x_N\}$ are, they will (if there are no ties) have the consecutive integers $\{1, 2, \ldots, N\}$ as ranks. Consequently, if the subjects are randomly divided into two groups of sizes m and n $(m + n = N)$, the sum of the ranks for one of the groups will have distribution, mean, and variance the same for all sets, $\{x_1, \ldots, x_N\}$ of untied scores. This mean and variance are, if f is the sum of the ranks for the group of size n, given by

$$\mu_f = \frac{n(N + 1)}{2},$$

$$\sigma_f^2 = \frac{mn(N + 1)}{12}.$$

These follow simply from the general formula, for f as a sum of scores in the group of size n,

$$\mu_f = n\mu_X,$$

$$\sigma_f^2 = n\sigma_X^2 \frac{N - n}{N - 1}.$$

SAMPLES WITH REPLACEMENT FROM POPULATIONS

For the sampling above n individuals were drawn, from N, either all at once or, if one at a time, without replacement between the successive draws. It is also possible to suppose that individuals are taken one at a time and that each drawn is returned to the set of N before the next is drawn. Thus, from the set of individuals $\{I_1, I_2, I_3, I_4, I_5\}$, the possible samples of size 2 are

$$\begin{array}{ccccc} (I_1, I_1) & (I_1, I_2) & (I_1, I_3) & (I_1, I_4) & (I_1, I_5) \\ (I_2, I_1) & (I_2, I_2) & (I_2, I_3) & (I_2, I_4) & (I_2, I_5) \\ (I_3, I_1) & (I_3, I_2) & (I_3, I_3) & (I_3, I_4) & (I_3, I_5) \\ (I_4, I_1) & (I_4, I_2) & (I_4, I_3) & (I_4, I_4) & (I_4, I_5) \\ (I_5, I_1) & (I_5, I_2) & (I_5, I_3) & (I_5, I_4) & (I_5, I_5) \end{array}$$

If these are taken to be equally likely, the sampling is called simple random, with replacement.

It is intuitively clear that there is no point to the inclusion of any individual in the sample more than once, when actually sampling (at a fixed time) from a finite set of individuals. However, there are at least two reasons for considering sampling in this manner. If the number N of individuals is large relative to the sample size n, a sampling theory, with replacement, is a reasonable approximation to a sampling theory without replacement, and the former theory is simpler in many respects. A more important reason for a theory of sampling with replacement is that some sources of observations produce sequences of observations that, for all practical purposes, can be regarded as successive draws, with replacement, from a set of individuals.

The destinations (cities) of phone calls, outgoing from a given central, provides an example. If a given set of destinations is regarded as the set of individuals from which the sample is to be taken, each call "selects" a destination. The fact that a given destination was selected on one draw does not preclude its selection on the next. For this sampling there would effectively be replacement; the sampling would not be simple random unless the set of destinations were carefully chosen. However, for any set of destinations, a model of simple random sampling which preserves the fact that some destinations are called more frequently can be constructed by including each destination several times. If there are only two destinations, Angola and Bayport, and, over a period, Angola receives three calls for each two which Bayport receives, then simple random sampling from the set of individuals $\{A_1, A_2, A_3, B_1, B_2\}$ would be such a model.

The assumption of simple random sampling—that, for $n = 2$, say, the 25 possible samples of size 2 are equally likely—does not follow from the replacement but is an additional assumption regarding the lack of influence that the selection of one destination has on the selection of the other. It would not be a plausible assumption, for example, if the phone center had only one trunk line to one of the destinations, or if there were communication among callers.

Many sources of observations produce observations so that sequences of n of them can be regarded as samples with the properties above. The sequence of yields, each year, of bushels of wheat on a given acre (for which the fertility is renewed yearly), a given dimension on a sequence of mass-produced parts, or the weights, at hatching, of a given variety of chickens are examples of such sequences.

The two kinds of sampling are often combined. If 10 eggs are selected from the output of a large flock, the weights of the newly hatched chicks can be regarded as a sample, with replacement. If 5 of these 10 are then selected at random for a treatment group, the weights of the 5 form a sample without replacement. The successive cards dealt in one hand are a sample of cards without replacement; the successive hands, in many games, are a sample of hands with replacement.

The sampling theory for sums of the observations in a simple random sample with replacement is similar to that for samples without replacement. If X is distributed in the population so that (that is, if the sampling distribution of X for samples of size 1 is such that) the mean is μ_X and the variance is σ_X^2, then the sum, for a sample, of the values of X will have mean $n\mu_X$ and variance $n\sigma_X^2$. The only difference in the formulas for sampling without, or with, replacement is the factor $(N - n)/(N - 1)$ for the variance of sums when there is no replacement. This factor is often called the *finite population correction factor*.

EXERCISES

10.1. a. For the trial "toss 3 coins" a list of possible outcomes is {HHH, HHT, HTH, HTT, THH, THT, TTH, TTT}. If the probabilities for these are each 1/8, find
(1) P(first is H), P(second is H), P(first and second are H).
(2) P(no heads), P(at least 1 head).
(3) P(at least two heads), P(at least 3 heads), P(exactly 3 heads).
b. Toss 3 coins 100 times and compare the relative frequencies for the events in Exercise 10.1a with their probabilities. Also, verify that these relative frequencies can be found from the relative frequencies of the eight outcomes in the list.
c. Which do you believe are more relevant to future tosses of three coins, your relative frequencies or the probabilities in Exercise 10.1a? Why?

10.2. In the same manner, repeat Exercise 10.1 for four coins.

10.3. If the following is a risk table, find the probabilities of the events
a. Payment is less than \$2000.
b. Payment is within \$1000 of \$3000.
c. Payment is at least as far from \$2000 as is \$1000.

Outcomes	*Probability*
\$00	.981
1000	.010
2000	.003
3000	.002
4000	.001
5000	.003

10.4. Verify, by computing the averages on both sides of the equations, that the relations

$$\mu_{(x-a)/b} = \frac{\mu_x - a}{b} \quad \text{and} \quad \sigma_{(x-a)/b} = \frac{\sigma_x}{b}$$

hold among the four populations on page 85.

10.5. Verify, for the distribution below, that the variance can be computed either as the weighted average of the squared deviations $(x - \mu)^2$ or as $\mu_{x^2} - (\mu_x)^2$.

x	$P \cdot 16$
0	1
1	4
2	6
3	4
4	1

10.6. Find the mean μ and standard deviation σ for each of the three populations below.

a.

x	P
10	1/10
11	1/10
17	1/10
34	1/10
46	1/10
52	1/10
75	1/10
78	1/10
83	1/10
88	1/10

b.

x	P
1	1/10
2	1/10
3	1/10
4	1/10
5	1/10
6	1/10
7	1/10
8	1/10
9	1/10
10	1/10

c.

x	P
−1	1/10
−1	1/10
−1	1/10
−1	1/10
−1	1/10
1	1/10
1	1/10
1	1/10
1	1/10
1	1/10

10.7. From the urn containing chips marked 2, 3, 5, 7,

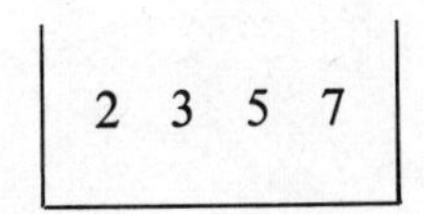

a. Enumerate, as (2, 3), (2, 5), . . ., the 16 possible outcomes if a chip is drawn, then replaced, and a second chip drawn.
b. For each outcome find the sum S of the two digits.
c. Assuming that each outcome has probability 1/16, compute the mean, variance, and standard deviation of the distribution for this sum.
d. Without repeating the computation (or with, if necessary), what are the mean and variance of $S/2$?

10.8. Repeat Exercise 10.7 with no replacement between the two draws.

10.9. Suppose that the scores {52, 35, 43, 40, 21} are replaced by -1, 0, or 1 according as they are above, equal to, or below their median $M = 40$. This substitution produces a "population" with scores X, {1, -1, 1, 0, -1}. If three are drawn at random without replacement for a treatment group, what is the mean μ_f and variance σ_f^2 for $f = n_t^+ - n_t^-$ defined to be the sum of the scores X of the draw? Assume no treatment effect.

10.10. From the populations of Exercise 10.6, find the mean and variance if 4 are drawn at random and without replacement, for each of

a. $f =$ sum of the scores.

b. $f =$ sum of the ranks among all 10 scores.

c. $f = n_t^+ - n_t^-$, where $n_t^+ =$ no. larger than median M of all 10, $n_t^- =$ no. smaller than M.

10.11. If, from 100 individuals with unequal scores X, 30 are drawn at random and without replacement, what are the mean and variance of the sum of the ranks (among all 100 scores)?

10.12. Repeat Exercise 10.10, assuming that the sampling was with replacement.

10.13. From the fact that the sample mean is, by definition, $1/n$ times the sum of the observations in the sample, find formulas for the mean and variance of the sample mean for simple random samples with replacement and without replacement.

10.14. In a population of 10,000 items, suppose that X is distributed so that $\sigma_X = 50$. If a sample of 10,000 is taken with replacement, what will be the standard deviation of the sample mean? What will it be if the sampling is without replacement?

CHAPTER 11

SOME PARTICULAR POPULATIONS

BINOMIAL DISTRIBUTIONS

The simplest example of binomial trials is the description of n ideal tosses of a (fair) coin. It is assumed that there are only two possible outcomes, H or T, for a single toss. The outcome of a sequence of n tosses can be described by a sequence of n of the symbols H and T. If $n = 5$, HTHTH and HHHHH are two of these possible outcomes. If it is supposed, for a given n, that these 2^n outcomes are equally likely, a population for the trial "toss a coin n times" (or for the trial "toss n coins once") is defined. For $n = 1, 2, 3$, and 4 these populations are those shown in Table 11.1.

Table 11.1

$n = 1$		$n = 2$		$n = 3$		$n = 4$	
Out-comes	*P*	*Out-comes*	*P*	*Out-comes*	*P*	*Out-comes*	*P*
H	1/2	HH	1/4	HHH	1/8	HHHH	1/16
T	1/2	HT	1/4	HHT	1/8	HHHT	1/16
		TH	1/4	HTH	1/8	HHTH	1/16
		TT	1/4	HTT	1/8	HHTT	1/16
				THH	1/8	HTHH	1/16
				THT	1/8	HTHT	1/16
				TTH	1/8	HTTH	1/16
				TTT	1/8	HTTT	1/16
						THHH	1/16
						THHT	1/16
						THTH	1/16
						THTT	1/16
						TTHH	1/16
						TTHT	1/16
						TTTH	1/16
						TTTT	1/16

The assumption that each possible sequence has the same probability has two important consequences. The first is that the probability for H is the same, and equal to 1/2, for each toss. For example, for $n = 2$ it is clear that P(first coin is H) = P(HT, HH) = 1/4 + 1/4 = 1/2, and that P(second coin is H) = P(HH, TH) = 1/2. Similarly, for $n = 3$ it is clear that P(first is H) = P(HHH, HHT, HTH, HTT) = 1/2, and that P(second is H) = P(third is H) = 1/2.

The second implication is that the tosses of the coin are independent; that is (see Exercise 11.2), the probability of any sequence is the product of the probabilities of the outcomes of each toss. For example, from Table 11.1, for $n = 2$, P(HH) = P(H)P(H), P(HT) = P(H)P(T), P(TH) = P(T)P(H), and P(TT) = P(T)P(T), since for each $1/4 = 1/2 \cdot 1/2$.

These implications are, for each n, also a characterization of the population. It can be defined as that for n independent trials, each of which can result in H or T, and for each of which P(H) = 1/2 [since P(T) = 1 − P(H), P(T) is also 1/2]. For $n = 2$, for example, these statements imply P(HH) = P(H)P(H) = 1/4, and in the same way, P(HT) = 1/4, P(TH) = 1/4, P(TT) = 1/4, so that the four possible sequences are equally likely.

The most common distribution (a distribution is a population whose outcomes are numbers) derived from the binomial population for sequences is the distribution of the number of heads. This distribution is called, for each n, the binomial distribution for n and $p = 1/2$. It can be found from the population for sequences by adding the probabilities for sequences with the same number of heads. For $n = 1$, the distribution is $P(1) = P(\text{H}) = 1/2$, $P(0) = P(\text{T}) = 1/2$ or, as arranged in a table:

x	P
0	1/2
1	1/2

For $n = 2$, P(exactly 0 heads) = P(TT) = 1/4, P(exactly 1 head) = P(HT, TH) = 1/2, and P(2 heads) = P(HH) = 1/4. In the same manner, the distributions for $n = 3$, 4 can be found (see Table 11.1), and the distributions for $n = 1, 2, 3, 4$ are as shown in Table 11.2.

For any n, the probability that the number of heads is x is given by the formula $\binom{n}{x}(1/2^n)$, for $x = 0, 1, 2, \ldots, n$. The number $\binom{n}{x}$ is called a *binomial coefficient* and is the number of subsets containing x objects which can be formed from a set of n objects. For $n = 3$, the eight subsets of (1, 2, 3) are

Table 11.2

$n = 1$		$n = 2$		$n = 3$		$n = 4$	
x	P	x	P	x	P	x	P
0	1/2	0	1/4	0	1/8	0	1/16
1	1/2	1	2/4	1	3/8	1	4/16
		2	1/4	2	3/8	2	6/16
				3	1/8	3	4/16
						4	1/16

(1, 2, 3), (1, 2), (1, 3), (2, 3), (1), (2), (3), and ( ). Of these, 1 has 3 objects, 3 have 2 objects, 3 have 1 object, and 1 has 0 objects. That is, $\binom{3}{3} = 1$, $\binom{3}{2} = 3$, $\binom{3}{1} = 3$, and $\binom{3}{0} = 1$. These are the coefficients of $(1/2)^3$ in Table 11.2 (see Exercise 11.1). The coefficient $\binom{n}{x}$ can also be computed as $\binom{n}{x} = n!/[x!(n - x)!]$, where $x!$ denotes the product of the digits $1, 2, \ldots, x$ and $0!$ denotes 1 (that is, $0! = 1$, $1! = 1$, $2! = 2 \cdot 1 = 2$, $3! = 3 \cdot 2 \cdot 1 = 6$, $4! = 4 \cdot 3 \cdot 2 \cdot 1 = 24, \ldots$).

An application of the binomial distribution, for $p = 1/2$, has already been used above in connection with the function, $f = |(\text{no. of } +\text{'s}) - n/2|$ for paired comparisons. There the 2^n possible assignments of signs were, with randomization, equally likely, so that the number of + signs has a binomial distribution with $p = 1/2$. The values of A_f were taken from this distribution by adding the probabilities for all points x which were as far, or farther, from $n/2$ as the number of + signs observed for the experiment.

There are many examples of sequences of trials which may be regarded as independent but for which the probability of H cannot reasonably be supposed to be 1/2. If one side of a symmetric six-sided die were labeled H and the other five sides were labeled T, the population for single tosses could be taken as $P(\text{H}) = 1/6$, $P(\text{T}) = 5/6$. In general, denoting now by H any fixed outcome for a single trial, and denoting by T the outcome, H did not occur, the population for a single trial would be

Outcomes	P
H	p
T	$1 - p$

for a number p with $0 \leq p \leq 1$. For a sequence of n of these trials the possible outcomes will be the 2^n sequences of the symbols H and T. However, these sequences will not be equally likely unless $p = 1/2$. The probability for each sequence is determined by the assumption of independence among the individual trials and the assumption that $P(\text{H})$ is p for each trial. For $n = 2$ the four possible sequences will have the probabilities $P(\text{HH}) = p \cdot p$, $P(\text{HT}) = p(1 - p)$, $P(\text{TH}) = (1 - p)p$, and $P(\text{TT}) = (1 - p)^2$. The distribution of the number of heads is

x	P
0	$(1 - p)^2$
1	$2p(1 - p)$
2	p^2

For $n = 3$, the probabilities are, for the eight possible sequences,

$$P(\text{HHH}) = p^3 \qquad P(\text{THH}) = (1 - p)p^2$$
$$P(\text{HHT}) = p^2(1 - p) \qquad P(\text{THT}) = (1 - p)p(1 - p)$$
$$P(\text{HTH}) = p(1 - p)p \qquad P(\text{TTH}) = (1 - p)^2p$$
$$P(\text{HTT}) = p(1 - p)^2 \qquad P(\text{TTT}) = (1 - p)^3.$$

The distribution of the number of heads is, for $n = 3$,

x	P
0	$(1 - p)^3$
1	$3p(1 - p)^2$
2	$3p^2(1 - p)$
3	p^3

For any n, the distribution of the number of heads is given by the formulas

x	P
0	$(1 - p)^n$
$\vdots$	
k	$\binom{n}{k}p^k(1 - p)^{n-k}$
$\vdots$	
n	p^n

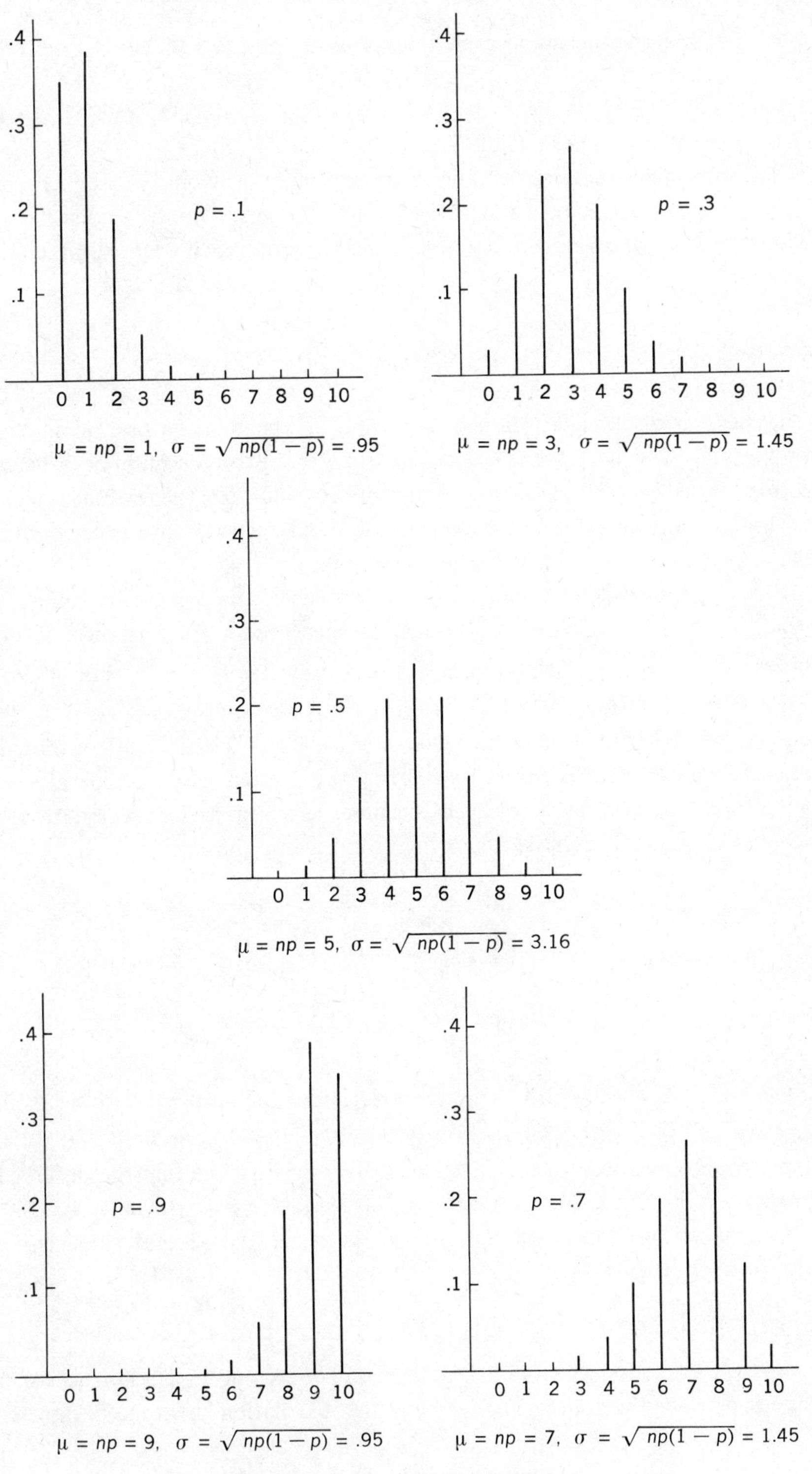

Figure 11.1. Various binomial distributions for $n = 10$.

For $n = 2, \ldots, 12$ and $p = .01, .05, .10, .15, \ldots, .90, .95$, and $.99$, these distributions are given in Table D.

The mean and standard deviation for a binomial distribution can be found from simple formulas in n and p. If X is the number, in n independent trials, of occurrences of an outcome whose probability, for each trial, is p, then

$$\mu_X = np,$$

$$\sigma_X = \sqrt{np(1 - p)}.$$

The mean is often called the *expectation* of X. Thus it can be said that, if in one trial the expected number of heads is p, the expected number of heads in n trials is np. The same statement can be made for the variance, $\sigma^2 = np(1 - p)$. In a single trial the expected squared deviation from the mean is $p(1 - p)$ and in n trials it is n times as large.

For example, if a fair coin is tossed 100 times, the expected number of heads is $100 \cdot 1/2 = 50$. The average, as measured by σ, distance of the observed number of heads from 50 is $\sqrt{100 \cdot 1/2 \cdot 1/2} = 5$. For 10,000 tosses the expected number of heads is 5000, the average distance of the observed number of heads from 5000 is $\sqrt{10{,}000 \cdot 1/2 \cdot 1/2} = 50$. Although the number of heads becomes more dispersed around its expected value as n increases, the proportion of heads becomes less dispersed. If X denotes the number of heads in n trials, X/n is the proportion of heads:

$$\mu_{X/n} = \frac{\mu_X}{n} \quad \text{and} \quad \sigma^2_{X/n} = \frac{{\sigma_X}^2}{n^2}.$$

Thus,

$$\mu_{X/n} = \frac{np}{n} = p \quad \text{and} \quad \sigma_{X/n} = \sqrt{\frac{np(1 - p)}{n^2}} = \sqrt{\frac{p(1 - p)}{n}}.$$

For $p = 1/2$, the mean and standard deviation of the proportion of heads in n tosses are $1/2$ and $1/[2\sqrt{n}]$, so that for either $n = 100$ or $n = 10{,}000$ the expected proportion of heads is $1/2$. The average distance that the observed proportion is from $1/2$ is $1/20$ for $n = 100$, while for $n = 10{,}000$ it is $1/200$.

Graphs of binomial distributions for 10 trials and several values of p are shown in Figure 11.1.

A CURVE A_f FOR BINOMIAL TRIALS

If x_0 is the observed number of a certain outcome in a sequence of n binomial trials, the problem of relating the observation x_0 to the parameter

$p =$ (the probability of the outcome in a single trial) is analogous to that already considered for randomized experiments. Each possible value of p can be regarded as a model for the experiment, and the class of models as the interval of numbers p with $0 \leq p \leq 1$.

Again, a convenient way to summarize the actions which would be taken in formal decision situations or to describe the experimental outcome and its relation to the class of models is given by a curve $A_f(p)$. The function f here will be taken as $|x - np|$ and $A_f(p)$ will be defined as the probability that x will be as far, or farther, from np than is the observation x_0. Or $A_f(p)$ will be the sum of the probabilities for all points x which are either the end points of, or are outside of, the interval determined by the two numbers $np + |x_0 - np|$ and $np - |x_0 - np|$, where the probabilities of x are given by $\binom{n}{x}p^x(1 - p)^{n-x}$.

As an example, suppose a trial consists of administering a fixed dose of a certain substance to a monkey, and p is the probability that a given reaction will occur. If the substance is given to each of 10 monkeys, there will be 10 trials ($n = 10$). Whether the 10 trials are binomial or not is a matter of experimental practice. If the monkeys are of uniform size, species, age, and general health, the assumption that p is a constant for the 10 trials would seem reasonable. Independence among the trials would, in many cases, be achieved by isolation of the monkeys. If the reaction were communicable, as could be the case if the substance were a vaccine, then without isolation the occurrence of the reaction in one monkey would increase the probability of its occurrence in another monkey and the trials would not be independent.

Suppose that the experimental practice was such that the trials were binomial and the observed number of reactions is $x_0 = 7$. The computation of $A_f(p)$ for $p = .5$ is as follows: $np = 10(.5) = 5$ and x is as far or farther from np as x_0 if x is 7 or more or if x is 3 or less. From Table D ($n = 10$, $p = .5$), the probability that x is 7 or more is .172, and the probability that x is 3 or less is .172. $A_f(.5)$ is $.172 + .172 = .344$. More briefly, $A_f(.5)$ is the sum of the P values for the entries $np + |x_0 - np| = 5 + |7 - 5| = 7$ and $np - |x_0 - np| = 5 - |7 - 5| = 3$.

For $p = .2$, $np + |x_0 - np| = 2 + |7 - 2| = 7$, and $np - |x_0 - np| = 2 - |7 - 2| = -3$, so that from Table D ($n = 10, p = .2$), $A_f(.2) = .001 + 0 = .001$.

For $p = .8$, $np + |x_0 - np| = 8 + |7 - 8| = 9$ and $np - |x_0 - np| = 8 - |7 - 8| = 7$ and, from Table D ($n = 10, p = .8$), $A_f(.8) = .376 + .322 = .698$.

For values of p by steps of .05 between 0 and 1, the values of $A_f(p)$ are given in Table 11.3. A graph of these values is in Figure 11.2.

Table 11.3

p	$A_f(p)$	p	$A_f(p)$
0	0	.55	.528
.05	.000	.60	.749
.10	.000	.65	1
.15	.000	.70	1
.20	.001	.75	1
.25	.004	.80	.698
.30	.011	.85	.377
.35	.049	.90	.070
.40	.101	.95	.012
.45	.202	1	0
.50	.344		

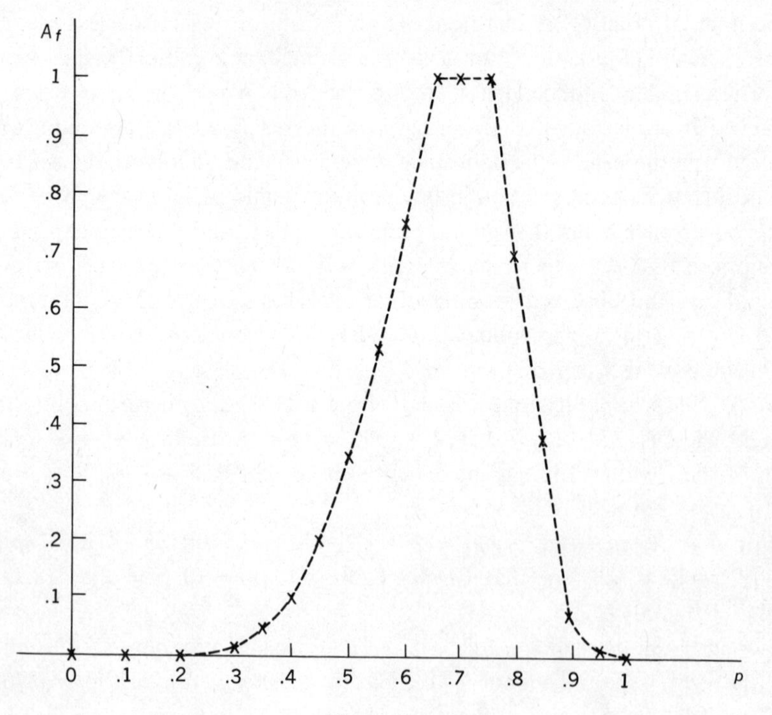

Figure 11.2.

The curve is defined for each p and here a close approximation to its values for points between multiples of .05 can be obtained by drawing a smooth curve through the values at these multiples.

The possible uses and interpretations of the curve are the same as for the ones constructed earlier. An estimate of p is given by the midpoint of the interval where $A_f = 1$. If the experiment had been conducted to test, with $\alpha = .2$, the hypothesis that $p = .4$, the hypothesis would be rejected. If it had been conducted to find a 75 per cent confidence interval for p, the interval would be (.47, .88). Descriptively, it can be stated that the models with p between .6 and .8 are in high agreement with the observed experimental outcome. The observed outcome gives almost no indication of agreement with models with p less than .3 or greater than .95.

HYPERGEOMETRIC DISTRIBUTIONS

A hypergeometric distribution is another model for sequences of trials in which each trial can have one of two outcomes. Note that a binomial distribution can be regarded as the distribution of the number of a certain outcome which occur in a sample of size n for simple random sampling, with replacement, from a population in which the proportion of the given outcome is p. If the population is taken as a set of N chips in an urn of which R are red and B are black and X denotes the number of red in a sample of size n, then X will have the same binomial distribution for simple random sampling with replacement from any urn in which the proportion, R/N, of red chips is the same. For example, the distribution of X will be binomial with $p = .5$ and $n = 10$ if 10 draws are made with replacement and so that all possible draws are equally likely from any of the urns

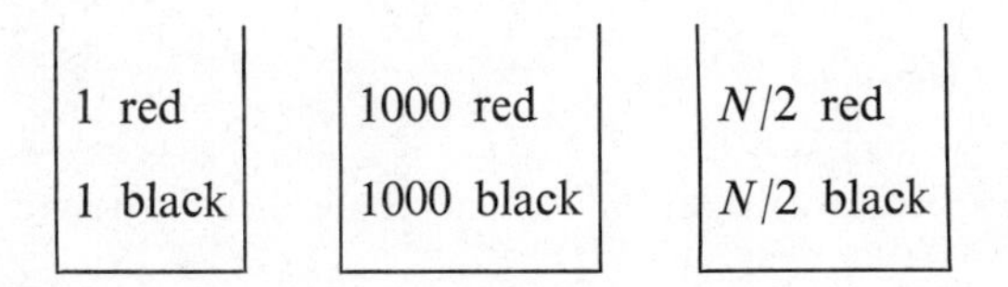

However, if the draws are made without replacement, the distribution of X will depend upon the numbers R and N of chips in the urn and not only on the proportion R/N. When these draws are made so that the possible samples of size n, from an urn with given contents, are equally likely, X is said to have a hypergeometric distribution with parameters N, R, and n. Necessarily, $n \leq N$.

As an example, suppose $N = 5$ and $R = 3$; the population would consist of $\{R_1, R_2, R_3, B_1, B_2\}$. If $n = 2$, the possible samples are

$$\begin{array}{ccccc} & (R_1, R_2) & (R_1, R_3) & (R_1, B_1) & (R_1, B_2) \\ (R_2, R_1) & & (R_2, R_3) & (R_2, B_1) & (R_2, B_2) \\ (R_3, R_1) & (R_3, R_2) & & (R_3, B_1) & (R_3, B_2) \\ (B_1, R_1) & (B_1, R_2) & (B_1, R_3) & & (B_1, R_3) \\ (B_2, R_1) & (B_2, R_2) & (B_2, R_3) & (B_1, B_2) & \end{array}$$

The assumption that these are equally likely defines a population of possible samples and a distribution for X = number of red in the sample. This distribution is

X	P
0	1/10
1	6/10
2	3/10

It is easily verified that these probabilities are given by

$$P(X = 0) = \frac{\binom{3}{0}\binom{2}{2}}{\binom{5}{2}}, \qquad P(X = 1) = \frac{\binom{3}{1}\binom{2}{1}}{\binom{5}{2}}, \qquad P(X = 2) = \frac{\binom{3}{2}\binom{2}{0}}{\binom{5}{2}}$$

(see Exercise 11.12).

In general, the probability that X, the number of red chips in the sample, is x will be given by

$$\frac{\binom{R}{x}\binom{N-R}{n-x}}{\binom{N}{n}}$$

if $\binom{a}{b}$ is defined as zero whenever $b > a$. These distributions are tabulated, for $N \leq 15$, in Table K. Note that Table K is abbreviated as follows. The urn scheme

R red
$N - R$ black

Draw n
No replacement

can be described by the numbers N, p, and q, where p is the smaller of $(n, N - n)$ and q is the smaller of $(R, N - R)$. The distribution given in Table K is that of the number of

> red which are in the sample if $p = n$ and $q = R$,
>
> black which are in the sample if $p = n$ and $q = N - R$,
>
> red which are left in the urn if $p = N - n$ and $q = R$,
>
> black which are left in the urn if $p = N - n$ and $q = N - R$.

The distribution of X = no. of red in the sample is easily obtained from the appropriate one of these by relabeling.

An application of the hypergeometric distributions has already been encountered in connection with the median test for the treatment and control experiment of Chapter 6. The test was based on n_t^+, the number of $(t_1', t_2', \ldots, t_n')$ which were above the median M of $(t_1', \ldots, t_n', c_1', \ldots, c_m')$. With randomization, the distribution of n_t^+ is hypergeometric with $N = n' + m'$, R = number of $(t_1', \ldots, t_n', c_1', \ldots, c_m')$ above M, and $n = n'$. [n' is the number of $(t_1', \ldots, t_n')$ not equal to M, m' is the number of $(c_1', \ldots, c_m')$ not equal to M.]

In actual practice of sampling from finite populations the usual case is that N and n are known, but R (and $N - R$) are not known. In quality-control applications N is often the lot size, that is, the number of items shipped in a container, red indicates a defective item, and a sample of n is taken from the container to gain information about R from X = no. of defectives in the sample.

An application of the hypergeometric distribution for which N is not known arises from the problem of estimating the number of individuals in populations that cannot be enumerated. The number of adult fish of a certain species in a given lake or in a given school is estimated by a capture–recapture method. In its simplest form, a number R of the fish are captured, marked, and then released. After a certain time, a second number n are captured and the number X of marked fish in the second sample are counted. The proportion X/n of marked fish in the second sample gives an indication of the value of N, the total number in the population. Whether any given probabilistic assumptions about the sampling are reasonable clearly depends upon the habits of the individuals in the population. As a first approximation it is often assumed that the sampling is simple random, so that, for each N, X is hypergeometric.

EXERCISES

11.1. A way to count the number of subsets of each size from finite spaces is that of Pascal's triangle:

$$\begin{array}{ccccccccc} &&&&1&&&& \\ &&&1&&1&&& \\ &&1&&2&&1&& \\ &1&&3&&3&&1& \\ 1&&4&&6&&4&&1 \end{array}$$

in which each element is the sum of the two elements above and immediately to the left and right of it. By enumeration of the subsets of n object sets for $n = 1, 2, 3, 4$, it is simple to verify that these numbers are

$$\begin{array}{ccccccccc} &&&&1&&&& \\ &&&\binom{1}{0}&&\binom{1}{1}&&& \\ &&\binom{2}{0}&&\binom{2}{1}&&\binom{2}{2}&& \\ &\binom{3}{0}&&\binom{3}{1}&&\binom{3}{2}&&\binom{3}{3}& \\ \binom{4}{0}&&\binom{4}{1}&&\binom{4}{2}&&\binom{4}{3}&&\binom{4}{4} \end{array}$$

that is, for $n = 4$ (for example),

there is 1 way to take 0 objects from $\{1, 2, 3, 4\}$;
there are 4 ways to take 1 object from $\{1, 2, 3, 4\}$;
there are 6 ways to take 2 objects from $\{1, 2, 3, 4\}$;
there are 4 ways to take 3 objects from $\{1, 2, 3, 4\}$;
there is 1 way to take 4 objects from $\{1, 2, 3, 4\}$.

That the numbers in the triangle will continue to be the numbers of subsets of size x, $\binom{n}{x}$, can be seen as follows. For n and x fixed, $x \neq 0$, the subsets of size x from $\{1, 2, \ldots, n\}$ can be divided into two groups, those which do not contain 1 and those which do contain 1. The subsets that do not contain 1 can be regarded as the subsets of size x from $\{2, \ldots, n\}$. The subsets which do contain 1 can be regarded, by ignoring the object 1, as the subsets of size $x - 1$ from $\{2, \ldots, n\}$. Hence there are $\binom{n-1}{x}$ which do not contain 1, and there are

$\binom{n-1}{x-1}$ which do contain 1. It follows that $\binom{n-1}{x-1} + \binom{n-1}{x} = \binom{n}{x}$, which is the relation of the triangle [for $x = 0$, $\binom{n}{x} = 1$, by definition].

a. By enumerating the subsets, carry out the division into two groups and the counting of the above argument for $n = 5$, $x = 3$.

b. Why is Pascal's triangle symmetric in each row?

c. Explain why the coefficients $\binom{n}{x}$ occur as they do in the formula

$$P(\text{exactly } x \text{ heads}) = \binom{n}{x} p^x (1-p)^{n-x}.$$

11.2. A motivation for the definition of independence, "two events A and B are independent if $P(AB) = P(A)P(B)$," can be given in terms of relative frequency. Suppose a trial is the observation of a person during his 16th and 17th year and the events are A = (was a driver involved in an auto accident during his 17th year), B = (had driver training during his 16th year). If n eighteen-year-olds are observed, there will be a relative frequency for A, for B, and for AB:

$$\text{fr}(A) = \frac{\text{number with accident during 17th year}}{n},$$

$$\text{fr}(B) = \frac{\text{number with driver training in 16th year}}{n},$$

$$\text{fr}(AB) = \frac{\text{number with both}}{n}.$$

The ratio $\text{fr}(AB)/\text{fr}(B)$ is called the conditional (given B) relative frequency of A and is the proportion among those who had driver training who had an accident. If this (relative) proportion is the same as the proportion who had an accident among all who were observed, then it would seem that the occurrence of the event, "had driver training in 16th year," did not influence the frequency of the event, "had an accident in 17th year." Also, if $\text{fr}(AB)/\text{fr}(B) = \text{fr}(A)$, then $\text{fr}(AB) = \text{fr}(A)\text{fr}(B)$.

Since probabilities are a model for relative frequencies, that is, an assumption about proportions in a population, the definition for a population of independence of events A and B is that $P(AB) = P(A)P(B)$.

Suppose that for 30 persons the frequencies for the joint occurrence of *acc*, *no-acc*, *dt*, and *no-dt* were

	dt	*no-dt*	
acc	1	2	3
no-acc	17	10	27
	18	12	30

a. What is the value of fr(*acc*|*dt*)?
b. What is the value of fr(*acc*)?
c. What is the value of fr(*dt*|*no-acc*)?
d. What is the value of fr(*dt*)?
e. What would you expect, for these marginal totals, the four frequencies of the joint occurrence to be if (*acc*) and (*dt*) were independent?

11.3. If $P(A) = x$, $P(B) = y$, and if A is independent of B, then the table

	A	not-A	
B	xy		y
not-B			$1 - y$
	x	$1 - x$	1

can be completed in two ways:

(1) By using the fact that the four cell probabilities must add to the marginal totals to give

	A	not-A	
B	xy	$y - xy$	y
not-B	$x - xy$	$1 - x - y + xy$	$1 - y$
	x	$1 - x$	1

(2) By multiplication of the marginal totals.

a. Show that the result of (2) is the same as that of (1).
b. Conclude that, if A is independent of B, then the same is true of any of the pairs of events (A, not-B), (B, not-A), (not-A, not-B).

11.4. Below are three sequences of trials in which the event (temperature at noon is at least 70°) can occur. Discuss, for each, whether, and why, or why not, the trials would be binomial trials.

a. Measure the temperature in Montreal on June 1, 1975; June 2, 1975; June 3, 1975; June 4, 1975.
b. Measure the temperature in Montreal on June 1, 1975; June 1, 1976; June 1, 1977; June 1, 1978.
c. Measure the temperature in Montreal on June 1, 1980; in Rome on June 1, 1980; in Phoenix on June 1, 1980; in Bombay on June 1, 1980.

11.5. Compute, for $n = 5$ and $p = .1$, the values of $\binom{n}{x}p^x(1 - p)^{n-x}$ for $x = 0, 1, 2, 3, 4, 5$. Compare the values you obtain with the entries in Table D.

11.6. Binomial trials can be regarded as samples, with replacement, from the population

X	P
0	$1 - p$
1	p

Use this fact to derive the mean and variance of a binomial distribution for n trials. Also, for the mean and variance of the proportion, that is, the sample mean, of the number of 1's in n trials.

11.7. Verify, from Table D, the values of $A_f(p)$ in Table 11.3 for $p = .1$ and $p = .6$.

11.8. Toss a coin five times and construct, from your observed value of x = number of heads, a curve $A_f(p)$ for $f = |x - np|$. Construct an 80 per cent confidence interval for p.

11.9. Suppose $p = 1/2$ and $n = 5$. For each of the possible observations x_0 from 0 to 5 draw (at multiples of .10) the corresponding curve, $A_f(p)$ with $f = |x - np|$. Hence, verify that the probability that a 90 per cent confidence interval covers $p = 1/2$ is .90.

11.10. a. Go to the local bowling lanes during league bowling hours. Starting with the first lane, observe whether the bowler there gets a spare on the first frame after you start observing. Repeat for the second, third, . . . , eighth lanes. Suppose that the eight observations are of binomial trials, and, compute, from your observation x_0, a curve $A_f(p), f = |x - np|$, for the probability of a spare. From this curve find an 80 per cent confidence interval for p.

b. Return the next week at the same time and count, for the same eight lanes, the number of spares in a large number (100 or more) of frames. Did your interval from eight frames catch the proportion in the 100 (or more) frames?

c. Comment on the appropriateness of the assumption that the true model is in the class of binomial models.

11.11. From the table on page 110 and the assumption that the 20 possible samples there are equally likely verify that

a. The probability of R on the first draw is the same as the probability of R on the second draw.

b. The conditional, given R on the first draw, probability of P on the second is not the same as the probability of R on the second.

11.12. In the formula

$$P(X = x) = \frac{\binom{R}{x}\binom{N-R}{n-x}}{\binom{N}{n}},$$

the denominator, $\binom{N}{n}$, represents the number of (equally likely) ways to draw n from N. "Explain" the numerator.

11.13. If n is small relative to R and $N - R$, then the fact of nonreplacement does not introduce very much dependence between successive draws. Verify this for $N = 20$, $R = 10$, and $n = 3$ by computing $P(X = 0)$, $P(X = 1)$, $P(X = 2)$, and $P(X = 3)$ from the hypergeometric formulas,

$$P(X = x) = \frac{\binom{R}{x}\binom{N-R}{3-x}}{\binom{N}{3}},$$

and from the binomial formulas

$$P(X = x) = \binom{3}{x}\left(\frac{R}{N}\right)^x\left(1 - \frac{R}{N}\right)^{n-x}.$$

11.14. Use the formulas for the mean and variance of sums for samples without replacement to show that if X is hypergeometric, then

$$\mu_x = n\left(\frac{R}{N}\right) \quad \text{and} \quad \sigma_x^2 = n\left(\frac{R}{N}\right)\left(1 - \frac{R}{N}\right)\frac{N-n}{N-1}.$$

Also, compute numerically from Table K μ_x and σ_x^2 for the distribution with $N = 10$, $n = 7$, and $R = 6$.

CHAPTER 12

CONTINUOUS DISTRIBUTIONS

Graphs of distributions have been constructed above with vertical bars, proportional in length to the corresponding probability, at each possible value of x. Other graphs are possible: one, the histogram, is made with contiguous rectangles, centered at each possible value of x, whose areas are equal to the corresponding probability. A distribution with this graph is shown in Figure 12.1. For this graph it can be stated that the probability that x is between $-.5$ and $.5$ (that is, that $x = 0$) is the area between $-.5$ and $.5$; the probability that x is at least 1 is the area above $.5$, the probability that x is properly between 0 and 3 is the area between $.5$ and 2.5.

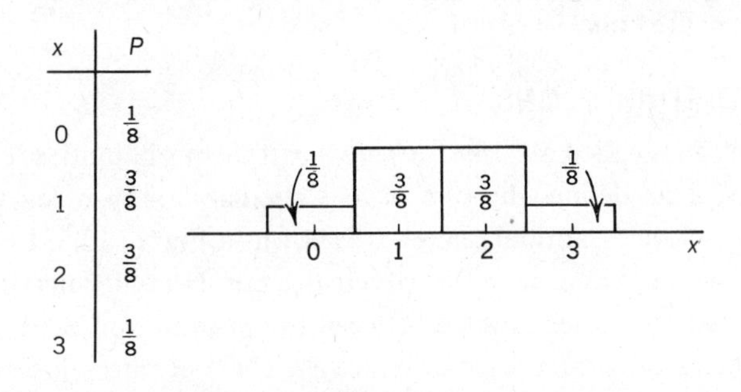

Figure 12.1.

In a similar manner, areas under any curve which lies above the horizontal axis and which has total area equal to 1 can be interpreted as probabilities to define a population. Populations defined in this manner are often a model for measurements of a quantity which, presumably, can have any value in some range. Such populations are called *continuous*. However, populations defined in this manner are also often used as approximations to discrete populations.

For a continuous distribution the probability that x falls in a given interval is, by definition, the area under the curve between the end points of the interval, as in Figure 12.2. The shaded area is the probability that x is between a and b, written $P(a < x < b)$. The unshaded area at the right is the probability that x exceeds b, written $P(x > b)$, and the unshaded area at the left is the probability that x does not exceed a, written $P(x < a)$.

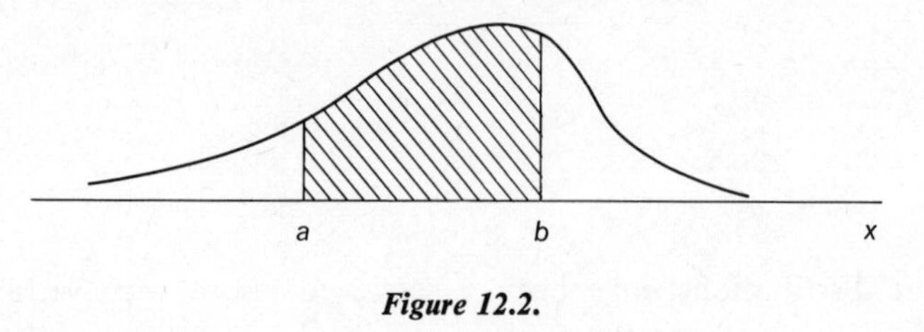

Figure 12.2.

It is interesting to note that, for a continuous population, the probability that x is exactly equal to a given number, say $P(x = 5)$, is zero. This may seem strange at first sight but it is reasonable. If time is being measured in seconds, the statement that a measured time is exactly 5 seconds means that it is 5 seconds no matter how fine the units, even thousandths, or millionths, of a second. If a small interval around 5 seconds is divided into many small pieces, the probability is extremely small that a measurement of time will result in a specified one.

NORMAL DISTRIBUTIONS

A distribution is called a *normal distribution* if the probabilities for intervals are taken as areas defined by one of a particular family of curves, called *normal curves*. Several normal curves are shown in Figure 12.3. In each case, the mean μ is the value of x for which the curve has its maximum. The standard deviation is the distance between the mean μ and the point where the curve changes from convex to concave. These remarks are helpful for sketching graphs of a normal curve; however, the calculation of areas under them is not elementary and these areas have been tabled. It is necessary to table only areas from a unit normal curve (Table E) for which the mean is zero and the standard deviation is 1. For a curve with mean μ and standard deviation σ, the area is related to that in a unit curve as shown in Figure 12.4. That is, the area below x_0 from a normal curve with mean μ and standard deviation σ is found by entering Table E with the entry $(x_0 - \mu)/\sigma$.

Table E is divided into two parts, an upper tail and a lower tail. The upper tail gives areas to the right of a positive entry $(x_0 - \mu)/\sigma$; the lower tail gives areas to the left of a negative entry $(x_0 - \mu)/\sigma$; see Figure 12.5. Since the area under the curve is 1, areas above a negative entry, or areas

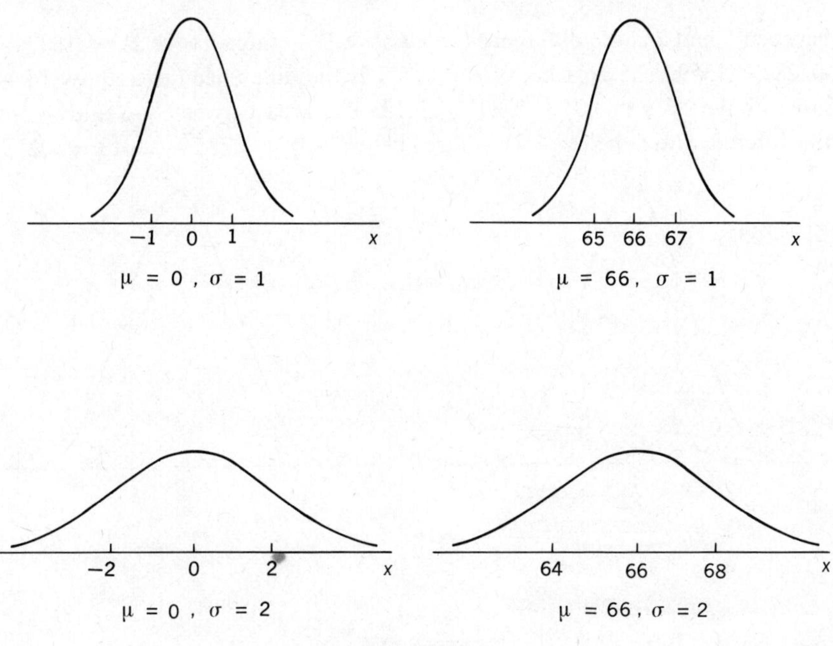

Figure 12.3.

below a positive entry, can be found by subtraction. Since the curve is symmetric, the area between x_0 and μ can be found by subtracting the area tabled for the entry $(x_0 - \mu)/\sigma$ from 1/2.

As an example, the areas for a unit normal curve are found, as indicated, for Figure 12.6. The area above 3 is read, from Table E, as .0013. The area

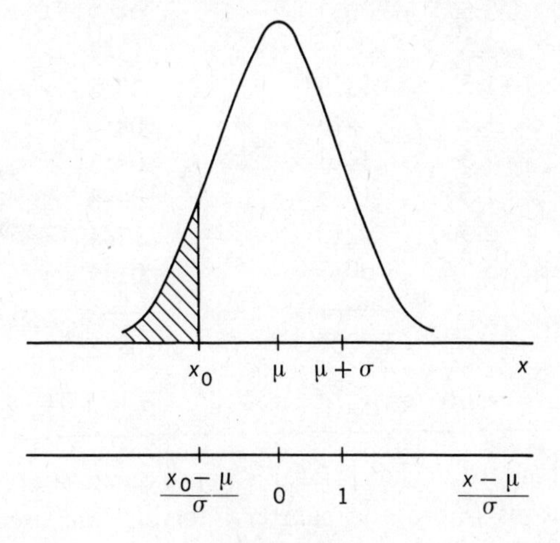

Figure 12.4.

between 1 and 2 is the difference (area above 1) − (area above 2) = .1587 − .0228 = .1359. The area between 0 and 1 is the difference (area above 0) − (area above 1) = .5000 − .1587 = .3413. The area between −3 and −2 is the difference (area below −2) − (area below −3) = .0228 − .0013 = .0215.

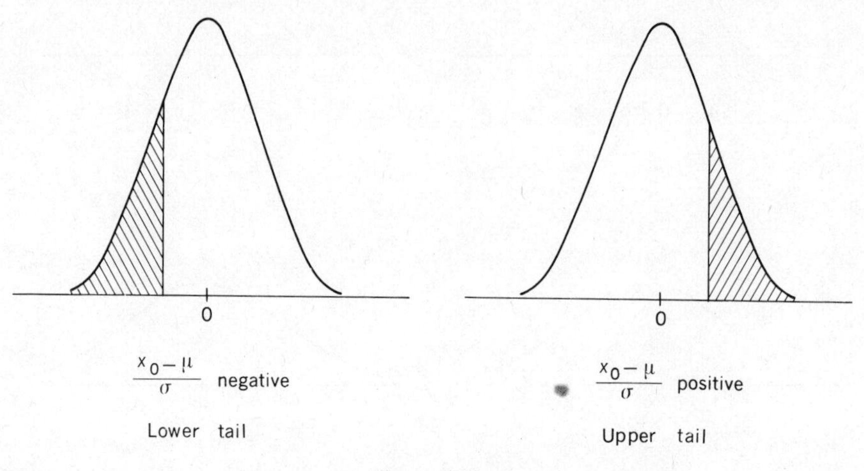

Figure 12.5.

A discrete distribution which approximates the unit normal distribution is given by supposing that these areas are probabilities concentrated on −3.5, −2.5, . . ., 3.5.

x	P	xP	x^2P
−3.5	.0013		.0159
−2.5	.0215		.1344
−1.5	.1359		.3058
−.5	.3413		.0853
.5	.3413		.0853
1.5	.1359		.3058
2.5	.0215		.1344
3.5	.0013		.0159
	1.0000	0	1.0828

$\mu = 0, \quad \sigma^2 = 1.0828 - 0^2, \quad \sigma = 1.04$

The mean and standard deviation of this approximation are 0 and 1.04. As finer approximations (more and shorter intervals) are used, the standard deviations will approach 1.

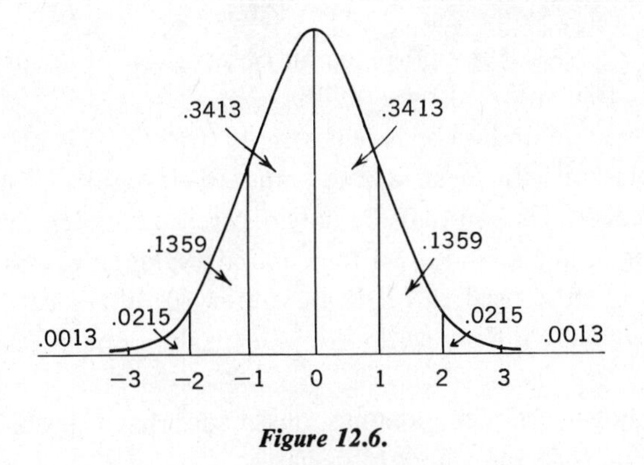

Figure 12.6.

As an example with $\mu \neq 0$ and $\sigma \neq 1$, suppose that $\mu = 22$ and $\sigma = 5$. The area above $x_0 = 26$ is found by entering Table E with

$$\frac{x_0 - 22}{5} = \frac{26 - 22}{5} = .80.$$

The area below $x_0 = 15.25$ is found by entering the table with

$$\frac{x_0 - 22}{5} = \frac{15.25 - 22}{5} = -1.35.$$

These areas are shown in Figure 12.7. The area between 22 and 26 or between 15.25 and 22 are found by subtracting the tabled areas from .5000.

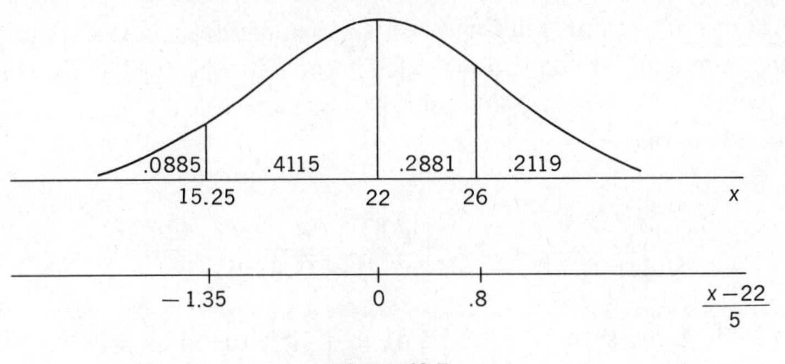

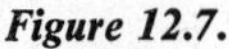
Figure 12.7.

SAMPLES FROM NORMAL POPULATIONS

Suppose observations $(c_1, c_2, \ldots, c_m)$ are obtained from m trials which are independent and for each of which it is true that the observation c is an observation from a normal population with mean μ_c and standard deviation

σ_c. Then $(c_1, c_2, \ldots, c_m)$ is said to be an observation of a sample from the normal population specified by μ_c and σ_c.

Suppose a second and independent sample $(t_1, \ldots, t_n)$ is observed from a normal population with mean μ_t and standard deviation σ_t. In some cases it is known that $\sigma_t = \sigma_c$, so that the only difference between the populations is that of their means μ_t and μ_c. If the common value of σ_t and σ_c is known, the analysis which is used to relate the observed difference $\bar{t}_0 - \bar{c}_0$ in the sample means to the difference $\theta = \mu_t - \mu_c$ in the population means is the following.

It can be shown, from the assumptions made, that $\bar{t} - \bar{c}$ is normal with mean $\mu_{\bar{t}-\bar{c}} = \mu_t - \mu_c$ and standard deviation

$$\sigma_{\bar{t}-\bar{c}} = \sigma\sqrt{\frac{1}{n} + \frac{1}{m}},$$

where σ is the common value of σ_t and σ_c. A curve $A_{|\bar{t}-\bar{c}|}(\theta)$ can then be defined as the probability, from this normal distribution, that $\bar{t} - \bar{c}$ will be farther from $\theta = \mu_t - \mu_c$ than is the observed $\bar{t}_0 - \bar{c}_0$. This probability is the area, from a unit normal curve, which is outside the interval defined by the two numbers

$$-\frac{|\bar{t}_0 - \bar{c}_0 - \theta|}{\sigma\sqrt{(1/n) + (1/m)}} \quad \text{and} \quad \frac{|\bar{t}_0 - \bar{c}_0 - \theta|}{\sigma\sqrt{(1/n) + (1/m)}}.$$

As an example, this curve $A_{|\bar{t}-\bar{c}|}(\theta)$ will be computed assuming that the observations of Example 1 in Chapter 1 were samples from normal populations with the same standard deviation, which is known to be 10. The observations there were $(c_1, c_2) = (21, 40)$ and $(t_1, t_2, t_3) = (35, 43, 52)$, $\bar{c}_0 = 30.50$, $\bar{t}_0 = 43.33$, so that $\bar{t}_0 - \bar{c}_0 = 12.83$.

For $\theta = 0$,

$$\pm\frac{|\bar{t}_0 - \bar{c}_0 - \theta|}{\sigma\sqrt{(1/n) + (1/m)}} = \pm\frac{|12.83 - 0|}{10\sqrt{(1/2) + (1/3)}} = \pm\frac{12.83}{9.13} = \pm 1.41.$$

From Table E the area outside -1.41 to 1.41 is found as $.0793 + .0793 = .1586 \doteq .16$, so that $A_{|\bar{t}-\bar{c}|}(0) = .16$.

For $\theta = 10$,

$$\pm\frac{|\bar{t}_0 - \bar{c}_0 - \theta|}{\sigma\sqrt{(1/n) + (1/m)}} \doteq \pm .31$$

so that $A_{|\bar{t}-\bar{c}|}(10) = .3783 + .3783 \doteq .76.$

In Table 12.1 the values of $A_{|\bar{t}-\bar{c}|}(\theta)$ are given for values of θ between -15 and 40. The graph of this curve is sketched in Figure 12.8, on which is superimposed the graph of $A_{|\bar{R}_t - \bar{R}_c|}(\theta)$ computed earlier from the assumption that a fixed set of five subjects was randomly divided into a treatment and a control group and that the treatment effect was additive.

Table 12.1

θ	$A_{\|\bar{t}-\bar{c}\|}(\theta)$	θ	$A_{\|\bar{t}-\bar{c}\|}(\theta)$
-15	.002	15	.810
-10	.012	20	.430
-5	.051	25	.184
0	.158	30	.060
5	.390	35	.015
10	.757	40	.003
12.83	1.00		

If the further assumption about this randomized experiment that the five subject were already a random selection from a normal population with mean μ and standard deviation $\sigma = 10$ is satisfied, the two sets of observations (c_1, c_2) and (t_1, t_2, t_3) will be those of independent samples from normal populations with means μ and $\mu + \theta$ and a common standard deviation $\sigma = 10$.

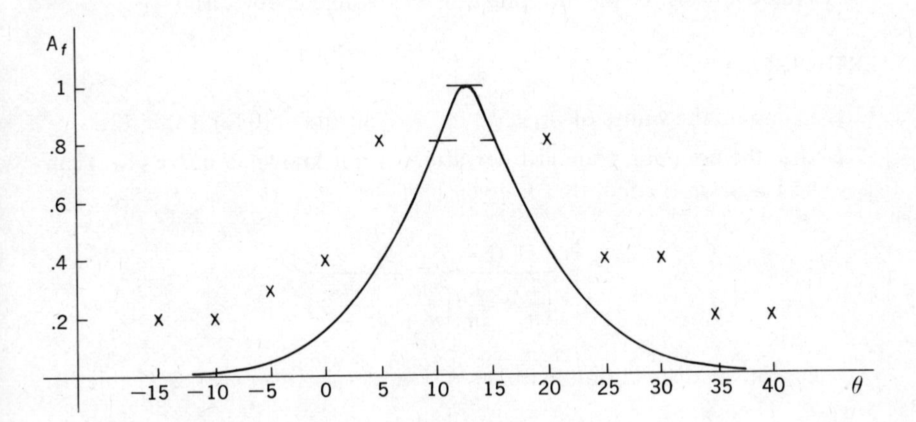

Figure 12.8.

The two curves in Figure 12.8 show how the knowledge of the population from which the subjects come can lead to a finer analysis. Confidence intervals will, as here, usually be smaller. Also, the curve A_f is smoother, since the knowledge about the population of subjects before treatment makes the curve less dependent upon these particular subjects. At the same time it is to be realized that to maintain the probabilistic properties of the finer and smoother curve requires the knowledge that the subjects are random samples from populations in which the scores are normal with $\sigma = 10$ (see Exercise 12.2 for an analysis that depends only on the normality). The curve based on $|\bar{R}_t - \bar{R}_c|$ requires only the knowledge that if θ is the treatment effect, the assignment of subjects to the treatment and control groups are equally likely. Any of the following assumptions, for instance, imply that, if θ is the treatment effect, the assignments are equally likely.

1. Fixed subjects were randomly divided into treatment and control groups of the given sizes n and m.

2. The $n + m$ subjects are a random sample from some population and (1).

3. The m control subjects are a random sample from some population, and the n treatment subjects are a random sample from a population which can be described as a translate of the control population. The distance of the translation is, in this case, identified as θ.

The reasonableness of these assumptions is simpler to establish than is that of normality; the first and second can be established by the use of a random-number table. If the analysis is only interpolatory, the advantages of as simple a basis for the interpolation as possible is obvious.

EXERCISES

12.1. Compute the values of $A_{|\bar{t}-\bar{c}|}(\theta)$ for $\theta = 30$ and -10 for Table 12.1.

12.2. If σ, the common standard deviation, is not known, a curve $A_f(\theta)$ can be based on the fact that f, given by

$$f = \frac{(\bar{t} - \bar{c} - \theta)^2}{\left(\frac{1}{n} + \frac{1}{m}\right)\left(\frac{m s_c^2 + n s_t^2}{n + m - 2}\right)}$$

has an F distribution with $\nu_1 = 1$ and $\nu_2 = n + m - 2$ (Table I).

$$s_c^2 = \frac{1}{m}\sum (c_i - \bar{c})^2 \qquad \text{and} \qquad s_t^2 = \frac{1}{n}\sum (t_i - \bar{t})^2.$$

$A_f(\theta)$ is the area above the point

$$\frac{(\bar{t}_0 - \bar{c}_0 - \theta)^2}{\left(\frac{1}{n} + \frac{1}{m}\right)\left(\frac{ms_c{}^2 + ns_t{}^2}{n + m - 2}\right)}.$$

For the same example, $(c_1, c_2) = (21, 40)$, $(t_1, t_2, t_3) = (35, 43, 52)$, compute this curve at $\theta = -10, 0, 10, 20$, and 30 and compare with that for σ known to be 10.

12.3. Compare this curve with the curve A_f for $f = |\bar{t} - \bar{c}|$ based on the randomization distribution (see Figure 4.3).

CHAPTER 13

OPTIMUM ANALYSES

An indication of the sort of considerations which can lead to the determination of an optimum analysis of observations will be given by the discussion of an example. Suppose that, in a laboratory, the installation of a machine has been proposed to replace a process which is presently carried out by hand. The output of the machine is not constant from one hour to the next, but it is known that the output x of any hour is an observation from a population. The only unknown characteristic of this population is its mean, θ, or, as is sometimes stated, the shape of the population is known but its location is not.

For example, it might be known that the population is normal with a known variance but whose mean θ is unknown. A few of these distributions are shown in Figure 13.1.

The common shape does not have to be normal. It could instead be known that the shape of the population is like those called *double exponential* in Figure 13.2, but the mean would be unknown.

From considerations of present costs and costs if the machine were to be installed, the laboratory has decided that if the mean hourly output θ of the machine is greater than a certain number θ_0, it would be desirable to install the machine. If θ does not exceed θ_0, the installation of the machine would be more disruptive than helpful.

To decide whether or not to install the machine, the laboratory can obtain independent observations, $(x_1, x_2, \ldots, x_n)$, of hourly outputs. Their problem is to select an analysis for the decision, that is, how to use these observations to decide whether to install the machine. The problem is still not sufficiently specified to determine a solution. Also needed are specifications, by the laboratory, of the control they wish over the risks of making wrong decisions. Such specifications can be given in many ways—a possible way is the following. The laboratory fixes a number, α, and chooses to consider only rules with the property that, if the mean hourly output θ of the machine is θ_0, then the

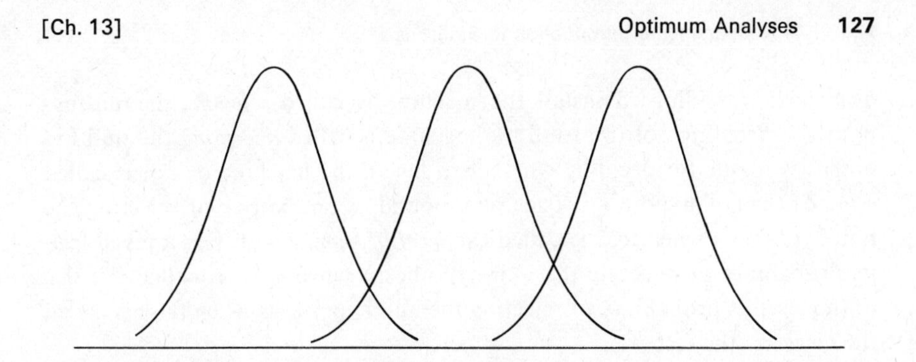

Figure 13.1. Several normal populations which are identical except for their means.

probability of installing the machine is to be no more than α. This specification is in the nature of a safeguard; it puts a bound on the risk that the laboratory runs of installing the machine without gain.

The laboratory wishes also to consider the risk of not installing the machine if θ is larger than θ_0. To simultaneously control the risks of these wrong decisions is not generally possible. However, the laboratory can select a value $\theta_1 > \theta_0$ of θ and ask for a rule for deciding whether to install the machine which satisfies the requirement above and which has a value as small as possible for the probability of not installing the machine if θ should be θ_1.

They have now reduced their problem to the following. Find a rule so that, for a population of known shape with mean at θ_0, the probability of deciding to install the machine is no more than α and so that, for a population of the same known shape with mean at θ_1, the probability of installing the machine is a maximum.

This problem is that of testing hypotheses; the statement "$\theta = \theta_0$" is called the *null hypothesis*; the statement "$\theta = \theta_1$" is called the *alternative*

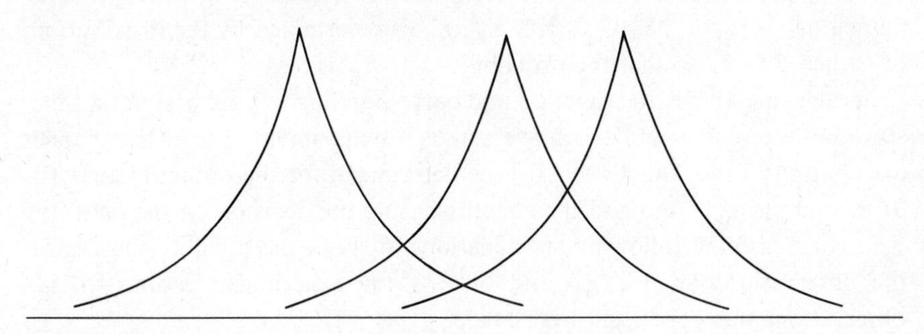

Figure 13.2. Several double exponential populations which are identical except for their means.

hypothesis. Deciding to install the machine is called *rejecting* the null hypothesis; deciding not to install the machine is called *accepting* the null hypothesis. A rule for deciding whether to install the machine or not is called a *test* of the null hypothesis. The upper bound, α, on the risk of rejecting the null hypothesis when true is called the *level of significance.* For a given test, its probability of rejecting the null hypothesis, when true, is called the *size* of the test; its probability of rejecting the null hypothesis when false is called the *power* of the test.

In these terms, the problem above has the statement: Find a test of the null hypothesis, $\theta = \theta_0$, which has size no more than α and which has maximum power at the alternative, $\theta = \theta_1$. The fundamental lemma of Neyman and Pearson gives the solution to this problem, as well as to others, and the extensions of the lemma can be applied to many more complicated problems. As applied here, the solution is the determination of a function $f = f(x_1, x_2, \ldots, x_n, \theta_0, \theta_1)$ and a constant K_α. When $(x_1, \ldots, x_n)$ is observed, the corresponding value, f_0, of f is determined. If $f_0 \geq K_\alpha$, the machine is installed; if $f_0 < K_\alpha$, the machine is not installed.

The function f can be called an *analysis* of the observations and it is interesting to consider, for the two examples above, how it depends upon the shape of the populations.

If the populations are normal, with means θ_1 and θ_0, the function f is $\sum (x_i - \theta_0)$, so that the hypothesis $\theta = \theta_0$ is to be rejected if $\sum (x_i - \theta_0) \geq K_\alpha$. K_α is determined from the distribution of $\sum (x_i - \theta_0)$ when the (normal) population mean is θ_0, so that the probability $\sum (x_i - \theta_0) \geq K_\alpha$ is α.

If the populations are double exponential, with means θ_0 and θ_1, the function f is dependent upon θ_1 in a somewhat complicated manner. For $\theta_1 - \theta_0$ small, f can be approximated by $f =$ [no. of $+$ signs among $(x_1 - \theta_0, \ldots x_n - \theta_0)$], so that $\theta = \theta_0$ is to be rejected if [no. of $+$ signs among $(x_1 - \theta_0, \ldots, x_n - \theta_0)$] $\geq K_\alpha'$. K_α' is determined by the distribution of f when $\theta = \theta_0$, so that the probability $f \geq K_\alpha'$ is α.

In each case above, the function and corresponding test are best in that the size of the test is α and the power, at θ_1, is maximum. For other-shaped distributions, other functions f will be determined for the optimum analysis of the data $(x_1, \ldots, x_n)$ and the rule for basing the decision on the data.

In each case the following specifications, of both the possible sources of the observations $(x_1, \ldots, x_n)$ and of why the experiment leading to the observations was conducted were made:

1. The set of decisions {install machine, don't install machine}.
2. The shape of the population whose mean θ was unknown.

3. A choice of θ_0 (here a breakeven point).

4. An upper bound α for the probability of installing the machine if θ should be θ_0.

5. The choice of a value $\theta_1 > \theta_0$ for which the probability of not installing the machine if the mean should be θ_1 is to be minimized.

In many problems a basis for such specifications does not exist. In these problems a best procedure cannot be defined, and some procedure which generally can be expected to be reasonable is followed.

For example, it might be that the shape of the population is known when the mean is θ_0 but not otherwise. In such a case it can be useful to choose a test by putting a precise condition, that the size of the test be α, only for $\theta = \theta_0$. How useful this practice is depends upon the ability to choose, on intuitive grounds, a function f which will give a test with high power for the alternatives it is important to reject. In the example above it was important to reject H_0 (that is, to install the machine) for populations with means larger than θ_0. It was also important to accept H_0 (that is, to not install the machine) for populations with means smaller than θ_0. These importances imply that a function f should be chosen that can be expected to be large if $\theta > \theta_0$ and small if $\theta < \theta_0$. For such an f, a value of K, so that the probability $f \geq K$ is α, is determined from the known distribution of f when $\theta = \theta_0$. Whether the function f selected will have any optimum properties for a particular alternative θ_1 will depend upon the shape of the distribution when θ is θ_1.

In some cases it can happen that the shape of the population when $\theta = \theta_0$ is also not completely known. If so, for many functions f it would not be possible to find K so that the probability that $f \geq K$ is α. However, for some functions the distribution of f is the same for many populations with mean θ_0. The function $f =$ [no. of $+$ signs among $(x_1 - \theta_0, \ldots, x_n - \theta_0)$] is an example. f has, for independent $(x_1, \ldots, x_n)$, a binomial distribution with $p = 1/2$ for any population symmetric around θ_0. Analyses with the property that their distribution is the same for a large class of populations (each expressing the same null hypothesis) are called *nonparametric* or *distribution-free*. They are also called *robust*; that is, they maintain the property that $P(f \geq K_\alpha) = \alpha$ in a great variety of circumstances (for many populations). Two other distribution-free analyses, which have already been introduced here, are Wilcoxon's signed rank test and the Fisher test. Their distributions are constant, not only for independent observations from populations symmetric at θ_0 but also for the randomized paired comparison experiment considered in Chapter 9.

To return to the list of specifications on pages 128 and 129, it has been seen that if the shape of the population is unknown, it is possible to proceed by selecting a function which can be expected to have power for the alternatives for which it is important to reject. Also, that by using nonparametric methods, it is possible to determine for such an f, a value K_α so that, if $\theta = \theta_0$ is true, the probability that $f \geq K_\alpha$ (and hence that H_0 is rejected) is α.

In the case of the laboratory, their necessity to choose between installing or not installing the machine determined the alternatives to $\theta = \theta_0$ for which it was important to reject the null hypothesis $\theta = \theta_0$. Without this necessity to decide, it might still be possible to single out a value θ_0 as a null hypothesis. The alternatives for which it is important to reject the null hypothesis might be the same as above or they might be different. For example, the question of whether to install the machine might be premature and the observations $(x_1, x_2, \ldots, x_n)$ have been taken to determine whether the machine should be considered at all. The null hypothesis θ_0 in this instance might be a smaller number than was θ_0 above; θ_0 could be the present hourly rate for the task, whereas the value above would presumably have been somewhat higher to justify the installation costs. Also, it could be important to reject θ_0 for alternatives θ either above or below θ_0. For example, if θ were considerably larger than θ_0, it might be clear that the machine should be put to a definitive test; if θ were considerably smaller than θ_0, it might be clear that the machine should be forgotten, whereas for θ near θ_0 the question of whether to consider the machine would still be open. Hence accepting θ_0 would be equivalent to not presently deciding whether to put the machine to a definitive test, but to wait for more information. Rejecting θ_0 would have a different meaning depending upon whether the evidence in $(x_1, \ldots, x_n)$ was that θ was considerably smaller than θ_0 or θ was considerably larger than θ_0. For such a case it would be indicated to reject θ_0, for the functions considered above, if the observed value of f were far from what would be expected if θ were θ_0. If it were desired that the risk of rejecting θ_0 when true be α, two numbers $K_\alpha{}^L < K_\alpha{}^U$ can be determined so that $P_{\theta_0}\{f \leq K_\alpha{}^L \text{ or } f \geq K_\alpha{}^U\} = P_{\theta_0}\{f \leq K_\alpha{}^L\} + P_{\theta_0}\{f \geq K_\alpha{}^U\} = \alpha$. The relative sizes of $P_{\theta_0}\{f \leq K_\alpha{}^L\}$ and $P_{\theta_0}\{f \geq K_\alpha{}^U\}$ can sometimes be determined by consideration of the relative seriousness of the errors "Don't reject θ_0 when $\theta > \theta_0$" and "Don't reject θ_0 when $\theta < \theta_0$." When the relative importance of these errors is obscure, one convention is to choose one constant, K_α, so that

$$P_{\theta_0}\{|f - \mu_f(\theta_0)| \geq K_\alpha\} = \alpha.$$

In the case just described, the null hypothesis θ_0 of interest might be different for different persons. If so, a report of the experiment in terms of several null hypothesis would be called for. Such a report is one interpretation of a confidence interval of coefficient $1 - \alpha$. It states, for each value of θ, whether that value of θ would be accepted with one of the family of tests, of size α, based on f used in its construction.

The value of α which would be set by different persons might not be the same. If so, a report of the experiment which described the confidence intervals for all values of α would be more helpful. That is, the reporting of a curve A_f for a reasonably chosen f would be indicated.

All the above discussion has been based on the assumption that observations $(x_1, \ldots, x_n)$ were taken so that their probabilistic properties, and hence those of A_f, were known. If the observations are not a random sample, or if no randomization were done, the curve A_f is still a useful summary. If the observations $x_1, \ldots, x_n$ have any relevance to θ, it will give some information. What is to be avoided is attributing any probabilistic properties to A_f, since any probabilistic assumptions made for its construction are not known to obtain. When such interpolatory assumptions are made, it is particularly important that a description of their nature be included with a description of the experimental outcome.

PART II

DESCRIPTIONS OF PARTICULAR ANALYSES

CHAPTER 14

TWO-SAMPLE PROBLEMS

Experiments leading to observations $(t_1, t_2, \ldots, t_n)$ from one source and $(c_1, \ldots, c_m)$ from another source are loosely referred to as *two-sample problems.*

The simplest assumptions about the sources of the observations are random assignment of $n + m$ subjects to a treatment group of n subjects and a control (or second treatment) group of m subjects, and a constant additive treatment effect (or treatment difference).

The hypothesis that a particular number θ is the treatment effect is tested by evaluating, for $(t_1 - \theta, \ldots, t_n - \theta)$, $(c_1, \ldots, c_m)$, a function f, and determining the proportion of the $\binom{n+m}{n}$ possible divisions of the $n + m$ numbers $(t_1 - \theta, \ldots, t_n - \theta, c_1, \ldots, c_m)$ into a group of m and a group of n which lead to value of f at least as large as the value for $(t_1 - \theta, \ldots, t_n - \theta)$, $(c_1, \ldots, c_m)$. If this proportion, $A_f(\theta)$, is no larger than a preassigned number α, the hypothesis "θ is the treatment effect" is rejected; otherwise it is accepted. Three functions that are often used are those of the Wilcoxon, Mann-Whitney test; the Fisher-Pitman test; and the median test. Of these, the Wilcoxon, Mann-Whitney has such simplicity and generally good properties that its use is to be recommended.

THE WILCOXON, MANN-WHITNEY TEST

$$f = \frac{nm}{n+m}|\bar{R}_{t-\theta} - \bar{R}_c| = \left|\sum R_{t-\theta} - \frac{n(n+m+1)}{2}\right|$$
$$= \left|\sum R_c - \frac{m(n+m+1)}{2}\right|,$$

where $R_{t-\theta}$ or R_c denotes a rank of a score $t - \theta$, or c, among $(t_1 - \theta, \ldots$ $t_n - \theta, c_1, \ldots, c_m)$. If there are no ties, the proportion of possible values of f which exceed the observed is given by twice the P value in Table B for

$\sum R_{t-\theta}$ if $n \leq m$, $\sum R_c$ if $m \leq n$ (or 1 if either $\sum R_{t-\theta}$ or $\sum R_c$ is the median of its distribution). Adjustments for ties and approximations are given there for larger sample sizes.

Example 1. For $n = 8$, $m = 7$, $(t_1, \ldots, t_8) = (-.1, .9, 1.1, 1.4, 1.3, .3, -1.0, 1.8)$, and $(c_1, \ldots, c_7) = (-.8, .1, -1.6, 1.0, .5, -.7, .2)$ were observed. To test the hypothesis that $\theta = .5$, the implied no-treatment observations are $(t_1 - .5, \ldots, t_8 - .5) = (-.6, .4, .6, .9, .8, -.2, -1.5, 1.3)$, $(c_1, \ldots, c_7) = (-.8, .1, -1.6, 1.0, .5, -.7, .2)$. Arranging these in order gives, with the ranks shown,

$$\begin{array}{ccccccccccccccc} -1.6, & -1.5, & -.8, & -.7, & -.6, & -.2, & .1, & .2, & .4, & .5, & .6, & .8, & .9, & 1.0, & 1.3 \\ 1, & 2, & 3, & 4, & 5, & 6, & 7, & 8, & 9, & 10, & 11, & 12, & 13, & 14, & 15 \end{array}$$

Consequently the ranks, for the two sets are

$$(R_{t_1-\theta}, \ldots, R_{t_8-\theta}) = (5, 9, 11, 13, 12, 6, 2, 15),$$
$$(R_{c_1}, \ldots, R_{c_7}) = (3, 7, 1, 14, 10, 4, 8).$$

To use Table B, the sum of the ranks for the smaller set is needed; here $\sum R_c = 3 + 7 + 1 + 14 + 10 + 4 + 8 = 47$. From Table B the proportion of rearrangements of $(t_1 - \theta, \ldots, t_8 - \theta, c_1, \ldots, c_7)$ into groups of sizes $n = 8$, $m = 7$ for which $|\sum R_c - [m(m + n + 1)/2]|$ is at least as large as $|47 - [m(m + n + 1)/2]|$ is $2(.168) = .34$.

If the normal approximation is used here,

$$\mu = \frac{m(m + n + 1)}{2} = 56,$$

$$\sigma = \sqrt{\frac{mn(m + n + 1)}{12}} = 8.64.$$

The normal approximation is twice the area below:

$$\frac{[(\sum R_c) + 1/2] - \mu}{\sigma} = \frac{47.5 - 56}{8.64} = -.98.$$

From Table E the approximation is seen to be $2(.1635) = .33$. [If m and n are not as nearly equal as here, or if θ is such that the ranges of $(t_1 - \theta, \ldots, t_n - \theta)$, $(c_1, \ldots, c_m)$ are more separated, the normal approximation will, generally, not be as good as above.]

THE FISHER-PITMAN TEST

$$f = \frac{nm}{n+m}|\bar{t} - \bar{c} - \theta| = \left|\sum t - \frac{n}{n+m}(n\bar{t} + m\bar{c} + m\theta)\right|$$
$$= \left|\sum c - \frac{m}{n+m}(n\bar{t} + m\bar{c} - n\theta)\right|.$$

Because the randomization distributions for this function depend upon the observations, it is not practical to table the distributions. For small samples the distribution can be found by enumeration. (See chapter 4.) For large samples an approximation to the proportion is given by twice the area above the value of f in a normal distribution with

$\mu = 0$,

$$\sigma = \left(\frac{mn}{n+m-1}\left[\frac{\sum t^2 + \sum c^2}{n+m} - \frac{(\sum t + \sum c)^2}{(n+m)^2} - \frac{nm}{(n+m)^2}(\bar{t} - \bar{c})^2 + \frac{nm}{(n+m)^2}\{\theta - (\bar{t} - \bar{c})\}^2\right]\right)^{\frac{1}{2}}.$$

Example 2. For the same observations and value of θ as in Example 1,

$$(t_1, \ldots, t_8) = (-.1, .9, 1.1, 1.4, 1.3, .3, -1.0, 1.8),$$
$$(c_1, \ldots, c_7) = (-.8, .1, -1.6, 1.0, .5, -.7, .2),$$

and the implied no-treatment observations

$$(t_1 - \theta, \ldots, t_8 - \theta) = (-.6, .4, .6, .9, .8, -.2, -1.5, 1.3),$$
$$(c_1, \ldots, c_7) = (-.8, .1, -1.6, 1.0, .5, -.7, .2),$$

it is not practicable to compute the randomization distribution for $\bar{t}' - \bar{c}'$. The computations for the normal approximation are given.

t	t^2	c	c^2
−.1	.01	−.8	.64
.9	.81	.1	.01
1.1	1.21	−1.6	2.56
1.4	1.96	1.0	1.00
1.3	1.69	.5	.25
.3	.09	−.7	.49
−1.0	1.00	.2	.04
1.8	3.24		
$\sum t = 5.7$	$\sum t^2 = 10.01$	$\sum c = -1.3$	$\sum c^2 = 4.99$

$$f = \left|\sum t - \frac{n}{n+m}(n\bar{t} + m\bar{c} + m\theta)\right|$$

$$= \left|5.7 - \frac{8}{15}(5.7 - 1.3 + 7(.5))\right| = 1.49,$$

$$\sigma = \left(\frac{nm}{n+m-1}\left[\frac{\sum t^2 + \sum c^2}{n+m} - \frac{(\sum t + \sum c)^2}{(n+m)^2} - \frac{nm}{(n+m)^2}(\bar{t}-\bar{c})^2 + \frac{nm}{(n+m)^2}\{\theta - (\bar{t}-\bar{c})\}^2\right]\right)^{\frac{1}{2}}$$

$$= \left(\frac{8\cdot 7}{14}\left\{\frac{10.01 + 4.99}{15} - \frac{(5.7-1.3)^2}{15^2} - \frac{8\cdot 7}{15^2}\left(\frac{5.7}{8} + \frac{1.3}{7}\right)^2 + \frac{8\cdot 7}{15^2}\left[.5 - \left(\frac{5.7}{8} + \frac{1.3}{7}\right)\right]^2\right\}\right)^{\frac{1}{2}}$$

$$= 1.73.$$

The normal approximation is twice the area in a unit normal distribution above:

$$\frac{f}{\sigma} = \frac{1.49}{1.73} = .86.$$

From Table E the approximation is seen to be 2(.1949) = .39.

THE MEDIAN TEST

$$f = \frac{n'm'}{2(n'+m')}\left|\frac{n_{t-\theta}^+ - n_{t-\theta}^-}{n'} - \frac{n_c{}^+ - n_c{}^-}{m'}\right| = \left|n_{t-\theta}^+ - \frac{(n_{t-\theta}^+ + n_c{}^+)n'}{n'+m'}\right|,$$

where n' is the number of $(t_1 - \theta, \ldots, t_n - \theta)$ not equal to the median M of $(t_1 - \theta, \ldots, t_n - \theta, c_1, \ldots, c_m)$, $n_{t-\theta}^+$ is the number of $(t_1 - \theta, \ldots, t_n - \theta)$ above M, and $n_{t-\theta}^-$ is the number below M. m', $n_c{}^+$, and $n_c{}^-$ are defined in the same way for $(c_1, \ldots, c_m)$.

The randomization distribution of $n_{t-\theta}^+$ is hypergeometric (Table K). To use this table it is helpful to construct the two-by-two-table as in Table 14.1.

Table 14.1

	$t - \theta$	c	
Above M	$n_{t-\theta}^+$	$n_c{}^+$	A
Below M	n_{t-c}^-	$n_c{}^-$	B
	n'	m'	$N' = A + B = n' + m'$

Let p = smaller of (n', m'), q = smaller of (A, B), and x equal the entry in the square corresponding to (p, q). The proportion of the possible divisions of the numbers $(t_1 - \theta, \ldots, t_n - \theta, c_1, \ldots, c_m)$ into a group of n and a group of m which lead to a value of f at least as large as $|x - [pq/(n' + m')]|$ is given by the sum of the probabilities of the points which are either the endpoints of, or, outside the interval determined by

$$\frac{pq}{n' + m'} - \left|x - \frac{pq}{n' + m'}\right| \quad \text{and} \quad \frac{pq}{n' + m'} + \left|x - \frac{pq}{n' + m'}\right|.$$

Approximations for larger sample sizes are given in the introduction to Table K.

Example 3. For the observations and the value of θ of the preceding two examples,

$$(t_1 - \theta, \ldots, t_8 - \theta) = (-.6, .4, .6, .9, .8, -.2, -1.5, 1.3),$$
$$(c_1, \ldots, c_7) = (-.8, .1, -1.6, 1.0, .5, -.7, .2).$$

The median M of these 15 numbers is easily seen to be .2. Table 14.1 is

	$t - \theta$	c	
Above M	5	2	$A = 7 \leftarrow q$
Below M	3	4	$B = 7$
	$n' = 8$	$m' = 6$ $\uparrow$ p	$N' = 14$

and, since $m' = 6 < 8 = n'$ and $A = 7 \leq 7 = B$, $p = 6$, $q = 7$, and the value of x is 2. Referring 2 and

$$\frac{2pq}{n' + m'} - 2 = \frac{2 \cdot 6 \cdot 7}{7 + 7} - 2 = 6 - 2 = 4$$

to Table K for $n' + m' = N' = 14$ gives the proportion of arrangements with f at least as large as for the observations as the sum of the P values for 2 and for 4 as $.296 + .296 = .59$.

The normal approximation is given by twice the area, from Table E, below $[(x + 1/2) - \mu]/\sigma$ with (see the introduction to Table K)

$$\mu = \frac{pq}{N'} = \frac{7 \cdot 6}{14} = 3,$$

$$\sigma = \sqrt{\frac{p \cdot q \cdot (n' + m' - p)(n' + m' - q)}{(n' + m')^2(n' + m' - 1)}} = \sqrt{\frac{6 \cdot 7 \cdot 8 \cdot 7}{14^2 \cdot 13}} = .96.$$

Since

$$\frac{(x + 1/2) - \mu}{\sigma} = \frac{(2 + 1/2) - 3}{.96} = -.52,$$

the approximation is $2(.3015) = .60$.

The median test can be applied without discarding the observations equal to the median. If there are relatively few equal to the median, not much will be gained by doing so. For the computation of the median test using all the observations, see Chapter 6.

There are other assumptions about the sources of the observations which lead to the same distribution theory for tests as above. Two of these, which are essentially equivalent, are

1. $n + m$ individuals are selected randomly from a population so that $(c_1, \ldots, c_{n+m})$ are a random sample from a distribution. n of the $n + m$ are randomly selected as treatment subjects for a treatment whose effect, θ, is additive (or for one of two treatments with an additive difference θ).
2. n individuals are selected randomly from one population and m individuals are selected independently and randomly from a second population, so that $(t_1, \ldots, t_n)$, $(c_1, \ldots, c_m)$ are independent samples from distributions which are translates, by θ, of each other.

In either case, if θ is the treatment effect, the conditional, given the values but not the treatment assignment, distribution of $(t_1 - \theta, \ldots, t_n - \theta, c_1, \ldots, c_m)$ is the randomization distribution. This has the implication that the tests given above are distribution-free, or nonparametric, and the size of a test, the probability of coverage of a confidence interval, and some basic properties of the estimate do not depend upon the population.

If the common distribution of $(t_1 - \theta, \ldots, t_n - \theta)$, $(c_1, \ldots, c_m)$ is known, it is sometimes possible to find a function f which gives tests with optimum power properties, confidence intervals with optimum probability of false coverage, and estimates with optimum properties.

For example, if the common distribution is normal, optimum tests are given by referring

$$f = \frac{|\bar{t} - \bar{c} - \theta|}{\sigma\sqrt{(1/n) + (1/m)}}$$

to a unit normal curve or, if σ is not known, referring

$$f = \frac{|\bar{t} - \bar{c} - \theta|}{\sqrt{\left(\frac{1}{n} + \frac{1}{m}\right)\frac{ns_t^2 + ms_c^2}{n + m - 2}}}$$

to a Student's t distribution (or referring f^2 to an F distribution with $\nu_1 = 1$, $\nu_2 = n + m - 2$). However, particularly for small samples, the size of these last two tests can be quite different from α if the underlying distribution is, in fact, not normal.

The question is whether the potential gain in power is worth the risk of not having the correct size. For instance, for large samples and small θ, the loss, if the underlying distribution is normal, from using the Wilcoxon test rather than Student's t amounts to only a reduction, in the effective number of observations, of about 5 per cent. The corresponding comparison for the median test is about 55 per cent. Small sample studies have shown the Wilcoxon test to compare as favorably with other tests.

Rank tests can be modified, for a given distribution, to have the correct size for all distributions and to have, at least asymptotically, the same power as the best test for the given distribution. For instance, replacing the ranks R by the $[R/(n + m + 1)]$th percentile of the unit normal distribution is such a modification for normal populations.

CHAPTER 15

ONE-SAMPLE PROBLEMS

Experiments leading to observations $(d_1, \ldots, d_n)$ are referred to as one-sample problems.

An example of a "source" for which the distribution theory is particularly simple is the paired comparison experiment. $2n$ subjects are matched, that is, arranged, before the experiment, in pairs, so that it is expected that the two subjects within each pair will, without treatment, have approximately the same response. Then, independently for all the n pairs, a treatment (or one of two treatments) is assigned, at random with probability 1/2, to one of the two subjects, reserving the other for control (or the second treatment). The observations $(d_1, \ldots, d_n)$ are $(t_1 - c_1, \ldots, t_n - c_n)$, where (t_i, c_i) are the observed scores from the experiment for the treatment subject and the control subject of the ith pair.

The hypothesis that a particular number θ is the additive treatment effect is tested by evaluating for $(d_1 - \theta, \ldots, d_n - \theta)$ a function f and determining the proportion of the 2^n possible assignments of + and − signs to $(d_1 - \theta, \ldots, d_n - \theta)$ which lead to values of f at least as high as that for $(d_1 - \theta, \ldots, d_n - \theta)$. If this proportion is no larger than a preassigned number α, the hypothesis is rejected; otherwise it is accepted.

Three functions that are often used are those of the Wilcoxon signed-rank test, the Fisher test, and the sign test.

THE WILCOXON SIGNED-RANK TEST

$$f = 1/2\left|\sum R^+_{|d-\theta|} - \sum R^-_{|d-\theta|}\right| = \left|\sum R^+_{|d-\theta|} - \frac{n'(n'+1)}{4}\right|,$$

where $R^+_{|d-\theta|}$ is the rank, among $(|d_1 - \theta|, \ldots, |d_n - \theta|)$, of an observation $d - \theta$ which is positive, $R^-_{|d-\theta|}$ is that of an observation which is negative, and n' is the number of $(d_1 - \theta, \ldots, d_n - \theta)$ which are not zero. If there are no ties among $(|d_1 - \theta|, \ldots, |d_n - \theta|)$, the proportion of possible assignments of signs that lead to as high or higher a value of f than that for the observations is given by twice the P value in Table C corresponding to the observed value of $\sum R^+_{|d-\theta|}$ [or by 1 if $\sum R^+_{|d-\theta|} = n'(n'+1)/4$]. Adjustments for ties and approximations for larger sample sizes are given in the introduction to Table C in Part III.

Example 1. For $n = 10$, $(d_1, \ldots, d_{10}) = (-.44, .02, .13, -.95, .18, .39, -.20, -1.65, .25, .61)$ were observed. To test the hypothesis that $\theta = .2$, the implied no-treatment differences are $(d_1 - \theta, \ldots, d_{10} - \theta) = (-.64, -.18, -.07, -1.15, -.02, .19, -.40, -1.85, .05, .41)$. Arranging these in order of their absolute value gives, with the ranks and the original signs shown:

−	+	−	−	+	−	+	−	−	−
.02,	.05,	.07,	.18,	.19,	.40,	.41,	.64,	1.15,	1.85
1	2	3	4	5	6	7	8	9	10

Consequently the ranks of $(d_1 - \theta, \ldots, d_{10} - \theta)$ among $(|d_1 - \theta|, \ldots, |d_n - \theta|)$ are (8, 4, 3, 9, 1, 5, 6, 10, 2, 7) and $\sum R^+_{|d-\theta|} = 2 + 5 + 7 = 14$.

From Table C, the proportion of possible assignments of signs for which $|\sum R^+_{|d-\theta|} - [n(n+1)/4]|$ is at least as large as $|14 - [n(n+1)/4]|$ is $2(.097) = .19$.

If the normal approximation is used here,

$$\mu = \frac{n'(n'+1)}{4} = \frac{10 \cdot 11}{4} = 27.5,$$

$$\sigma = \sqrt{\frac{1}{24} n'(n'+1)(2n'+1)} = \sqrt{\frac{1}{24} 10(11)(21)} = 9.81.$$

The normal approximation is twice the area below:

$$\frac{(\sum R^+_{|d-\theta|} + \frac{1}{2}) - \mu}{\sigma} = \frac{14.5 - 27.5}{9.81} = 1.33.$$

From Table E the approximation is seen to be $2(.0918) = .18$.

THE FISHER TEST

$$f = n|\bar{d} - \theta| = |\sum (d - \theta)| = |\sum d - n\theta|.$$

Because the randomization distributions for this function depend upon the observations, it is not practical to tabulate the distributions. For small samples the distribution can be found by enumeration. For larger samples an approximation to the proportion is given by twice the area above the value of f in a normal distribution with

$$\mu = 0,$$

$$\sigma = \sqrt{\sum d^2 - \frac{(\sum d)^2}{n} + n(\bar{d} - \theta)^2}.$$

Example *2.* For the same observations and value of θ in Example 1,

$$(d_1, \ldots, d_{10}) = (-.44, .02, .13, -.95, .18, .39, -.20, -1.65, .25, .61),$$

$$(d_1 - \theta, \ldots, d_{10} - \theta)$$

$$= (-.64, -.18, -.07, -1.15, -.02, .19, -.40, -1.85, .05, .41),$$

it is not practicable to compute, by hand, the randomization distribution of $\bar{d} - \theta$. The computations for the normal approximation are given below.

d	d^2
−.44	.1936
.02	.0004
.13	.0169
−.95	.9025
.18	.0324
.39	.1521
−.20	.0400
−1.65	2.7225
.25	.0625
.61	.3721
$\sum d = -1.66$	$\sum d^2 = 4.4950$

$$f = |\sum d - n\theta|$$
$$= |-1.66 - 10(.2)| = 3.66$$

$$\sigma = \sqrt{\sum d^2 - \frac{(\sum d)^2}{n} + n(\bar{d} - \theta)^2}$$

$$= \sqrt{4.4950 - \frac{(1.66)^2}{10} + 10(-.166 - .2)^2} = 2.36.$$

The approximation is twice the area in Table E (in Part III) above $f/\sigma = 3.66/2.36 = 1.55$, which is seen to be $2(.0606) = .12$.

THE SIGN TEST

$$f = \tfrac{1}{2}|n^+ - n^-| = \left|n^+ - \frac{n'}{2}\right|,$$

where $n^+(n^-)$ is the number of $(d_1 - \theta, \ldots, d_n - \theta)$ which are greater (smailer) than zero and n' is the number of $(d_1 - \theta, \ldots, d_n - \theta)$ which are not zero.

The randomization distribution of n^+ is binomial (Table D in Part III). The proportion of possible assignments of signs that lead to as high or higher a value of f than that for the observations is given by twice the P value in Table D, with $p = 1/2$, corresponding to the observed value of n^+ (or by 1 if $n^+ = n'/2$). Approximations for larger sample sizes are given in the introduction to Table D.

Example 3. For the observations and the value of θ of the preceding two examples,

$$(d_1, \ldots, d_{10}) = (-.44, .02, .13, -.95, .18, .39, -.20, -1.65, .25, .61),$$

$$(d_1 - \theta, \ldots, d_{10} - \theta)$$
$$= (-.64, -.18, -.07, -1.15, -.02, .19, -.40, -1.85, .05, .41),$$

and $n^+ = 3$. Referring $n^+ = 3$ to Table D for $n = 10$, $p = 1/2$, gives the proportion of assignments of signs with f at least as large as for the observations as $2(.172) = .34$.

The normal approximation is given by twice the area in Table E below $[(n^+ + \frac{1}{2}) - \mu]/\sigma$ with

$$\mu = n'p = 10 \cdot \tfrac{1}{2} = 5,$$
$$\sigma = \sqrt{n'p(1 - p)} = \sqrt{10\tfrac{1}{2}\tfrac{1}{2}} = 1.58.$$

Since

$$\frac{(n^+ + \frac{1}{2}) - \mu}{\sigma} = \frac{(3 + \frac{1}{2}) - 5}{1.58} = -.96,$$

the approximation is $2(.1685) = .34$.

There are other assumptions about the sources of the observations which lead to the same distribution theory for tests as above. Three of these are

1. n individuals are selected randomly from a population and the same characteristic measured before and after treatment, so that the differences $(d_1, \ldots, d_n)$ are a sample from a distribution symmetric about θ. Then the conditional, given the absolute values but not the + or − signs, distribution of $(d_1 - \theta, \ldots, d_n - \theta)$ is that above.

2. $2n$ individuals are taken at random from some population so that $(y_1, \ldots, y_{2n})$ is a sample from a distribution. The $2n$ are put in pairs on some basis before the experiment. If the subjects within each pair are randomly, with $p = 1/2$, assigned to treatment and control (or a second treatment) and $d_i = t_i - c_i$ is defined as above, then the conditional, given the absolute values but not the + or − signs, distribution of $(d_1 - \theta, \ldots, d_n - \theta)$ is that above.

3. n individuals are selected at random from a population so that their scores $(y_1, \ldots, y_n)$ are a sample from a distribution that is symmetric around θ. Then, the conditional, given the absolute values but not the + or − signs, distribution of $(y_1 - \theta, \ldots, y_n - \theta)$ is the same as that above.

In connection with paired comparison experiments, it is not to be taken for granted that any arbitrary pairing will give more precision than would dividing the $2n$ subjects randomly into a treatment and a control group. Roughly speaking, the pairing should tend to give the value zero to the (non-observable) no-treatment difference between the scores of subjects in the same pair.

Again, as for the two-sample problem, the tests above are distribution-free. With knowledge of the population it is possible to find optimum tests. For example, if the common distribution of $(d_1 - \theta, \ldots, d_n - \theta)$ is normal, optimum tests are given by referring

$$f = \frac{|\bar{d} - \theta| \sqrt{n}}{\sigma}$$

to a unit normal curve or, if σ is not known,

$$f = \frac{|\bar{d} - \theta| \sqrt{n}}{\sqrt{[1/(n-1)]\{\sum d^2 - [(\sum d)^2/n]\}}}$$

to a Student's t distribution (or referring f^2 to an F distribution with $\nu_1 = 1$, $\nu_2 = n - 1$).

Example 4. For the observations and value of θ as in the Examples 1, 2 and 3

$$(d_1, \ldots, d_{10}) = (-.44, .02, .13, -.95, .18, .39, -.20, -1.65, .25, .61),$$

$$f = \frac{|\bar{d} - \theta|}{\sqrt{[1/(n-1)]\{\sum d^2 - [(\sum d)^2/n]\}}} \sqrt{n}$$

$$= \frac{|-.166 - .20|}{\sqrt{\frac{1}{9}\{4.4950 - [(1.66)^2/10]\}}} \sqrt{10} = 1.69,$$

$$f^2 = 2.86.$$

Referring $f^2 = 2.86$ to the F distribution with $\nu_1 = 1$ and $\nu_2 = 10 - 1 = 9$ gives $A_f(.20) = .14$.

The considerations of whether to attempt to select a function f optimum for a known (?) distribution or to use the signed-rank test are as for two-sample problems.

CHAPTER 16

k-SAMPLE PROBLEMS

Experiments leading to observations

$$
\begin{aligned}
&(t_{1,1}, t_{1,2}, \ldots, t_{1,n_1}) \text{ for treatment 1}\\
&(t_{2,1}, t_{2,2}, \ldots, t_{2,n_2}) \text{ for treatment 2}\\
&\qquad\quad\vdots\\
&(t_{k-1,1}, t_{k-1,2}, \ldots, t_{k-1,n_{k-1}}) \text{ for treatment } k-1\\
&(t_{k,1}, t_{k,2}, \ldots, t_{k,n_k}) \text{ for control (or treatment } k)
\end{aligned}
$$

are referred to as k-sample problems.

The simplest assumptions about the source of the observations are random assignment of $N = \sum n_i$ subjects to k groups of $n_1, n_2, \ldots, n_k$ subjects as follows.

n_1 subjects are selected at random from N for treatment 1
n_2 subjects are selected at random from the remaining $N - n_1$ for treatment 2
$\vdots$
n_{k-1} subjects are selected at random from the remaining $N - n_1 - n_2 - \cdots - n_{k-2}$ for treatment $k - 1$
The remaining n_k subjects are assigned to the control group (to treatment k).

The hypothesis that $\theta_1, \ldots, \theta_{k-1}$ are the additive treatment effects (or, if "control" is a kth treatment, that the treatment differences are $\theta_1 = \theta_1' - \theta_k'$, $\theta_2 = \theta_2' - \theta_k', \ldots, \theta_{k-1} = \theta'_{k-1} - \theta_k'$) is tested by evaluating, for $[(t_{1,1} - \theta_1, t_{1,2} - \theta_1, \ldots, t_{1,n_1} - \theta_1), (t_{2,1} - \theta_2, t_{2,2} - \theta_2, \ldots, t_{2,n_2} - \theta_2), \ldots, (t_{k-1,1} - \theta_{k-1}, t_{k-1,2} - \theta_{k-1}, \ldots, t_{k-1,n_{k-1}} - \theta_{k-1}), (t_{k,1}, t_{k,2}, \ldots, t_{k,n_k})]$, a function f, and determining the proportion of possible rearrangements of these implied no-treatment observations into k groups of sizes $n_1, n_2, \ldots, n_k$ for which f is at least as large as for the observed division. If this proportion is no larger than a preassigned number α, the hypothesis "$\theta_1, \theta_2, \ldots, \theta_{k-1}$ are the treatment effects" is rejected; otherwise it is accepted.

Two functions that are often used are those of the Kruskal–Wallis, Rijkoort test; and the Mood–Brown test.

THE KRUSKAL-WALLIS, RIJKOORT TEST

$$f = \frac{12}{N(N+1)} \sum_{i=1}^{k} n_i(\bar{R}_i - \bar{R})^2 = \frac{12}{N(N+1)} \left[\sum_{i=1}^{k} \frac{R_i^2}{n_i} - \frac{N(N+1)^2}{4} \right]$$

$$= \frac{12}{N(N+1)} \sum_{i=1}^{k} \frac{R_i^2}{n_i} - 3(N+1),$$

where R_i is the sum of the ranks, among $[(t_{1,1} - \theta_1, \ldots, t_{1,n_1} - \theta_1), \ldots, (t_{k-1,1} - \theta_{k-1}, \ldots, t_{k-1,n_{k-1}} - \theta_{k-1}), (t_{k,1}, \ldots, t_{k,n_k})]$, of the implied no-treatment observations in the ith group,

$$\bar{R}_i = \frac{R_i}{n_i} \quad \text{and} \quad \bar{R} = \frac{1}{N} \sum_{i=1}^{k} R_i = \frac{N+1}{2}.$$

If there are no ties, the proportion of rearrangements of the implied no-treatment observations into k groups of sizes $n_1, n_2, \ldots, n_k$ for which f is at least as large as the observed value of f is given by the P value in Table F opposite H. This proportion can also (and more easily) be found by computing, instead of f, $f_1 = \sum_{i=1}^{k}(R_i^2/n_i)$; the proportion is then found in Table F opposite x. Adjustments for ties and approximations for more samples and larger sample sizes are given in the introduction to Table F.

Example 1. For $n_1 = 3$, $n_2 = 5$, $n_3 = 4$, $(t_{1,1}, \ldots, t_{1,3}) = (-.8, -.2, .4)$, $(t_{2,1}, \ldots, t_{2,5}) = (.3, -.7, -2.3, .8, -.9)$ and $(t_{3,1}, \ldots, t_{3,4}) = (.2, -1.6, 1.0, .5)$ were observed. To test the hypothesis that $\theta_1 = -.5$, $\theta_2 = .2$, the implied no-treatment observations are $(t_{1,1} - \theta_1, \ldots, t_{1,3} - \theta_1) = (-.3, .3, .9)$, $(t_{2,1} - \theta_2, \ldots, t_{2,5} - \theta_2) = (.1, -.9, -2.5, .6, -1.1)$, $(t_{3,1}, \ldots, t_{3,4}) = (.2, -1.6, 1.0, .5)$. Arranging these observations in order gives, with the ranks shown,

$$\begin{array}{cccccccccccc} -2.5, & -1.6, & -1.1, & -.9, & -.3, & .1, & .2, & .3, & .5, & .6, & .9, & 1.0 \\ 1, & 2, & 3, & 4, & 5, & 6, & 7, & 8, & 9, & 10, & 11, & 12 \end{array}$$

Consequently, the ranks for the three sets are

Treatment 1 (5, 8, 11),
Treatment 2 (6, 4, 1, 10, 3),
Control (7, 2, 12, 9),

so that $R_1 = 5 + 8 + 11 = 24$, $R_2 = 6 + 4 + 1 + 10 + 3 = 24$, $R_3 = 7 + 2 + 12 + 9 = 30$:

$$f_1 = \sum_{i=1}^{k} \frac{R_i^2}{n_i} = \frac{24^2}{3} + \frac{24^2}{5} + \frac{30^2}{4} = 192 + 144 + 225 = 561.$$

From Table F the proportion of rearrangements of the 12 implied no-treatment observations into groups of sizes 3, 5, and 4 for which f_1 is at least 561 is .131.

The χ^2 approximation is the area in Table H for $k - 1 = 2$ degrees of freedom above

$$f = \frac{12}{N(N+1)} \sum_{i=1}^{k} \frac{R_i^2}{n_i} - 3(N+1) = \frac{12}{12 \cdot 13}(561) - 3(13) = 4.15.$$

From Table H the approximation is seen to be .13.

For $k = 3$ the surface $A_f(\theta_1, \theta_2)$ with f of the Kruskal–Wallis, Rijkoort test can be constructed as follows.

1. Form the $n_1 \cdot n_2 \cdot n_3$ triples (t_{1u}, t_{2v}, t_{3w}) by, for each triple, taking one observation from each group.
2. For each triple, compute

$$x = t_{1u} - t_{3w},$$
$$y = t_{2v} - t_{3w}.$$

3. Plot the $n_1 \cdot n_2 \cdot n_3$ points defined by (x, y) as in step 2 on a graph whose horizontal axis is labeled θ_1 and whose vertical axis is labeled θ_2, as in Figure 16.1.
4. Through each of the $n_1 \cdot n_2 \cdot n_3$ points draw a vertical line, a horizontal line, and a 45-degree (diagonal) line as shown.

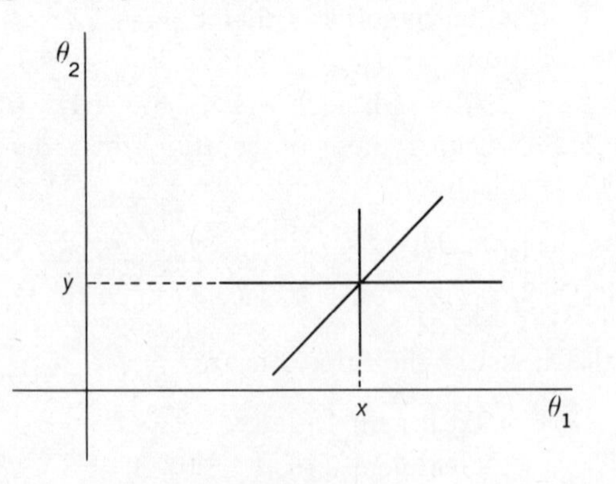

Figure 16.1.

5. $A_f(\theta_1, \theta_2)$ will be constant within each of the regions of the (θ_1, θ_2) plane defined by the lines in step 4. Hence the value for any (θ_1, θ_2) can be found by choosing a point within each region and computing f for that point. [Points (θ_1, θ_2) on lines correspond to ties (see Exercise 5.8).]

Example 2. For the observations

$$(t_{11}, t_{12}) = (4, 9),$$
$$(t_{21}, t_{22}) = (8, 11),$$
$$(t_{31}) = (10),$$

the $n_1 \cdot n_2 \cdot n_3 = 4$ triples (t_{1u}, t_{2v}, t_{3w}) and the differences x and y are

t_{1u}	t_{2v}	t_{3w}	x	y
4	8	10	−6	−2
4	11	10	−6	1
9	8	10	−1	−2
9	11	10	−1	1

Figure 16.2 is constructed as in Figure 16.1, where in each region the value of A_f is indicated. (The numbers in parentheses are the approximations to A_f found by using the χ^2 approximation. From these it is obvious that it is not advisable to use this approximation for such small sample sizes.)

For preassigned α, a confidence region for (θ_1, θ_2) is given by those θ_1, θ_2 for which $A_f(\theta_1, \theta_2) > \alpha$. For the probability of coverage, $1 - \alpha$, large, relative to the sample sizes, these regions will generally not be bounded; that is, they will extend to infinity in various strips.

For $1 - \alpha = .25$, the 25 per cent confidence region for Example 2 is shown in Figure 16.3. It is the region, from Figure 16.2, where $A_f > .75$. Simultaneous confidence intervals for all functions $g(\theta_1, \theta_2)$ are obtained by finding the maximum and minimum of $g(\theta_1, \theta_2)$ as (θ_1, θ_2) varies over the confidence set. For linear functions, $a\theta_1 + b\theta_2$, these simultaneous confidence intervals are easily found as follows. Draw the line $a\theta_1 + b\theta_2 = 0$ and a line through the origin perpendicular to it. Evaluate $a\theta_1 + b\theta_2$ for the extreme points of the set in the direction of this perpendicular. For the example of Figure 16.3 the simultaneous 25 per cent confidence intervals for θ_1, θ_2, and $\theta_1 - \theta_2$ are seen to be

$$-6 \leq \theta_1 \leq -1,$$
$$-4 \leq \theta_2 \leq 3,$$
$$-7 \leq \theta_1 - \theta_2 \leq 1.$$

If there are three treatments with treatment effects θ_1', θ_2', θ_3' (so that $\theta_1 = \theta_1' - \theta_3'$, $\theta_2 = \theta_2' - \theta_3'$), simultaneous intervals for the differences between the three treatment effects are

$$-6 \le \theta_1' - \theta_3' \le -1,$$
$$-4 \le \theta_2' - \theta_3' \le 3,$$
$$-7 \le \theta_1' - \theta_2' \le 1.$$

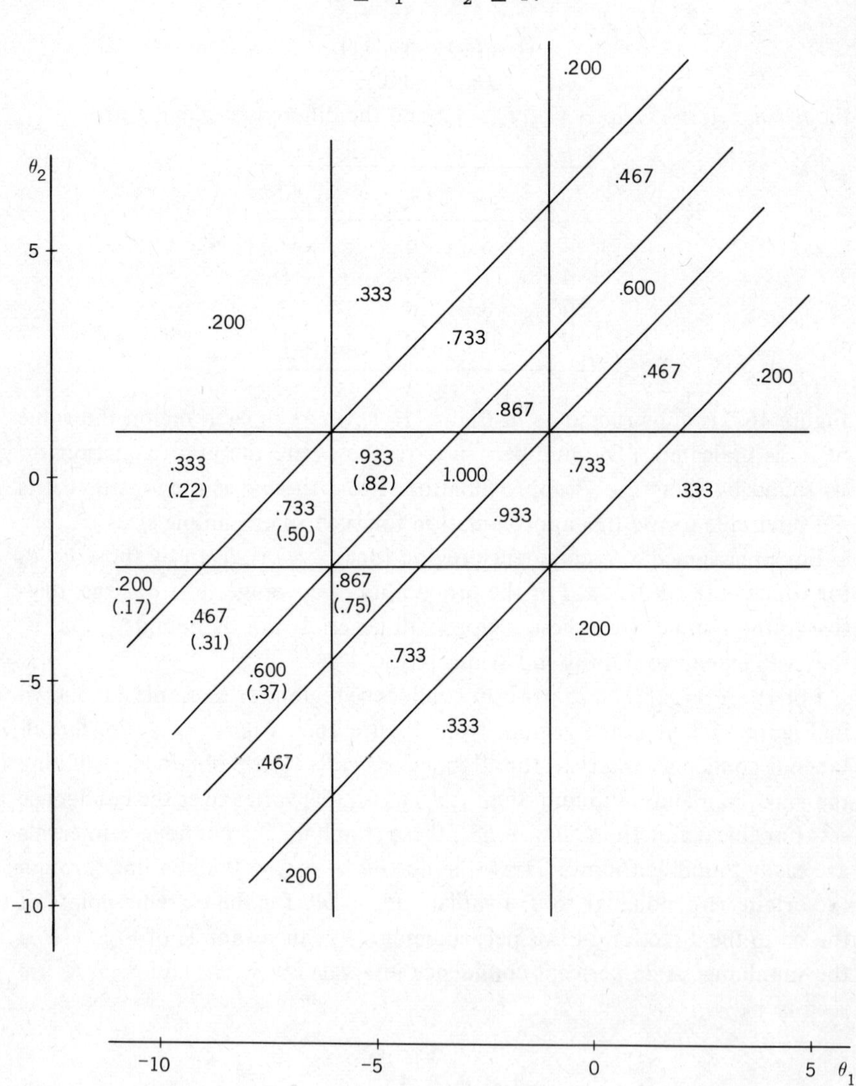

Figure 16.2.

Or, since only the first of these intervals does not contain zero, it is sometimes stated; at the 75 per cent level of significance this experiment has "shown" a significant difference between treatments 1 and 3, but not between treatments 1 and 2 and not between treatments 2 and 3.

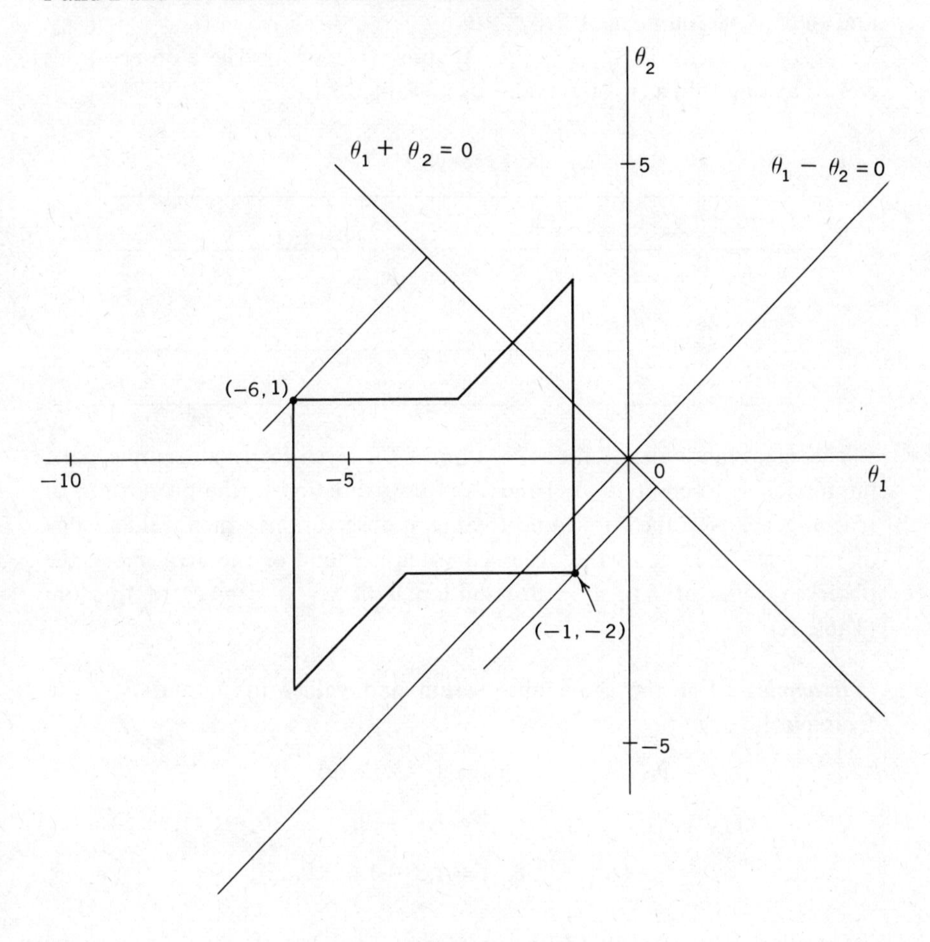

Figure 16.3.

THE MOOD-BROWN MEDIAN TEST

$$f = \frac{(N')^2}{AB} \sum_{i=1}^{k} \frac{[n_i^+ - (n_i'A/N')]^2}{n_i'}$$

$$= \frac{1}{AB} \sum_{i=1}^{k} \frac{(n_i^+N' - n_i'A)^2}{n_i'},$$

where n_i' is the number of implied no-treatment observations in the ith group not equal to the median M of $[(t_{1,1} - \theta_1, \ldots, t_{1,n_1} - \theta_1), \ldots, (t_{k-1,1} - \theta_{k-1}, \ldots, t_{k-1,n_{k-1}} - \theta_{k-1}), (t_{k,1}, \ldots, t_{k,n_k})]$. $n_i^+(n_i^-)$ is the number of implied no-treatment observations in the ith group above (below) M, $N' = \sum n_i'$, and $A(B)$ is the number of $[(t_{1,1} - \theta_1, \ldots, t_{1,n_1} - \theta_1), \ldots, (t_{k-1,1} - \theta_{k-1}, \ldots, t_{k-1,n_{k-1}} - \theta_{k-1}), (t_{k,1}, \ldots, t_{k,n_k})]$ above (below) M. These observations can be arranged in a two-by-k table as in Table 16.1.

Table 16.1

Treatment	1	2	. . .	k	
Above M	n_1^+	n_2^+	. . .	n_k^+	A
Below M	n_1^-	n_2^-	. . .	n_k^-	B
	n_1'	n_2'	. . .	n_k'	$N' = A + B = \sum n_i'$

The exact randomization distribution of f is, even for small sample sizes, impracticable to compute by hand. An approximation to the proportion of rearrangements of the implied no-treatment observations which yield a value of f at least as large as the observed value is found as the area above the observed value of f in a χ^2 distribution with $k - 1$ degrees of freedom (Table H).

Example 3. For the same observation and values of θ_1 and θ_2 as in Example 1,

$$(t_{1,1} - \theta_1, \ldots, t_{1,3} - \theta_1) = (-.3, .3, .9),$$

$$(t_{2,1} - \theta_2, \ldots, t_{2,5} - \theta_2) = (.1, -.9, -2.5, .6, -1.1),$$

$$(t_{3,1}, \ldots, t_{3,4}) = (.2, -1.6, 1.0, .5),$$

the median M is .15. Table 16.1 is

Treatment	1	2	3	
Above M	2	1	3	6
Below M	1	4	1	6
	3	5	4	12

and

$$f = \frac{1}{AB} \sum_{i=1}^{k} \frac{(n_i{}^+N' - n_i'A)^2}{n_i'}$$

$$= \frac{1}{6.6}\left[\frac{(2 \cdot 12 - 3 \cdot 6)^2}{3} + \frac{(1 \cdot 12 - 5 \cdot 6)^2}{5} + \frac{(3 \cdot 12 - 6 \cdot 4)^2}{4}\right] = 3.13.$$

Referring this value of f to a χ^2 table with $k - 1 = 2$ degrees of freedom, gives, for the approximation to the proportion, .21.

As for the two-sample and single-sample problems, there are other assumptions about the sources of the observations which lead to the same distribution theory for tests as above. Two of these, which are essentially equivalent are:

1. $N = \sum_{i=1}^{k} n_i$ individuals are selected randomly from a population so that $(c_1, \ldots, c_N)$ are a random sample from a distribution. n_1 of the N are randomly selected for treatment 1, n_2 are randomly selected from the remaining $N - n_1$ for treatment $2, \ldots, n_{k-1}$ are randomly selected for treatment $k - 1$, and the remaining $N - n_1 - \cdots n_{k-1} = n_k$ are assigned to control (or a kth treatment), where the treatment effects $\theta_1, \ldots, \theta_{k-1}$ (or the treatment differences if "control" is a kth treatment) are additive.

2. n_1 individuals are selected randomly from a population, n_2 are selected randomly from a second population, $\ldots$, n_k are selected randomly from a kth population, so that $[(t_{1,1}, \ldots, t_{1,n_1}), \ldots, (t_{k,1}, \ldots, t_{k,n_k})]$ are independent samples from distributions which are translates, by $\theta_1, \ldots, \theta_{k-1}$, of the kth one.

In either case, if $\theta_1, \ldots, \theta_{k-1}$ are the treatment effects, the conditional, given the values but not the treatment assignment, distribution of $[(t_{1,1} - \theta_1, \ldots, t_{1,n_1} - \theta_1), \ldots, (t_{k-1,1} - \theta_{k-1}, \ldots, t_{k-1,n_{k-1}} - \theta_{k-1}), (t_{k,1}, \ldots, t_{k,n_k})]$ is the randomization distribution. That is, the tests given above are distribution-free.

As for the previous problems, knowledge of the population, when the samples are from populations, can lead to better tests. For instance, when the populations are normal with a common variance, the optimum (in a certain sense) test that the effects are $\theta_1, \ldots, \theta_{k-1}$ is that of the analysis of variance. This analysis compares, for the implied no-treatment observations, the average sum of squares about the means within each sample with the sum of squares of the sample means about the mean of all these observations. The usual method of calculation for the k-sample problem is shown in Table 16.2, where

$$[(t'_{1,1}, \ldots, t'_{1,n_1}), \ldots, (t'_{k-1,1}, \ldots, t_{k-1,n_{k-1}}), (t'_{k,1}, \ldots, t'_{k,n_k})]$$
$$= [(t_{11} - \theta_1, \ldots, t_{1,n_1} - \theta_1), \ldots, (t_{k-1,1} - \theta_{k-1}, \ldots, t_{k-1,n_{k-1}} - \theta_{k-1}), (t_{k,1}, \ldots, t_{k,n_k})].$$

Table 16.2

Source	*Sum of squares*	*d.f.*	*Mean square*	*F*
Total (T)	$\sum_i \sum_j t_{ij}'^2 - \frac{\left(\sum_i \sum_j t_{ij}'\right)^2}{N}$	$N - 1$		
Within (W)	$T - B$	$N - k$	$w = \frac{T - B}{N - k}$	$F = \frac{b}{w}$
Between (B)	$\sum_i \frac{\left(\sum_j t_{ij}'\right)^2}{n_i} - \frac{\left(\sum_i \sum_j t_{ij}'\right)^2}{N}$	$k - 1$	$b = \frac{B}{k - 1}$	

$A_F(\theta_1, \ldots, \theta_{k-1})$, from this analysis of variance, is the area above the observed value of F in the F distribution (Table I) for $\nu_1 = k - 1$ and $\nu_2 = N - k$.

Example 4. For the same observations and values of θ_1 and θ_2 as in Example 1, that is, for

$(t_{1,1}, \ldots, t_{1,3}) = (-.8, -.2, .4)$ for treatment 1,
$(t_{2,1}, \ldots, t_{2,5}) = (.3, -.7, -2.3, .8, -.9)$ for treatment 2,
$(t_{3,1}, \ldots, t_{3,4}) = (.2, -1.6, 1.0, .5)$ for control,
$\theta_1 = -.5, \theta_2 = .2,$

the computations for the analysis of variance are given as follows:

$t_{1j}' = t_{1j} - \theta_1 = t_{1j} + .5$	$t_{ij}'^2$	$t_{2j}' = t_{2j} - \theta_2 = t_{2j} - .2$	$t_{2j}'^2$	$t_{3j}' = t_{3j}$	$t_{3j}'^2$
−.3	.09	.1	.01	.2	.04
.3	.09	−.9	.81	−1.6	2.56
.9	.81	−2.5	6.25	1.0	1.00
		.6	.36	.5	.25
		−1.1	1.21		
$\sum t_{1j}' = .9$	$\sum t_{1j}'^2 = .99$	$\sum t_{2j}' = -3.8$	$\sum t_{2j}'^2 = 8.64$	$\sum t_{3j}' = .1$	$\sum t_{3j}'^2 = 3.85$

$$\sum_i \sum_j t_{ij}' = .9 - 3.8 + .1 = -2.8,$$

$$\left(\sum_i \sum_j t_{ij}'\right)^2 = (2.8)^2 = 7.84,$$

$$\sum_i \sum_j t_{ij}'^2 = .99 + 8.64 + 3.85 = 13.48,$$

$$\sum_i \frac{\left(\sum_j t_{ij}'\right)^2}{n_i} = \frac{(.9)^2}{3} + \frac{(3.8)^2}{5} + \frac{(.1)^2}{4} = 3.16,$$

and Table 16.2 becomes

Source	Sum of squares	d.f.	Mean square	F
Total (T)	$13.48 - \frac{7.84}{12} = 12.83$	$N - 1 = 12 - 1 = 11$		
Within (W)	$12.83 - 2.51 = 10.32$	$N - k = 12 - 3 = 9$	$w = \frac{10.32}{9} = 1.15$	$F = \frac{b}{w}$
Between (B)	$3.16 - \frac{7.84}{12} = 2.51$	$k - 1 = 3 - 1 = 2$	$b = \frac{2.51}{2} = 1.26$	$= \frac{1.26}{1.15} = 1.10$

$A_F(-.5, .2)$ is the area above $F = 1.10$ in Table I with $\nu_1 = k - 1 = 2$ and $\nu_2 = N - k = 9$. From Table I this area is seen to be .40.

As a further example, $A_F(\theta_1, \theta_2)$ will be found for all (θ_1, θ_2) assuming that the three samples are independent and from normal populations with means $\mu + \theta_1$, $\mu + \theta_2$, μ, and a common standard deviation. From Table 16.2 and the implied no-treatment observations

Treatment 1	*Treatment* 2	*Control*
$t_{1,1} - \theta_1$	$t_{2,1} - \theta_2$	$t_{3,1}$
$t_{1,2} - \theta_1$	$t_{2,2} - \theta_2$	$t_{3,2}$
$\vdots$	$\vdots$	$\vdots$
$t_{1,n_1} - \theta_1$	$t_{2,n_2} - \theta_2$	t_{3,n_3}

the value of F is seen to be

$$F = \frac{N-3}{2} \frac{\sum_{i=1}^{3} n_i[(\bar{t}_i - \bar{T}) - (\theta_i - \bar{\theta})]^2}{W},$$

where W is the within sum of squares (see Table 16.2), $\bar{t}_i$ the mean of the observations in the ith sample, $\bar{T} = (n_1\bar{t}_1 + n_2\bar{t}_2 + n_3\bar{t}_3)/N$, θ_1 and θ_2 the treatment effects of treatment 1 and 2, $\theta_3 = 0$, and $\bar{\theta} = (1/N) \sum_{i=1}^{2} n_i\theta_i$. $A_F(\theta_1, \theta_2)$ is for each θ_1, θ_2 the area above F from the F distribution (Table I) with $\nu_1 = 2$, $\nu_2 = N - 3$. These areas, that is, $A_F(\theta_1, \theta_2)$, are constant as a function of (θ_1, θ_2) whenever

$$F = \frac{N-3}{2} \frac{\sum_{i=1}^{3} n_i[(\bar{t}_i - \bar{T}) - (\theta_i - \bar{\theta})]^2}{W}$$

is constant. Choosing this constant as the $(1 - s)$th percentile, k_s, of the F distribution gives those (θ_1, θ_2), for which $A_F(\theta_1, \theta_2) = s$ as those (θ_1, θ_2) for which

$$F = \frac{N-3}{2} \frac{\sum_{i=1}^{3} n_i[(\bar{t}_i - \bar{T}) - (\theta_i - \bar{\theta})]^2}{W} = k_s.$$

For each s these points (θ_1, θ_2) lie on an ellipse and the ellipses are concentric for different values of s.

Example 5. For Example 2, the observations are

Treatment 1	*Treatment* 2	*Control*
4	8	10
9	11	

and

t_{1j}	t_{1j}^2	t_{2j}	t_{2j}^2	t_{3j}	t_{3j}^2
4	16	8	64	10	100
9	81	11	121		
—	—	—	—	—	—
13	99	19	185	10	100

so that

$$\bar{t}_1 = \frac{13}{2} = 6.5, \quad \bar{t}_2 = \frac{19}{2} = 9.5, \quad \bar{t}_3 = \frac{10}{1} = 10, \quad \bar{T} = \frac{13 + 19 + 10}{5} = 8.4,$$

$$\bar{t}_1 - \bar{T} = -1.9, \qquad \bar{t}_2 - \bar{T} = 1.1, \qquad \bar{t}_3 - \bar{T} = 1.6,$$

$$\sum_i \sum_j t_{ij}^2 = 99 + 185 + 100 = 384,$$

$$\sum_i \frac{\left(\sum_j t_{ij}\right)^2}{n_i} = \frac{(13)^2}{2} + \frac{(19)^2}{2} + \frac{(10)^2}{1} = 365, \qquad W = 384 - 365 = 19,$$

$$F = \frac{2}{2}\frac{1}{19}\{2[-1.9 - (\theta_1 - \bar{\theta})]^2 + 2[1.1 - (\theta_2 - \bar{\theta})]^2 + 1[1.6 + \bar{\theta}]^2\}$$

$$= \frac{2(9.5 + 3\theta_1 - 2\theta_2)^2 + 2(5.5 + 2\theta_1 - 3\theta_2)^2 + (8 + 2\theta_1 + 2\theta_2)^2}{25 \cdot 19}.$$

The ellipses for $s = .50$, $.75$, and $.90$ are given in Figure 16.4. The center of these ellipses is the point $(\bar{t}_1 - \bar{t}_3, \bar{t}_2 - \bar{t}_3) = (-3.5, -.5)$.

In the same manner as from Figure 16.2, a 25 per cent confidence region for (θ_1, θ_2) is those (θ_1, θ_2) within the contour labeled .75. Also, in the same manner, simultaneous 25 per cent intervals for functions, $g(\theta_1, \theta_2)$, are given by the maximum and minimum values of g for (θ_1, θ_2) in the same ellipse. For linear combinations, $a\theta_1 + b\theta_2$, these are given by the value of $a\theta_1 + b\theta_2$ at the extremes, in the direction of the perpendicular $-b\theta_1 + a\theta_2 = 0$ of the ellipse. Hence Scheffé's simultaneous 25 per cent intervals for θ_1, θ_2, and $\theta_1 - \theta_2$ are

$$-6.6 < \theta_1 < -.4,$$
$$-3.6 < \theta_2 < 2.6,$$
$$-5.5 < \theta_1 - \theta_2 < -.5.$$

Because of the discontinuities in Figure 16.2, a direct comparison of the lengths here with the lengths given for the corresponding intervals there is not appropriate. A comparison of lengths for the $\alpha = .733$ intervals from Figure 16.2 with these from the ellipse is more appropriate. These are

$$-9 < \theta_1 < 2,$$
$$-7 < \theta_2 < 6,$$
$$-7 < \theta_1 - \theta_2 < 1.$$

The greater lengths of these intervals gives, again, an idea of the greater precision in analyses if it is known that the observations are samples from given (here normal with equal standard deviations) populations. However,

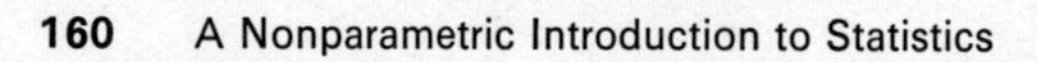

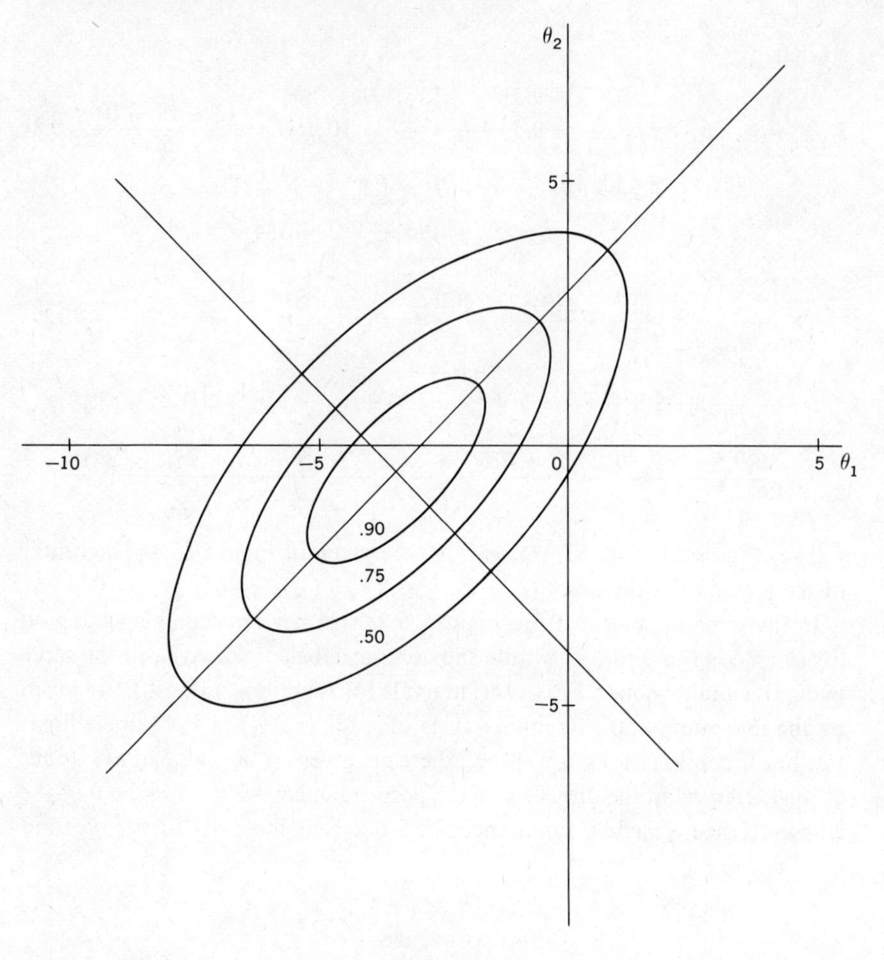

Figure 16.4.

when, as usually is the case, the populations are not known, the intervals of Figure 16.3 have the stated probability of coverage under any of the distribution assumptions given above.

CHAPTER 17

RANDOMIZED BLOCKS

The simplest form of randomized blocks is the paired comparison experiment (see Chapter 15) in which each block contains two subjects and one of two treatments is assigned to each subject in the same block.

In this chapter a design with k treatments (or $k - 1$ treatments and a control) will be considered. Let $m \cdot k$ subjects be arranged, before the experiment, in m k-tuples, so that the k subjects within a k-tuple can, without treatment, be expected to have approximately the same response. For example, in an agricultural experiment, each block might be a set of plots in one locality or of one type of soil and the experiment comprise blocks in several localities or of several soil types.

Independently within each of the k-tuples, the k treatments are assigned at random to the k subjects. The observations can be arranged as follows:

	Treatment 1	Treatment 2	...	Treatment $k-1$	Control or treatment k
Block 1	$t_{1,1}$	$t_{1,2}$		$t_{1,k-1}$	$t_{1,k}$
Block 2	$t_{2,1}$	$t_{2,2}$		$t_{2,k-1}$	$t_{2,k}$
⋮	⋮	⋮		⋮	⋮
Block m	$t_{m,1}$	$t_{m,2}$		$t_{m,k-1}$	$t_{m,k}$

The treatment effects $\theta_1, \theta_2, \ldots, \theta_{k-1}$ (or, if "control" is a kth treatment, the treatment differences $\theta_1' - \theta_k', \ldots, \theta_{k-1}' - \theta_k'$) are assumed to be additive and, for each treatment, the same regardless of which block the treatment is in.

The hypothesis that a particular set of numbers $\theta_1, \ldots, \theta_{k-1}$ are the treatment effects is tested by evaluating for the implied no-treatment observations a function f, and determining the proportion of the $(k!)^m$ possible assignments of the k treatments to the k subjects in each block which lead to values of f at

	Treatment 1	...	*Treatment* $k-1$	*Control*
Block 1	$t_{1,1} - \theta_1$		$t_{1,k-1} - \theta_{k-1}$	$t_{1,k}$
⋮	⋮		⋮	⋮
Block m	$t_{m,1} - \theta_1$		$t_{m,k-1} - \theta_{k-1}$	$t_{m,k}$

least as high as the observed value. If this proportion is no larger than a preassigned number α, the hypothesis is rejected; otherwise it is accepted.

A function f that is often used is that of Friedman's method of m rankings. For each block separately, the implied no-treatment observations ($t_{i1} - \theta_1, \ldots, t_{i,k-1} - \theta_{k-1}, t_{i,k}$) are replaced by their ranks among themselves and for each treatment the sum of these ranks is computed. Denoting these sums of ranks by $R_1, \ldots, R_k$ and $\bar{R} = (1/k) \sum_{j=1}^{k} R_j$,

$$f = \frac{12}{m^2k(k^2 - 1)} \sum_{j=1}^{k} (R_j - \bar{R})^2.$$

If there are no ties among the implied no-treatment observations within the blocks, the proportion of possible assignments of the treatments to the subjects within the blocks which lead to a value of f at least as high as the observed value is given in Table G opposite x. This proportion can also be found by computing $f_1 = \sum_{i=1}^{k} (R_i - \bar{R})^2$ and reading Table G opposite S.

Adjustments for ties and approximations for more blocks and more treatments are given in the introduction to Table G.

Note that this analysis is, for paired comparisons, the sign test.

Example 1. Suppose that for three treatments and four blocks the following observations were obtained and arranged as follows:

	Treatment 1	*Treatment* 2	*Control or treatment* 3
Block 1	1.5	−.2	1.0
Block 2	.9	−.6	1.9
Block 3	−.2	−.8	.1
Block 4	1.2	−2.0	2.3

To test the hypothesis that the treatment effects are $\theta_1 = .4$, $\theta_2 = -.3$, the implied no-treatment observations are

	Treatment 1	*Treatment* 2	*Control or treatment* 3
Block 1	1.1	.1	1.0
Block 2	.5	−.3	1.9
Block 3	−.6	−.5	.1
Block 4	.8	−1.7	2.3

The ranks of these implied no-treatment observations within the blocks are

	Treatment 1	*Treatment* 2	*Control or treatment* 3	
Block 1	3	1	2	
Block 2	2	1	3	
Block 3	1	2	3	
Block 4	2	1	3	
	$R_1 = 8$	$R_2 = 5$	$R_3 = 11$	$\bar{R} = \frac{8 + 5 + 11}{3} = 8$

and $f_1 = (8 - 8)^2 + (5 - 8)^2 + (11 - 8)^2 = 18$. Table G gives for the proportion of assignments that lead to a value of f_1 at least equal to 18 the value .125.

An approximation to the proportion is given by the area above

$$\frac{12S}{mk(k + 1)} = \frac{12 \cdot 18}{4 \cdot 3 \cdot 4} = 4.5$$

in a χ^2 distribution (Table H) with $\nu = k - 1 = 2$ degrees of freedom. From Table H this approximation is seen to be .11.

For $k = 3$ the surface $A_f(\theta_1, \theta_2)$, with

$$f = \frac{12}{m^2k(k^2 - 1)} \sum_{j=1}^{k} (R_j - \bar{R})^2,$$

can be constructed as follows. Compute, for each of the blocks, the differences

$$x = t_{i,1} - t_{i,3}, \qquad y = t_{i,2} - t_{i,3}.$$

Plot the m points (x, y) in a plane with the axes labeled θ_1 and θ_2 as

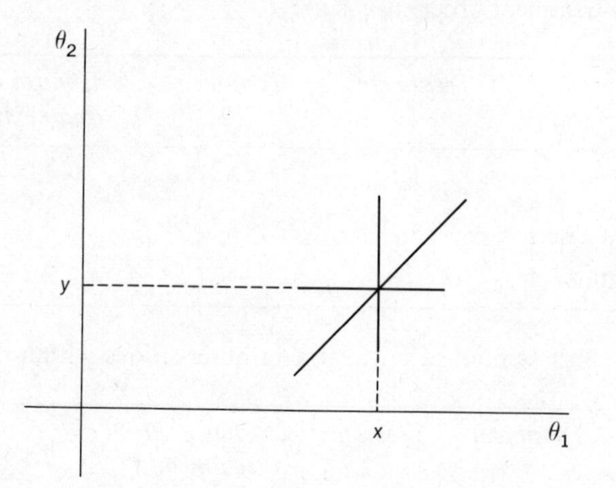

and draw, through each point, a horizontal line, a vertical line, and a 45-degree line (diagonal). $A_f(\theta_1, \theta_2)$ is constant within each of the regions of the plane defined by these lines, so that the surface $A_f(\theta_1, \theta_2)$ can be found by computing $A_f(\theta_1, \theta_2)$ for one point in each region.

Example 2. Suppose for three treatments and two blocks the following observations were obtained:

	Treatment 1	*Treatment* 2	*Treatment* 3
Block 1	3.5	1.9	4.7
Block 2	.3	−.5	1.1

The $m = 2$ points (x, y) are the points $(3.5 - 4.7, 1.9 - 4.7) = (-1.2, -2.8)$ and $(.3 - 1.1, -.5 - 1.1) = (-.8, -1.6)$. The surface $A_f(\theta_1, \theta_2)$ for this example is given in Figure 17.1. [The numbers in parentheses are approximations to $A_f(\theta_1, \theta_2)$ from the χ^2 approximation.]

Simultaneous confidence intervals for functions $g(\theta_1, \theta_2)$ can be found as described in Chapter 16. For this example the simultaneous 16.7 per cent intervals for θ_1, θ_2, and $\theta_1 - \theta_2$ are seen to be

$$-2.0 \leqq \theta_1 \leqq 0,$$
$$-2.8 \leqq \theta_2 \leqq -1.6,$$
$$-3.6 \leqq \theta_1 - \theta_2 \leqq -2.8.$$

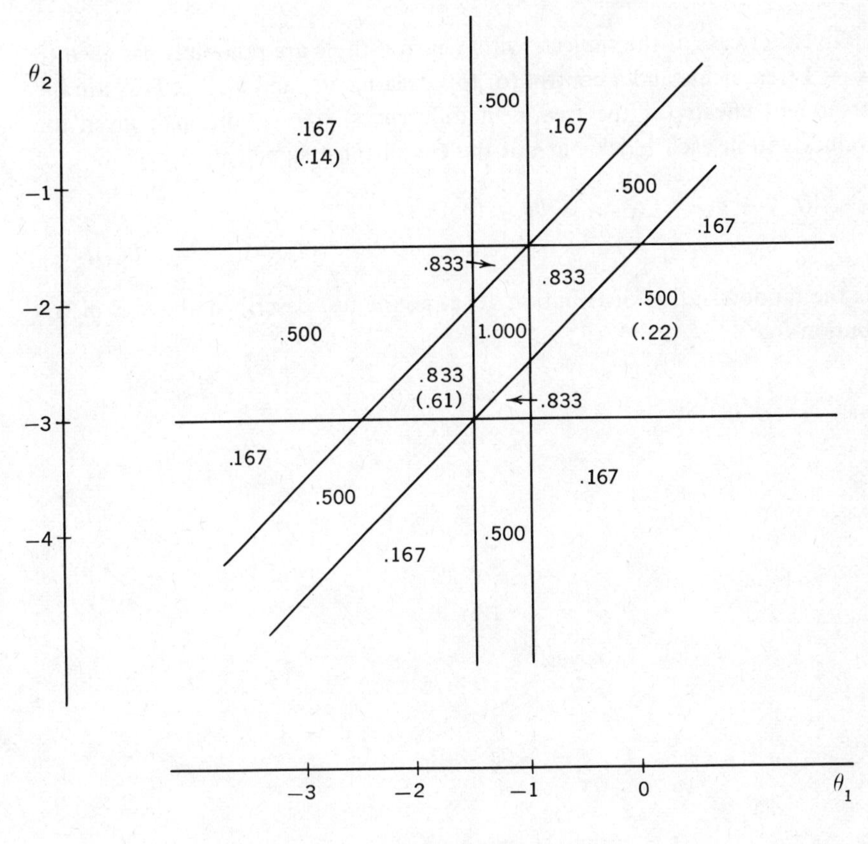

Figure 17.1.

As for the foregoing designs, there are other assumptions about the sources of the observations which lead to the same distribution theory for the test above. Two of these are

1. $k \cdot m$ subjects are taken at random from some population, so that $(y_1, \ldots, y_{km})$ is a sample from a distribution. The $k \cdot m$ subjects are, before the experiment, put in m k-tuples on some basis, usually on the basis of the value of a variable x whose value is known and that is correlated with y.

2. k subjects are taken from population 1, so that $y_{1,1}, \ldots, y_{1,k}$ is a sample from a distribution, a second set of k subjects is taken from population 2, so that $y_{2,1}, \ldots, y_{2,k}$ is a sample from a distribution, . . ., an mth set of k subjects is taken from population m, so that $y_{m,1}, \ldots, y_{m,k}$ is a sample from a distribution, where the m distributions are translates of each other.

In either case, if the subjects within each k-tuple are randomly assigned to $k - 1$ treatments and a control (or to k treatments) and $\theta_1, \ldots, \theta_{k-1}$ are the treatment effects (or the treatment differences), the conditional, given the values within each block but not the treatment assignment, distribution of

$$[(t_{1,1} - \theta_1, \ldots, t_{1,k-1} - \theta_{k-1}, t_{1,k}), \ldots, (t_{m,1} - \theta_1, \ldots, t_{m,k-1} - \theta_{k-1}, t_{m,k})]$$

is the randomization distribution. That is, the test described above is distribution-free.

CHAPTER 18

GOODNESS-OF-FIT TESTS

ONE-SAMPLE GOODNESS-OF-FIT TESTS

For a sample $(x_1, \ldots, x_n)$ from a distribution, the question can arise whether $(x_1, \ldots, x_n)$ is a sample from a given distribution $F(x)$. Two tests for the null hypothesis that a sample is a sample from a given distribution function are given here.

The Kolmogorov-Smirnov Test

This test is based on the function

$$D_n = \sup |F_n(t) - F(t)|,$$

where $F_n(t)$ is the sample distribution function defined by

$$F_n(t) = \frac{\text{no. of } x_i \leqq t}{n},$$

and F is a hypothetical continuous distribution function. A_f for $f = D_n$ and the hypothesis that $(x_1, \ldots, x_n)$ is a sample from F is found from Table M, with $x = nD_n$, as the P value for x. The null hypothesis, F, is rejected if A_f is no larger than a preassigned number α; otherwise it is accepted.

Approximations for larger sample sizes are given in the introduction to Table M.

Example 1. Suppose the sample $(y_1, \ldots, y_n) = (10, 4, 20, 8, 28, 2, 7, 12, -13, -7)$ is observed and the hypothesis that the sample was a sample from a normal distribution with mean 5 and standard deviation 10 is to be tested. This hypothesis may also be stated: The sample $(x_1, \ldots, x_n)$, where $x_i = (y_i - 5)/10$, is a sample from a unit normal distribution. The observations $(x_1, \ldots, x_n)$ for the example are $(.5, -.1, 1.5, .3, 2.3, -.3, .2, .7, -1.8, -1.2)$.

$F(t)$ is, for each t, found from Table E as the area below t. The graphs of $F_n(t)$ and $F(t)$ are given in Figure 18.1. From this graph it is clear that D_n can be found by computing, for all observations, $F(x_i)$, $F_n(x_i^+)$, and $F_n(x_i^-)$, where $F_n(x_i^+)$ is the right-hand limit, at x_i, of $F_n(t)$ and $F_n(x_i^-)$ is the left-hand limit, at x_i, of $F_n(t)$. The computations are given in the following table:

x_i	$F(x_i)$	$F_n(x_i^+)$	$F_n(x_i^-)$	$\lvert F_n(x_i) - F_n(x_i^+)\rvert$	$\lvert F_n(x_i) - F_n(x_i^-)\rvert$
−1.8	.0359	.1	0	.0641	.0359
−1.2	.1151	.2	.1	.0849	.0151
−.3	.3821	.3	.2	.0821	.1821
−.1	.4602	.4	.3	.0602	.1602
.2	.5793	.5	.4	.0793	.1793
.3	.6179	.6	.5	.0179	.1179
.5	.6915	.7	.6	.0085	.0915
.7	.7580	.8	.7	.0420	.0580
1.5	.9332	.9	.8	.0332	.1332
2.3	.9893	1	.9	.0107	.0893

so that $D_n = .1821$ and $nD_n = 10(.1821) = 1.821$. From Table M, A_f for the hypothesis that the sample $(y_1, \ldots, y_n)$ was a sample from a normal distribution with mean 5 and standard deviation 10 is seen to be .80. Using the approximation of Table O gives $\sqrt{n}\, D_n = (\sqrt{10})(.1821) = .58$, so that an approximate value of .89 for A_f is obtained.

A confidence band, with confidence coefficient $1 - \alpha$, for the distribution from which the sample was taken, consists of a band around $F_n(x)$ containing

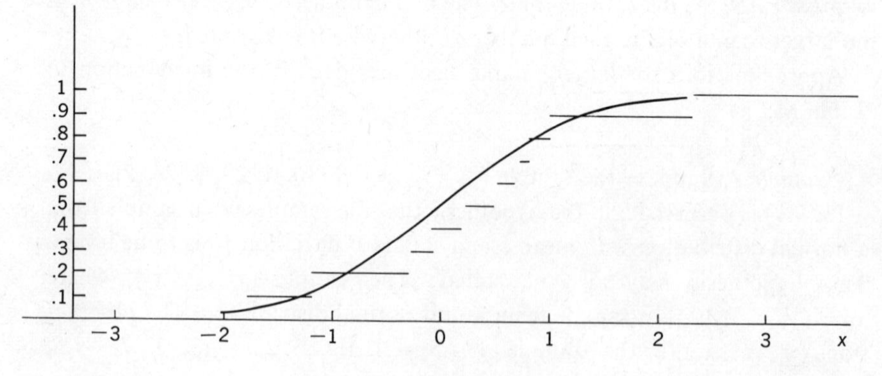

Figure 18.1.

all continuous distributions F for which the hypothesis that $(x_1, \ldots, x_n)$ was a sample from F, is not rejected at level α.

For the above example with $\alpha = .25$, this band contains all distribution functions F for which (see Table M)

$$nD_n \leq 3$$

or

$$\sup |F_n(t) - F(t)| \leq .3 \,.$$

For Example 1 this band is given in Figure 18.2.

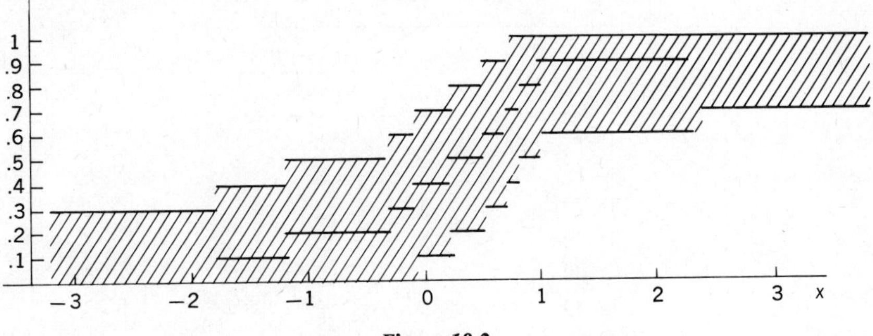

Figure 18.2.

The χ^2 Goodness-of-Fit Test

Suppose that n individuals are independently classified into k classes, so that the probability that an individual is assigned to any given class is the same for all individuals. A test of the null hypothesis that $p_1, \ldots, p_k (\sum p_i = 1)$ are the probabilities that an individual is assigned to the classes $1, \ldots, k$, respectively, is based on $A_f(p_1, \ldots, p_k)$, where

$$f = \chi^2 = \sum \frac{(n_i - np_i)^2}{np_i},$$

where n_i is the observed number of individuals in the ith class.

The exact null distribution of χ^2 depends upon $p_1, \ldots, p_k$ and n, and tables are lengthy unless n and k are small (for $n = 2$ the exact distribution of χ^2 can be obtained from the binomial distribution, Table D). The usual approximation is to refer the observed value of χ^2 to a χ^2 distribution with $\nu = k - 1$ degrees of freedom. For this approximation sufficient grouping of the classes is done, so that $np_i \geq 5$ for each class.

If the individuals are sorted on the basis of their values of observations from a distribution F and the numbers $p_1, \ldots, p_k$ are computed from F, the test above is a test of the null hypothesis that F is the distribution of the observations.

Example 2. Suppose that the entries in a random-number table (Table A) are read down successive pairs of columns from the beginning. The hypothesis that the first 50 pairs of digits so obtained are observations from a uniform distribution on 0 to 99 can be tested as follows. Classify each pair into one of the classes (0, 9), (10, 19), . . ., (90, 99), to obtain the counts in Table 18.1. The computation of χ^2 is shown there.

Table 18.1

Classes	n_i	np_i	$\frac{(n_i - np_i)^2}{np_i}$
0–9	5	5	0.0
10–19	2	5	1.8
20–29	4	5	.2
30–39	5	5	0
40–49	6	5	.2
50–59	6	5	.2
60–69	4	5	.2
70–79	6	5	.2
80–89	9	5	3.2
90–99	3	5	.8
	50		6.8 = χ^2

From Table H, with $\nu = 9$, $A_{\chi^2}(\text{H}_o) = .56$; that is, random digits would, among approximately 56 per cent of sets of 50 pairs, give a value of χ^2 at least as large as 6.8.

The grouping in Table 18.1 is arbitrary. It should not be based on properties of the observed n_i, although the usual practice of dividing the range of a set of observations into equal classes will ordinarily not alter the significance level appreciably. Note that the grouping determines the hypothesis being tested. The value of χ^2 in Table 18.1 would have been the same if the entire second column of Table A had consisted of 3's. In general, a coarser grouping amounts to stating the hypothesis less precisely, finer grouping amounts to stating it more precisely. At the same time, coarser grouping gives a better approximation, by Table H, to the distribution of the χ^2 statistic.

Often the hypothesis of interest is not whether independent observations $(x_1, \ldots, x_n)$ are from a given distribution but whether their distribution belongs to a given parametric class of distributions. The general procedure to test such an hypothesis is to estimate, from the observations, the parameters and compute χ^2 as though the hypothesis were the distribution in the class corresponding to the estimated values of the parameters. The estimation of the parameters reduces the degrees of freedom by one for each essential parameter estimated.

Example 3. Suppose that the hypothesis is that the independent observations in Table 18.2 are from some Poisson distribution.

Table 18.2

X	n_i
0	8
1	10
2	11
3	11
4	4
5	2
6	2
7	1
8	1
	50

Table 18.3

X	n_i		np_i		$(n_i - np_i)^2/np_i$
0	8		4.85		2.05
1	10		11.20		.13
2	11		13.05		.32
3	11		10.20		.06
4	4		6.05		.69
5	2	6	2.90	4.65	.39
6	2		1.20		
7	1		.40		
8	1		.15		
					$3.64 = \chi^2$

The parameter λ of a Poisson distribution is estimated by the mean $\bar{X} = (1/n)\sum n_i X_i$, which from Table 18.2 is easily seen to be 2.36. Interpolation, in Table L, gives the values of $p_0, \ldots, p_8$ so that np_i are as shown in Table 18.3. The last four classes there are grouped so that all cell expected frequencies are about 5 or more. There are, for these computations, six classes after grouping and one estimated parameter, so that the number of degrees of freedom is $6 - 2 = 4$. Reference to Table H gives $A_{\chi^2}(\mathrm{H_o}) = .46$.

TWO-SAMPLE GOODNESS-OF-FIT TESTS

There are forms of both the Kolmogorov–Smirnov test and the χ^2 test to test the hypothesis that two independent sets $(x_1, \ldots, x_n)$ and $(y_1, \ldots, y_m)$ of independent observations are from the same distribution. For the Kolmogorov–Smirnov test the hypothesis that the two sets of observations are from the same continuous population is tested by computing

$$D_{mn} = \sup|F_n(t) - G_m(t)|$$

where F_n and G_m are the sample cumulatives for x and y. When the sample sizes are equal (and $= n$) the exact distribution of nD_{nn} is given in Table N. Approximations for other cases are given in the introduction to Table N.

Example 4. For the observations $(x_1, x_2, x_3, x_4, x_5) = (-.6, .3, -.8, 1.0, -1.5)$ and $(y_1, y_2, y_3, y_4, y_5) = (.6, 2.0, .4, 3.0, -.7)$, the computation of $D_{5,5} = .6$ is shown in Table 18.4.

Table 18.4

X	Y	F_n	G_m	$\|F_n - G_m\|$	
−1.5		.2	0	.2	
−.8		.4	0	.4	
	−.7	.4	.2	.2	
−.6		.6	.2	.4	
.3		.8	.2	.6	← max.
	.4	.8	.4	.4	
	.6	.8	.6	.2	
1.0		1.0	.6	.4	
	2.0	1.0	.8	.2	
	3.0	1.0	1.0	0	

nD_{nn} is equal to 5(.6) = 3 and from Table N $A_{D_{nn}}(\text{H}_o) = .36$. The approximation from Table O is computed by finding

$$\sqrt{\frac{m \cdot n}{m + n}}\, D_{mn} = \sqrt{\frac{5 \cdot 5}{5 + 5}}\,(.6) = .95,$$

and referring this to Table O gives the approximation $A_{D_{nn}}(\text{H}_o) = .33$.

The two-sample χ^2 test for the hypothesis that two independent sets of independent observations are from the same distribution is applied by classifying the observations in the two sets into the same set of k classes and computing, as expected frequencies for each cell, the products of its marginals totals divided by the total number of observations. χ^2 is computed, as above, from the resulting observed and theoretical frequencies. The approximate distribution of the χ^2 statistic is that of Table H with $k - 1$ degrees of freedom.

Example 5. Observations, already grouped, are given in Table 18.5 along with the table of expected frequencies and the computation of χ^2. From Table H, with $\nu = 4$, $A_{\chi^2}(\text{H}_o) = .003$.

Table 18.5

Observed frequencies (n_i)			*Expected frequencies* (e_i)			$\frac{(n_i - e_i)^2}{e_i}$	
X	Y		X	Y		X	Y
2	10	12	4.8*	7.2	12	1.63	1.09
6	21	27	10.8	16.2	27	2.13	1.42
8	15	23	9.2	13.8	23	.16	.10
13	7	20	8.0	12.0	20	3.12	2.08
11	7	18	7.2	10.8	18	2.45	1.63
40	60	100	40.0	60.0	100	$\chi^2 = 15.8$	

* $4.8 = \frac{40 \cdot 12}{100}$.

CHAPTER 19

INDEPENDENCE, CORRELATION, AND REGRESSION

INDEPENDENCE

For each individual, in a sample of N individuals from a population, two characteristics are often measured and it is of interest to ask whether they are independent, that is, whether the proportion, in the population, of individuals having one of the characteristics is the same among both those with and those without the second characteristic. If the individuals are classified, and counted, according as they have or have not each of the characteristics, the counts can be arranged in a two-by-two table as in Table 19.1.

Table 19.1

	With C_1	*Without* C_1	
With C_2	n_{11}	n_{12}	A
Without C_2	n_{21}	n_{22}	B
	n	m	N

A test of the null hypothesis, H_o, that the two characteristics are independent can be based on the function

$$f = \left|n_{11} - \frac{nA}{N}\right| = \left|n_{21} - \frac{nB}{N}\right| = \left|n_{12} - \frac{mA}{N}\right| = \left|n_{22} - \frac{mB}{N}\right|.$$

$A_f(H_o)$ is found from the hypergeometric distribution (Table K) as follows. Let p = smallest of (n, m), q = smallest of (A, B), and let x be the entry in the cell in Table 19.1 corresponding to p and q. $A_f(H_o)$ is the sum of the two values in Table K (for N, p, q) for x and, from the other tail, outside of, and including, $(2pq/N) - x$ (or 1 if $x = pq/N$).

The hypothesis of independence is rejected if $A_f(H_o)$ is no larger than a preassigned number α; otherwise the hypothesis is accepted.

For approximations for larger sample sizes, see the introduction to Table K.

An approximation, essentially equivalent to the normal approximation to the hypergeometric, is obtained by referring

$$\chi^2 = \frac{[n_{11} - (nA/N)]^2}{nA/N} + \frac{[n_{21} - (nB/N)]^2}{nB/N} + \frac{[n_{12} - (mA/N)]^2}{mA/N} + \frac{[n_{22} - (mB/N)]^2}{mB/N}$$

$$= \frac{[n_{11} - (nA/N)]^2}{nmAB} N^3 = \frac{f^2N^3}{nmAB}$$

to a χ^2 distribution (Table H) with $\nu = 1$ degree of freedom. The null hypothesis of independence is rejected if the area above the observed value of χ^2 is no larger than a preassigned number α; otherwise it is accepted.

The presence or absence of a characteristic as above can be regarded as two "levels" of a characteristic. If there are more than two levels of either characteristic, the individuals are classified, and counted, according to the levels of the two characteristics (Table 19.2). For example, characteristic 1

Table 19.2

	Characteristic 1				
Characteristic 2	*Level* 1	*Level* 2	⋯	*Level k*	
Level 1	n_{11}	n_{12}	⋯	$n_{1,k}$	s_1
Level 2	n_{21}	n_{22}	⋯	$n_{2,k}$	s_2
.	.	.	⋯	.	.
.	.	.	⋯	.	.
.	.	.	⋯	.	.
Level r	$n_{r,1}$	$n_{r,2}$	⋯	$n_{r,k}$	s_r
	n_1	n_2	⋯	n_k	N

could be the state in which an individual resides (Alabama, Alaska, ...) and characteristic 2 could be the number of years of school completed.

A test of the null hypothesis H_o that the two characteristics are independent can be based on the function χ^2, which is computed from the observations as follows. For the cell in the ith row and jth column, compute

$$f_{i,j} = \frac{[n_{i,j} - (n_i s_j/N)]^2}{n_i s_j/N}.$$

χ^2 is the sum of the $f_{i,j}$ for all cells; that is, $\chi^2 = \sum\sum f_{ij}$.

The exact distribution of χ^2 is a function of all the marginal totals $n_1, \ldots, n_k, s_1, \ldots, s_r$ and tables of them are not included. The usual approximation is to refer the observed χ^2 to a χ^2 distribution (Table H) with $\nu = (k - 1)(r - 1)$ degrees of freedom. $A_{\chi^2}(\mathrm{H_o})$ is then approximately the area above the observed value of χ^2 and the hypothesis of independence is rejected if $A_{\chi^2}(\mathrm{H_o})$ is no larger than a preassigned number α; otherwise it is accepted.

When, for each individual, in a sample of n individuals from a population, scores (x, y) are observed, a test that x and y are independent in the population can be conducted by classifying the individuals into classes defined in terms of x and y, and using the χ^2 test above.

CORRELATION

Characteristics which are not independent are sometimes called *associated* or *correlated.* Most measures of correlation are sensitive only to certain specific forms of dependence. The simplest of these is linear correlation; however, it is important to distinguish between linear correlation and dependence. Most tests for linear correlation, including the ones to be described here, will fail to reject the null hypothesis of independence for certain forms of dependence and nonlinear correlation.

A test for linear correlation often used is that based on Spearman's rank correlation coefficient. The function f for this test is defined as follows. The x_i are replaced by their ranks among themselves, the y_i are replaced by their ranks among themselves, so that, for each pair of scores (x_i, y_i), a pair of ranks (R_i, R_i') is obtained. The function f is the absolute value of the correlation coefficient between these two sets of ranks; that is,

$$f = \frac{\left|\sum RR' - \frac{1}{n}\sum R \sum R'\right|}{\sqrt{\sum (R - \bar{R})^2 \sum (R' - \bar{R})^2}} = \left|1 - \frac{6\sum d^2}{n(n^2 - 1)}\right|,$$

where

$$\bar{R} = \frac{1}{n}\sum R = \frac{n+1}{2} \quad \text{and} \quad \sum d^2 = \sum (R - R')^2.$$

The distribution of f if all permutations, of either the x's or the y's, are equally likely can be found by enumeration and is in Table J. $A_f(\mathrm{H_o})$ can be found, if there are no ties, from Table J as twice the P value opposite x, or, equivalently, twice the P value opposite $\sum d^2$.

The null hypothesis of independence, which implies that the permutations are equally likely, is rejected if $A_f(\mathrm{H_o})$ is no larger than a preassigned number α; otherwise it is accepted.

Approximations for larger sample sizes and adjustments for ties are given in the introduction to Table J.

One of the approximations for $A_f(\mathrm{H_o})$ is obtained by referring $(n-2)f^2/(1-f^2)$ to an F distribution (Table I) with $\nu_1 = 1$ and $\nu_2 = n - 2$ degrees of freedom. If the individuals are a sample from a population such that $(x_1, y_1), \ldots, (x_n, y_n)$ are a sample from a bivariate normal distribution and f is computed from the scores (x, y) instead of the ranks, this approximation provides an exact test of the null hypothesis of independence.

Example 6. Suppose, for $n = 5$, the following pairs of scores were obtained:

x	1.3	.4	.2	1.6	−.9
y	2.2	−.6	−1.8	1.9	−1.3

The two sets of ranks and their differences d are

R	4	3	2	5	1
R'	5	3	1	4	2
d	−1	0	1	1	−1

so that $\sum d^2 = (-1)^2 + 0^2 + 1^2 + 1^2 + (-1)^2 = 4$ and

$$f = \left|1 - \frac{6\sum d^2}{n(n^2-1)}\right| = \left|1 - \frac{6\cdot 4}{5\cdot 24}\right| = .8.$$

From Table J it is seen that $A_f(\mathrm{H_o}) = 2(.067) = .13$.

As an approximation, the F distribution gives

$$\frac{(n-2)f^2}{1-f^2} = \frac{3(.8)^2}{1-(.8)^2} = 5.33.$$

From Table I this approximation is seen to be .10. The computations for the coefficient of (linear) correlation, r, computed from the scores (x, y) instead of the ranks, are as follows:

x	x^2	y	y^2	xy
1.3	1.69	2.2	4.84	2.86
.4	.16	−.6	.36	−.24
.2	.04	−1.8	3.24	−.36
1.6	2.56	1.9	3.61	3.04
−.9	.81	−1.3	1.69	1.17
2.6	5.26	.4	13.74	6.47

so that

$$r^2 = \frac{[6.47 - \frac{1}{5}(2.6)(.4)]^2}{\left[5.26 - \frac{(2.6)^2}{5}\right]\left[13.74 - \frac{(.4)^2}{5}\right]} = .73.$$

If the pairs (x, y) are a sample from a bivariate normal population, reference of $[(n - 2)r^2]/(1 - r^2)$ to an F distribution with $\nu_1 = 1$ and $\nu_2 = n - 2 = 3$ degrees of freedom provides a test of the null hypothesis of independence. From Table I, $A_f(\text{H}_o)$, for this example and under the assumption of normality, is seen to be .07.

Sometimes individuals receive scores on several measurements and it is of interest to ask whether these measurements generally tend to increase together. For example, if several judges each rank the same set of subjects, independence among their rankings would suggest, for instance, that the judges were either responding to different characteristics of the subjects or that there were no differences among the subjects. Kendall's coefficient of concordance provides a test of the null hypothesis that the rankings by m judges are ranking the k subjects independently and at random. The computations and distribution theory for this test are the same as for the m-ranking analysis given for randomized blocks in Chapter 17. A possible interpretation of the m-ranking analysis there is that it asks whether the "judge" consisting of the k subjects in a given block ranks the treatments at random relative to the other $m - 1$ blocks.

REGRESSION

Regression theory is closely related to that for correlation. The distinction is that for regression theory the "levels" of one characteristic are fixed and the number of subjects at each level is fixed. Most of the analyses proposed for correlation theory are conditional (given certain marginal totals) analyses, so that they apply also to some regression problems.

As an example, suppose that for a given sequence of times, $t_1 < t_2 < \cdots < t_n$, independent observations of a continuous variable Y are made, one at each time, to give

Time	t_1	t_2	t_3	$\cdots$	t_n
Y	y_1	y_2	y_3	$\cdots$	y_n

If there is no "dependence" of the distributions of Y on t, that is, if the distributions are constant in t, the permutations of y are equally likely. This affords a basis for tests to detect various forms of dependence of the distribution of Y on t.

The simplest form of dependence is that Y tends to increase, or to decrease, with t. A test for this is based on Spearman's rank correlation coefficient above. The distribution of this coefficient if the observations are independent with a distribution constant in t is the same as above. It is easily verified that the distribution of the $\sum d^2$ is the same if the ranks of one variate (here, t) are fixed and the permutations of the other are equally likely as when all possible permutations of either are equally likely.

If there is more than one observation for each t, Spearman's rank correlation coefficient can be computed for the $n_1 + \cdots + n_k = n$ pairs $[(y_{11}, t_1), (y_{12}, t_1), \ldots, (y_{1,n_1}, t_1)] \cdots [(y_{k,1}, t_k) \cdots (y_{k,n_k}, t_k)]$. There will be ties among the ranks of the t's.

Kendall's rank correlation coefficient (τ) is an alternative to Spearman's which offers certain advantages, particularly that the approximation of its distribution by a normal distribution is better. If there are no ties in either the y's or the t's, Kendall's τ is defined by $\tau = 2S/n(n - 1)$, where S is defined as follows. Let $[(y_1, t_1), (y_2, t_2)]$, with $t_1 < t_2$, be one of the possible such $(n^2 - n)/2$ pairs of observations. Let N^+ be the number of these pairs with $y_1 < y_2$ and N^- be the number with $y_1 > y_2$. Then $S = N^+ - N^-$.

If there are ties, S has the same definition, since only pairs $[(y_1, t_1), (y_2, t_2)]$ with $t_1 < t_2$ and $y_1 \neq y_2$ are to be considered. However, the definition of τ is

$$\tau = \frac{2S}{\sqrt{n^2 - T_1}\sqrt{n^2 - T_2}}$$

where T_1 is the sum of squares of the sizes of the ties (untied observations are counted as "ties" of size 1) among the y's and T_2 is the same for the t's.

τ can also be computed as a sum of Wilcoxon statistics as follows. Let S_1 be the sum of the ranks, among all the y's, for the y's at t_1. Let S_2 be the sum of the ranks, among the y's for $t_2, t_3, \ldots, t_k$, of the y's at t_2. $S_3, \ldots, S_{k-1}$ are defined analogously. S_{k-1} is the sum of the ranks among the y's for t_{k-1} and t_k of the y's at t_{k-1}. $R = S_1 + S_2 + \cdots + S_{k-1}$ is a linear function of τ. The distribution of R if there are no ties among the y's is approximately normal with

$$\mu = \frac{n^2 - T_2}{4} + \frac{1}{2}\sum_{1}^{k-1} n_i(n_i + 1),$$

$$\sigma = \sqrt{\frac{1}{72}\left[n(n + 1)(2n + 1) - \sum_{1}^{k} n_i(n_i + 1)(2n_i + 1)\right]}.$$

Example 7. Suppose for $n_1 = 2$, $n_2 = 3$, $n_3 = 3$, the following observations were obtained:

t_1	t_2	t_3
1	−2	7
−6	8	12
	3	5

Replacing these observations by their ranks gives

t_1	t_2	t_3
3	2	6
1	7	8
	4	5

so that S_1 = the sum of the ranks of the observations at t_1 among all observations $= 3 + 1 = 4$. Ranking the observations at t_2 and t_3 gives

t_2	t_3
1	4
5	6
2	3

so that S_2 = (the sum of the ranks of the observations at t_2 among the observations at t_2 and t_3) $= 1 + 5 + 2 = 8$ and $R = S_1 + S_2 = 4 + 8 = 12$. For the normal approximation,

$$\mu = \frac{n^2 - T_2}{4} + \frac{1}{2}\sum_{1}^{k-1} n_i(n_i + 1)$$

$$= \frac{(2 + 3 + 3)^2 - (2^2 + 3^2 + 3^2)}{4} + \frac{1}{2}(2 \cdot 3 + 3 \cdot 4) = 19.5,$$

$$\sigma = \sqrt{\frac{1}{72}\left[n(n + 1)(2n + 1) - \sum_{1}^{k} n_i(n_i + 1)(2n_i + 1)\right]}$$

$$= \sqrt{\frac{1}{72}[8 \cdot 9 \cdot 17 - (2 \cdot 3 \cdot 5 + 3 \cdot 4 \cdot 7 + 3 \cdot 4 \cdot 7)]} = 3.77$$

and

$$\frac{R - \mu}{\sigma} = \frac{12 - 19.5}{3.77} = -1.99$$

can be referred to a unit normal distribution for approximate significance levels.

PART III

TABLES

LIST OF TABLES

GENERAL INTRODUCTION

The tables following are either cumulative to the mean from both extremes or cumulative toward zero from the right-hand extreme. In either case, probabilities for any interval, or collection of intervals, can be found by differences among the tabled values. For tables cumulative from both extremes, examples of intervals and the calculation of their probabilities from tabled values are shown in Figure 1. If the distribution of X is continuous, all intervals can be considered as either open, closed, or open on one side and closed on the other. If the distribution of X is discrete, and the possible values are integers, $P\{X \leq x\} = P\{X < x + 1\}$ and $P\{X = x\} = P\{X \leq x\} - P\{X \leq x - 1\}$, or $P\{X \geq x\} = P\{X > x - 1\}$ and $P\{X = x\} = P\{X \geq x\} - P\{X \geq x - 1\}$, can be used to relate probabilities of closed and open intervals.

Interval	Probability
$x\,]$ μ — X	$P\{X \leq x\}$ = (Lower tail entry for x)
μ $[\,x$ — X	$P\{X \geq x\}$ = (Upper tail entry for x)
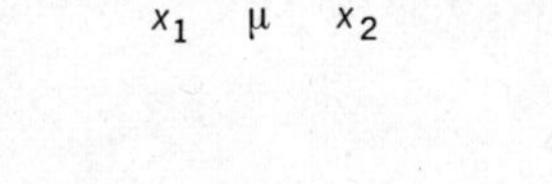 μ $[\,x_1$ $x_2\,)$ — X	$P\{x_1 \leq X < x_2\}$ = (Upper tail entry for x_1) − (Upper tail entry for x_2)
$(\,x_1$ μ $x_2\,)$ — X	$P\{x_1 < X < x_2\}$ = 1 − (Lower tail entry for x_1) − (Upper tail entry for x_2)

Figure 1.

For tables cumulative from the right-hand extreme, examples of intervals and their probabilities are shown in Figure 2. The changes necessary when intervals are altered by the inclusion or exclusion of end points are as described in the preceding paragraph.

The descriptions of tests in the text are almost all for tests symmetric (in x) about the mean. The use of the tables for one-sided tests, or for two-sided tests symmetric in the tail probabilities, is straightforward.

All the tables included are complete distributions, so that they can be used for tests, or confidence intervals, with any level of significance, or for every level of significance, if a curve descriptive of a relationship between observations and a class of models is desired.

The ranges of sample sizes for the table are adequate for most instructional purposes, where the number of observations is ordinarily chosen so that lengthy calculations will not distract from the purposes and rationale of the statistical analyses. The ranges are also adequate for the sample sizes often encountered in many exploratory studies.

For many analyses, with small or intermediate sample sizes, machines can be programmed to either compute, or to call for, tables as they are needed. When computers are used for statistical analyses, it is to be recommended that the same analysis as being done by the machine be carried out, by hand, for a portion of the data or analogous data. Doing so is an aid to understanding the problem and the output, and, if the pilot problem is input in the same run as the actual problems, can provide a check against some machine errors, programming errors, and, with "canned" programs, errors in the description of the program.

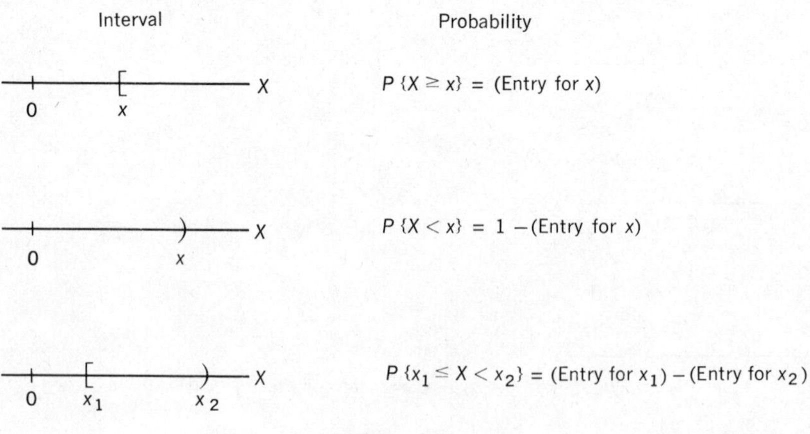

Figure 2.

Approximations for sample sizes beyond the ranges of the tables are given in the introductions to the separate tables. Only bare indications of the accuracies of these approximations have been given in the introductions. Conditions under which an approximation will have a given relative, or absolute, error are detailed and technical when known at all. When the accuracy is important, reference can be made to a larger table, to exact computation, or consultation with someone who has experience with approximations. Experience with at least the problems that can arise when using approximations can be gained by approximating the exact distributions for sample sizes within and particularly near the "edges" of the ranges of the tables here. When the distribution assumptions for an analysis are interpolatory, often the question of whether to use an approximation is more nearly a question of whether to change the basis for interpolation than a question of accuracy.

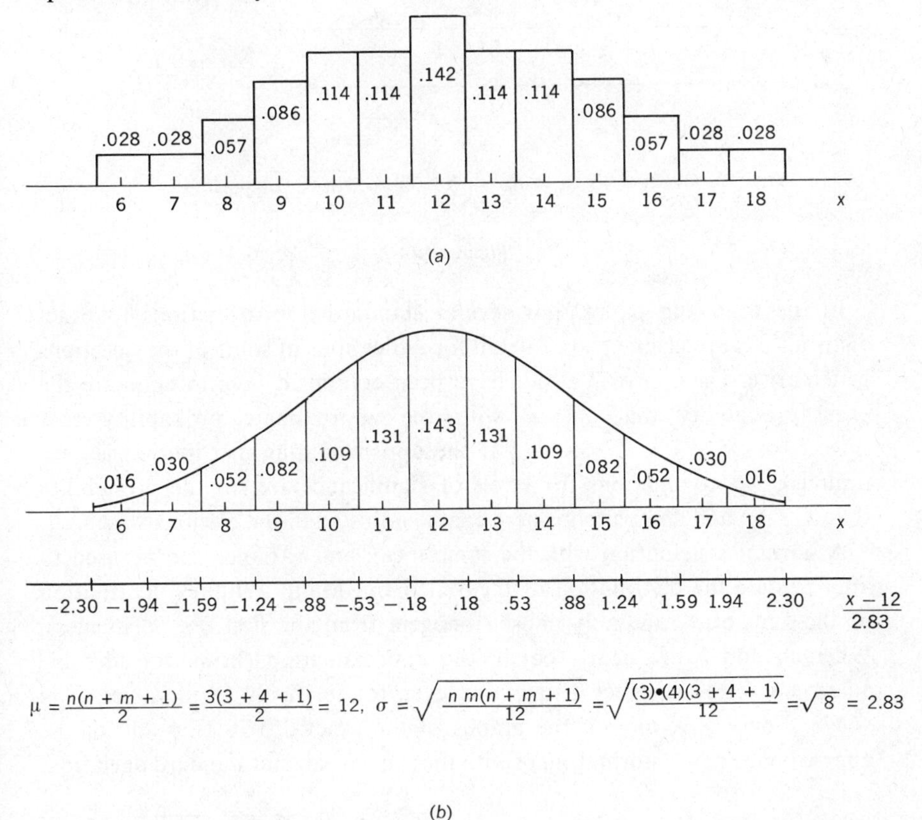

Figure 3.

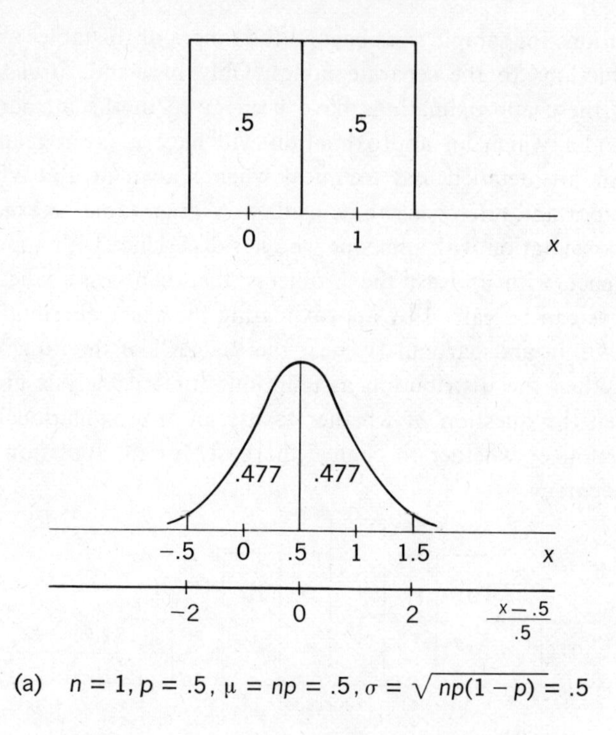

(a) $n = 1, p = .5, \mu = np = .5, \sigma = \sqrt{np(1-p)} = .5$

Figure 4(a).

In the following paragraphs several standard approximations to exact distributions are given in some detail for indications of some of the questions which arise. The approximations have been computed here to compare the exact probability that $X = k$ with the approximate probability that $X = k$ (or, $k - \frac{1}{2} < X < k + \frac{1}{2}$ if the approximating distribution is continuous). Approximations for levels of significance are for the probability that $X \leq x$, and comparisons here can be adjusted in the obvious way.

A normal distribution with the same mean and variance can be used to approximate the distribution of the Wilcoxon, Mann–Whitney distribution of the sum of n randomly chosen integers from the first $n + m$ integers. When m and n are nearly equal, the approximation shows considerable agreement with the exact distribution even for relatively small values of m and n. For $n = 3$, $m = 4$, the graphs of the exact distribution and of the approximation by a normal curve with the same mean and standard deviation,

$$\mu = \frac{n(n + m + 1)}{2} = 12 \quad \text{and} \quad \sigma = \sqrt{\frac{nm(n + m + 1)}{12}} = 2.83$$

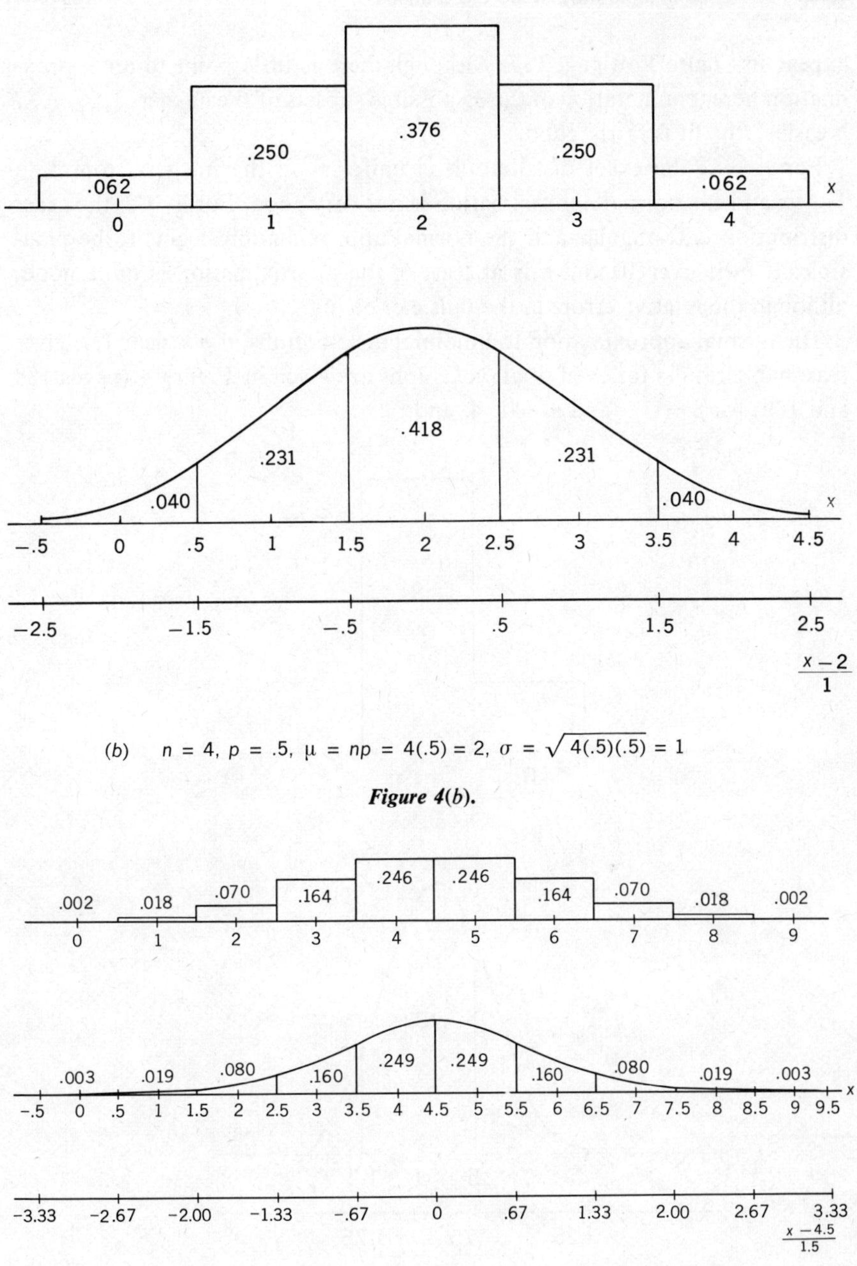

(b) $n = 4,\ p = .5,\ \mu = np = 4(.5) = 2,\ \sigma = \sqrt{4(.5)(.5)} = 1$

Figure 4(b).

(c) $n = 9,\ p = .5,\ \mu = np = 9(.5) = 4.5,\ \sigma = \sqrt{9(.5)(.5)} = 3(.5) = 1.5$

Figure 4(c).

appear in Figure 3 on page 187. Although there is little point to an approximation here (enumeration of the 35 possible subsets of the integers 1, 2, . . . , 7 is easier), the fit is fairly good.

For $n = 1$, the exact distribution is uniform on the integers from 1 to $1 + m$ and the normal approximation is not very good. For $n = 2$, the exact distribution is triangular and the normal approximation begins to be plausible. If m is over 10 and n is at least 5, the approximation is quite good, although the relative errors in the tails can be high.

The normal approximation to binomial distributions, if p is near 1/2, gives reasonable results for even small n. Graphs are given in Figure 4 (pages 188 and 189) for $p = 1/2$ and $n = 1$, 4, and 9.

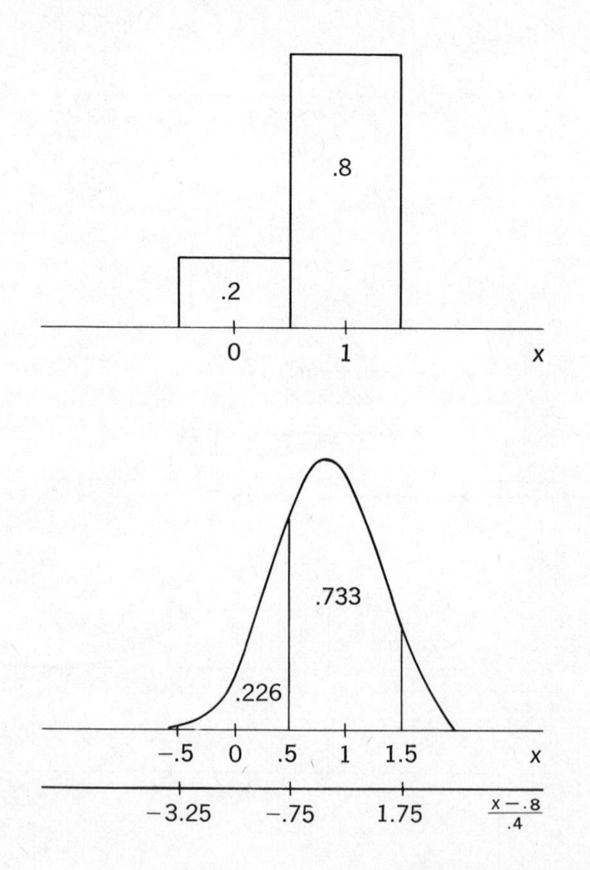

(a) $n = 1$, $p = .8$, $\mu = np = .8$, $\sigma = \sqrt{np(1-p)} = \sqrt{1(.8)(.2)} = \sqrt{.16} = .4$

Figure 5(a).

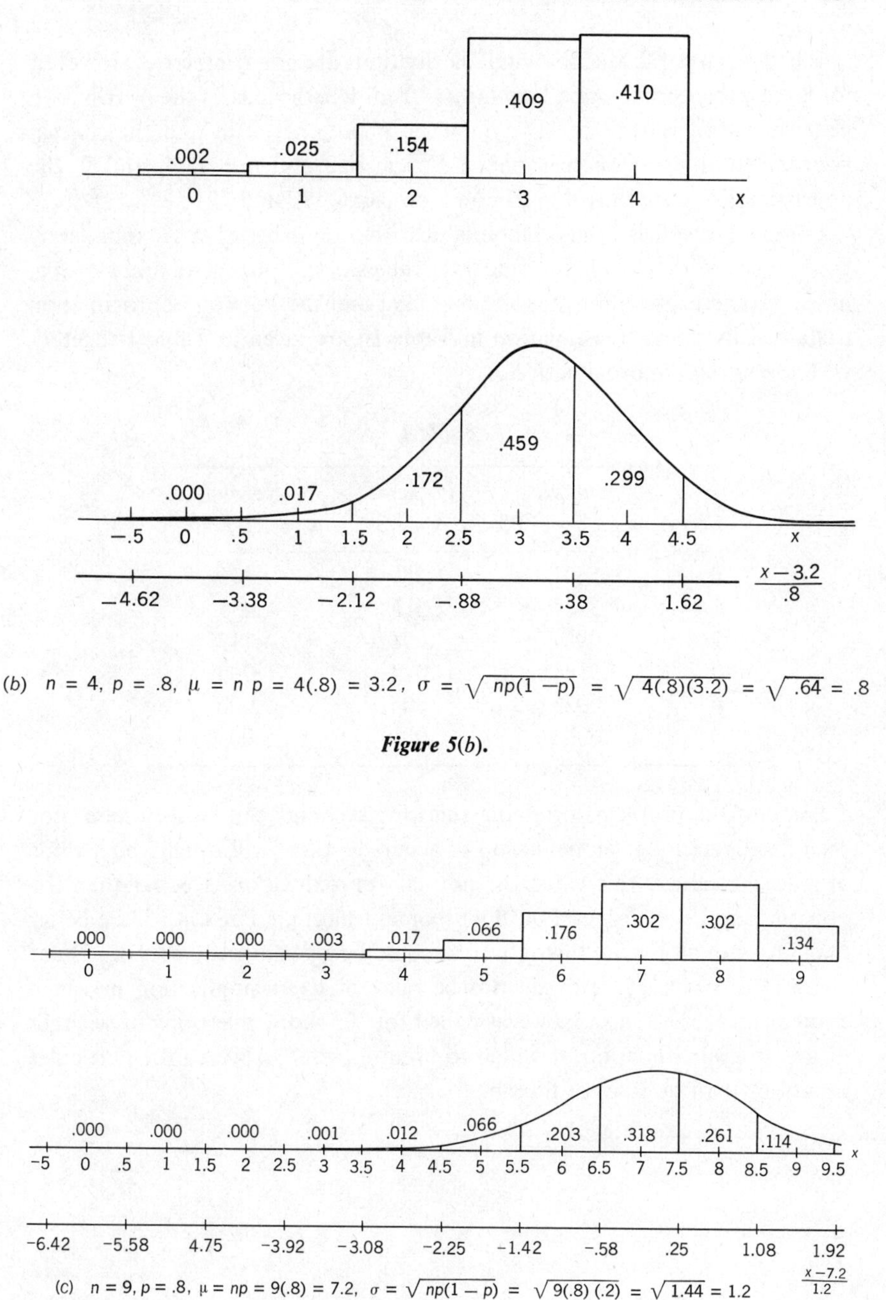

(*b*) $n = 4,\ p = .8,\ \mu = np = 4(.8) = 3.2,\ \sigma = \sqrt{np(1-p)} = \sqrt{4(.8)(3.2)} = \sqrt{.64} = .8$

Figure 5(b).

(c) $n = 9,\ p = .8,\ \mu = np = 9(.8) = 7.2,\ \sigma = \sqrt{np(1-p)} = \sqrt{9(.8)(.2)} = \sqrt{1.44} = 1.2$

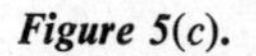

Figure 5(c).

When p is not 1/2, the binomial distributions are not symmetric. However, for large n, depending upon how far p is from 1/2, the part of the distribution near the mean is very nearly symmetric about the mean and the normal approximation is again reasonable. For $p = .8$ and $n = 1$, 4, and 9, the approximations are shown in Figure 5 on pages 190 and 191.

For smaller values of p, a binomial distribution is better approximated by the Poisson, with $\lambda = np$, for moderate values of n. For $n = 12$ and $p = .05$, $np = .6$. The probabilities for the binomial and the Poisson approximation (obtained by linear interpolation in Table L) are given in Table 1 together with the normal approximation.

Table 1

X	*Binomial:* $n = 12, p = .05$	*Poisson:* $\lambda = .6$	*Normal:* $\mu = .6, \sigma = .76$
0	.540	.559	.375
1	.342	.316	.433
2	.098	.098	.113
3	.018	.022	.006
4	.002	.005	.000
5	.000	.000	.000

Some of the problems of giving rules for accuracy can be seen here. For each fixed p and a given definition of accuracy, there will usually be a value of n so that above this value the normal approximation is better than the Poisson, and below (at least until n becomes small) the Poisson will be better than the normal. Even if this value of n could be given in terms of a particular measure of accuracy, it might not be relevant to an application in which another measure of accuracy was called for. In short, questions of whether to use an approximation or which to use are better answered for particular situations than by rules of thumb.

TABLE A

RANDOM DIGITS*

Table A is a sequence of 12,500 random digits. These digits were produced, by the Rand Corporation, by the conversion of electronic shot noise. They have been substantially tested and can be regarded as though they were produced by successive independent rolls of a symmetric ten-sided die, or by successive single draws from an urn, with replacement and thorough mixing between draws. It may be read in groups of digits of any fixed size and in any prescribed direction. Descriptions of some of the applications of Table A to sampling are given in Chapter 7.

* From the pp. 6–10 of *A Million Random Digits* by The Rand Corporation, The Free Press (1955). Reproduced with kind permission from The Rand Corporation.

Table A. Random Digits

59467	58309	87834	57213	37510	33689	01259	62486	56320	46265
73452	17619	56421	40725	23439	41701	93223	41682	45026	47505
27635	56293	91700	04391	67317	89604	73020	69853	61517	51207
86040	02596	01655	09918	45161	00222	54577	74821	47335	08582
52403	94255	26351	46527	68224	90183	85057	72310	34963	83462
49465	46581	61499	04844	94626	02963	41482	83879	44942	63915
94365	92560	12363	30246	02086	75036	88620	91088	67691	67762
34261	08769	91830	23313	18256	28850	37639	92748	57791	71328
37110	66538	39318	15626	44324	82827	08782	65960	58167	01305
83950	45424	72453	19444	68219	64733	94088	62006	89985	36936
61630	97966	76537	46467	30942	07479	67971	14558	22458	35148
01929	17165	12037	74558	16250	71750	55546	29693	94984	37782
41659	39098	23982	29899	71594	77979	54477	13764	17315	72893
32031	39608	75992	73445	01317	50525	87313	45191	30214	19769
90043	93478	58044	06949	31176	88370	50274	83987	45316	38551
79418	14322	91065	07841	36130	86602	10659	40859	00964	71577
85447	61079	96910	72906	07361	84338	34114	52096	66715	51091
86219	81115	49625	48799	89485	24855	13684	68433	70595	70102
71712	88559	92476	32903	68009	58417	87962	11787	16644	72964
29776	63075	13270	84758	49560	10317	28778	23006	31036	84906
81488	17340	74154	42801	27917	89792	62604	62234	13124	76471
51667	37589	87147	24743	48023	06325	79794	35889	13255	04925
99004	70322	60832	76636	56907	56534	72615	46288	36788	93196
68656	66492	35933	52293	47953	95495	95304	50009	83464	28608
38074	74083	09337	07965	65047	36871	59015	21769	30398	44855
01020	80680	59328	08712	48190	45332	27284	31287	66011	09376
86379	74508	33579	77114	92955	23085	92824	03054	25242	16322
48498	09938	44420	13484	52319	58875	02012	88591	52500	95795
41800	95363	54142	17482	32705	60564	12505	40954	46174	64130
63026	96712	79883	39225	52653	69549	36693	59822	22684	31661
88298	15489	16030	42480	15372	38781	71995	77438	91161	10192
07839	62735	99218	25624	02547	27445	69187	55749	32322	15504
73298	51108	48717	92926	75705	89787	96114	99902	37749	96305
12829	70474	00838	50385	91711	80370	56504	56857	80906	09018
76569	61072	48568	36491	22587	44363	39592	61546	90181	37348
41665	41339	62106	44203	06732	76111	79840	67999	32231	76869
58652	49983	01669	27464	79553	52855	25988	18087	38052	17529
13607	00657	76173	43357	77334	24140	53860	02906	89863	44651
55715	26203	65933	51087	98234	40625	45545	63563	89148	82581
04110	66683	99001	09796	47349	65003	66524	81970	71262	14479
31300	08681	58068	44115	40064	77879	23965	69019	73985	19453
26225	97543	37044	07494	85778	35345	61115	92498	49737	64599
07158	82763	25072	38478	57782	75291	62155	52056	04786	11585
71251	25572	79771	93328	66927	54069	58752	26624	50463	77361
29991	96526	02820	91659	12818	96356	49499	01507	40223	09171
83642	21057	02677	09367	38097	16100	19355	06120	15378	56559
69167	30235	06767	66323	78294	14916	19124	88044	16673	66102
86018	29406	75415	22038	27056	26906	25867	14751	92380	30434
44114	06026	79553	55091	95385	41212	37882	46864	54717	97038
53805	64150	70915	63127	63695	41288	38192	72437	75075	18570

Table A. Random Digits

52065	08853	30104	79937	66913	53200	84570	78079	28970	53859
37632	80274	35240	32960	74859	07359	55176	03930	38984	35151
82576	82805	94031	12779	90879	24109	25367	77861	09541	85739
69023	64971	99321	07521	95909	43897	71724	92581	05471	64337
98949	03606	78236	78985	29212	57369	34857	67757	58019	58872
96526	28749	56592	37871	72905	70198	57319	54116	47014	18285
33692	72111	60958	96848	17893	40993	50445	14186	76877	87867
50335	09513	44346	26439	55293	06449	44301	63740	40158	72703
88321	85062	57345	66231	15409	03451	95261	43561	15673	28956
90303	62469	82517	43035	36850	15592	64098	59022	31752	04370
50486	11885	23085	41712	80692	48492	16495	99721	36912	28267
27882	16269	64483	11273	02680	01616	46138	54606	14761	05134
45144	63213	49666	27441	86989	29884	54334	06740	08368	80051
81020	17882	74973	74531	94994	24927	64894	22667	20466	82948
66831	47427	76033	31197	59817	20064	61135	28556	29695	80179
74058	18293	09963	35278	13062	83094	23373	90287	33477	48865
30348	70174	11468	25994	25343	22317	01587	30682	00001	67814
59557	23362	13746	82244	42093	24671	79458	93730	45488	60234
67098	09899	25775	00332	36636	57594	19958	85564	58977	12247
60774	66371	69442	20385	14486	91330	50332	46023	75768	59877
60081	92936	72302	75064	85727	52987	05750	19384	33684	78859
80458	69902	34870	88684	49762	40801	86291	18194	90366	82639
53844	96326	65728	48563	26027	52692	62406	76294	41848	63010
69841	29451	36170	21529	16525	64326	22086	24469	57407	96033
37771	31002	18311	93285	31948	14331	58335	15977	80336	81667
27286	24361	61638	57580	95270	46180	76990	53031	94366	02727
49944	19278	05756	51875	53445	33342	01965	07937	10054	97712
87693	58124	46064	39133	77385	09605	65359	70113	90563	86637
94282	12025	31926	24541	23854	58407	32131	92845	20714	27898
26917	50326	35145	50859	72119	95094	29441	42301	62460	75252
94267	38422	73047	24200	85349	72049	91723	97802	98496	12734
73432	10371	57213	53300	80847	46229	07099	72961	13767	65654
31102	82119	96946	65919	81083	03819	57888	57908	16849	77111
41429	92261	45263	01172	55926	78835	27697	48420	58865	41207
21406	08582	10785	36233	12237	07866	13706	92551	11021	63813
71512	65206	37768	94325	14721	20990	54235	71986	05345	56239
52028	01419	07215	55067	11669	21738	66605	69621	69827	08537
18638	60982	28151	98885	76431	25566	03085	23639	30849	63986
73287	26201	36174	14106	54102	57041	16141	64174	03591	90024
73332	31254	17288	59809	25061	51612	47951	16570	43330	79213
11354	55585	19646	99246	37564	32660	20632	21124	60597	69315
31312	57741	85108	21615	24365	27684	16124	33888	14966	35303
69921	15795	04020	67672	86816	63027	84470	45605	44887	26222
79888	58982	22466	98844	48353	60666	58256	31140	93507	69561
06256	88526	18655	00865	75247	00264	65957	98261	72706	36396
46065	85700	32121	99975	73627	78812	89638	86602	96758	65099
52777	46792	13790	55240	52002	10313	91933	71231	10053	78416
54563	96004	42215	30094	45958	48437	49591	50483	13422	69108
59952	27896	40450	79327	31962	46456	39260	51479	61882	48181
50691	64709	32902	10676	12083	35771	79656	56667	76783	03937

Table A. Random Digits

99859	10362	57411	40986	35045	02838	29255	64230	84418	34988
77644	39892	77327	74129	53444	35487	95803	38640	20383	55402
25793	14213	87082	42837	95030	97198	61608	97723	79390	35290
34683	81419	87133	70447	53127	97146	28299	56763	12868	01145
12147	58158	92124	60934	18414	97510	07056	54488	20719	53743
91037	44797	52110	08512	18991	20129	31441	51449	14661	71126
23180	68124	18807	70997	21913	19594	70355	73637	68266	60775
43164	52643	96363	77989	79332	39890	65379	20405	52935	43816
92740	95319	04538	60660	28982	15328	80475	34690	02293	19646
46524	96627	33159	42081	08816	74931	20674	08697	66169	46460
46326	39923	60625	28386	22919	19415	75766	43668	31626	70301
67053	03949	70082	02303	48642	38429	94053	38770	68137	68441
52928	70244	91954	17401	92693	98342	21451	84988	80487	33807
73797	49494	41878	76635	83227	76618	11946	13451	87591	78381
21407	90038	72638	69692	51599	86413	32019	64856	74730	41531
11064	01790	58817	86400	66213	92599	70905	78324	54326	43659
34206	63132	38837	40210	96346	16967	81619	96503	14881	89405
32205	49508	98425	02451	35423	56072	36810	30332	85998	49358
92748	84147	79835	94867	41224	61794	35066	82220	66684	20096
02754	41731	37068	32753	91059	13407	05607	69384	53329	95909
44968	11397	92973	50014	92997	80968	93761	57598	74703	07768
37978	73873	33475	09720	97852	98449	48722	84977	11271	11728
68318	22312	78792	87508	88466	72976	47099	84126	38595	85124
64405	90020	07492	52413	95111	34455	86311	68892	01074	60274
28136	19328	38161	57475	13771	63562	84207	94121	18901	52768
33801	82087	86091	59969	90398	56870	55756	78841	98450	54165
55106	50343	70519	14567	36780	55450	19606	83749	67562	64765
38543	16585	86841	73742	08766	39252	75678	75379	78760	37279
15280	13558	95916	89759	76686	76467	67147	63110	94008	08037
35263	53710	16667	79008	11231	29397	67136	18601	64502	90228
89109	72849	22711	65547	34542	26686	81678	87765	77654	23664
96352	14106	32938	28083	18633	80286	65507	46197	52722	75476
77816	47204	34876	45963	79262	90181	84041	03745	90041	30780
27226	92847	85572	15308	80688	05761	82638	13464	23683	81015
54214	64175	43701	86845	15569	50687	52679	87696	08285	97444
47599	94472	64150	87753	68652	60726	26213	17320	64553	81285
98126	12158	52095	64833	00492	35817	55571	91300	97812	37507
04209	53515	64342	21223	16662	43265	68219	03529	43636	68417
53640	95326	93381	37113	80751	76469	96677	43054	22937	31954
13266	34140	27253	02734	99070	60077	57988	93211	92795	83795
57477	03941	39007	14619	38320	93449	31336	25279	97030	26245
47394	39475	90621	23820	29344	94859	91604	14033	41868	14816
04075	66644	87803	97815	99552	78666	03942	08175	22345	19983
76783	99044	20851	84981	59052	77178	72109	76475	21619	73017
06812	56633	50612	55289	04671	84419	94072	94446	80603	32188
93415	23464	43947	43728	74284	67177	57105	31059	10642	13803
69602	46961	66567	19359	84676	63918	40650	12923	15974	79732
20225	92525	71179	04859	91208	60430	05239	61458	24089	68852
60171	29603	42535	86365	93905	28237	45317	60718	82001	41679
20679	56304	70043	87568	21386	59049	78353	48696	77379	55309

Table A. Random Digits

23780	28391	05940	55583	81256	59418	97521	32846	70761	90115
45325	05490	65974	11186	15357	03568	00450	96644	58976	36211
88240	92457	89200	94696	11370	91157	48487	59501	56983	89795
42789	69758	79701	29511	55968	41472	89474	84344	80517	07485
97523	17264	82840	59556	37119	30985	48866	60605	95719	70417
59083	95137	76538	44155	67286	57897	28262	04052	00919	86207
79932	44236	10089	44373	65670	44285	06903	20834	49701	95735
21149	03425	17594	31427	14262	32252	68540	39427	44026	47257
45055	95091	08367	28381	57375	41562	83883	27715	10122	67745
46497	28626	87297	36568	39483	11385	63292	92305	78683	06146
81905	15038	38338	51206	65749	34119	71516	74068	51094	06665
91884	66762	11428	70908	21506	00480	94183	78484	66507	75901
25728	52539	86806	69944	65036	27882	02530	04918	74351	65737
89178	08791	39342	94963	22581	56917	17541	83578	75376	65202
30935	79270	91986	99286	45236	44720	81915	70881	45886	43213
49789	97081	16075	20517	69980	25310	91953	01759	67635	88933
54558	18395	73375	62251	58871	09870	70538	48936	07757	90374
56631	88862	30487	38794	36079	32712	11130	55451	25137	38785
83558	31960	69473	45950	18225	09871	88502	75179	11551	75664
74321	67351	27703	83717	18913	42470	08816	37627	14288	62831
44047	67612	72738	26995	50933	63758	50003	43693	52661	55852
52372	59042	37595	04931	73622	68387	86478	40997	05245	75300
24902	59609	35653	15970	37681	69365	22236	86374	65550	00343
98377	35354	65770	15365	41422	71356	16630	40044	19290	66449
53629	79452	71674	30260	97303	06487	62789	13005	70152	22501
49867	89294	59232	31776	54919	99851	05438	01096	72269	50486
16719	06144	82041	38332	64452	31840	99287	59928	25503	08407
46970	45907	99238	74547	19704	72035	26542	54600	79172	58779
35747	78956	11478	41195	58135	63856	33037	45753	60159	25193
71838	07526	07985	60714	88627	75790	38454	96110	39237	19792
34534	70169	24805	63215	38175	38784	38855	24826	50917	25147
17082	26997	32295	10894	21805	65245	85407	37926	69214	38579
84721	23544	88548	65626	75517	69737	55626	52175	21697	19453
16908	82841	24060	40285	19195	80281	89322	15232	70043	60691
86370	91949	19017	83846	77869	14321	95102	87073	71467	31305
64677	80358	52629	79419	22359	87867	48296	50141	46807	82184
95812	84665	74511	59914	04146	90417	58508	62875	17630	21868
09199	30322	33352	43374	25473	04119	63086	14147	14863	38020
44757	98628	57916	22199	11865	42911	62651	78290	09392	77294
63168	21043	17409	13786	27475	75979	89668	43596	74316	84489
54941	95992	45445	41059	55142	15214	42903	16799	88254	95984
48575	77822	21067	57238	35352	96779	89564	23797	99937	46379
27119	16060	30302	95327	12849	38111	97090	07598	78473	63079
18570	72803	70040	91385	96436	96263	17368	56188	85999	50026
36050	73736	13351	48321	28357	51718	65636	72903	21584	21060
39829	15564	04716	14594	22363	97639	65937	17802	31535	42767
98761	30987	57657	33398	63053	25926	20944	19306	81727	02695
97479	79172	72764	66446	78864	12698	15812	97209	38827	91016
91281	57875	45228	49211	69755	99224	43999	62879	08879	80015
74396	57146	64665	31159	06980	79069	37409	75037	69977	85919

Table A. Random Digits

42826	06974	61063	97640	13433	92528	91311	08440	38840	22362
93929	01836	36590	75052	89475	15437	65648	99012	70236	12307
83585	00414	62851	48787	28447	21702	57033	29633	44760	34165
27548	37516	24343	63046	02081	20378	19510	42226	97134	68739
32982	56455	53129	77693	25022	55534	99375	30086	98001	07432
67126	76656	29347	28492	43108	64736	32278	84816	80440	30461
00818	09136	01952	48442	91058	92590	10443	05195	34009	32141
62209	43740	54102	76895	98172	31583	04155	66492	58981	16591
11331	06838	03818	77063	12523	45570	68970	70055	77751	73743
71732	04704	61384	57343	66682	44500	89745	10436	67202	36455
42467	88801	91280	01056	27534	81619	79004	25824	66362	33280
20706	31929	57422	18730	96197	22101	47592	02180	18287	82310
60430	59627	26471	07794	60475	76713	45427	89654	14370	81674
41246	98416	08669	48883	77154	09806	94015	60347	20027	08405
33150	27368	53375	70171	59431	14534	34018	85665	77797	17944
49602	74391	48830	55029	10371	94261	16658	68400	44148	28150
40364	90913	73151	64463	50058	78191	84439	82478	62398	03113
17578	12830	06571	95934	09132	25287	78731	80683	67207	76597
42096	34934	76609	52553	47508	71561	08038	83011	72577	95790
40076	20292	32138	61197	95476	23123	26648	13611	48452	39963
85857	04855	27029	01542	72443	53688	82635	56264	07977	23090
93553	65434	12124	91087	87800	95675	99419	44659	30382	55263
82514	86800	16781	65977	65946	13033	93895	04056	75895	47878
91309	51233	81409	46773	69135	56906	84493	34530	84534	38312
54574	92933	77341	20839	36126	01143	35356	35459	07959	98335
53266	36146	78047	50607	22486	63308	08996	96056	39085	26567
06779	62663	30523	47881	41279	49864	82248	78333	29466	48151
41957	93235	53308	22682	90722	54478	07235	34306	15827	20121
96837	06283	80172	66109	92592	48238	76428	94546	45430	16288
74839	00740	25553	83767	35900	05998	07493	46755	11449	88824
44906	33143	07454	56652	34755	63992	59674	65131	46358	12799
96988	51158	73176	01184	49925	63519	11785	29073	72850	47997
75172	55187	15313	40725	33225	56643	10465	38583	86440	97967
26401	17078	38765	33454	19136	57712	48446	98790	27315	71074
10157	57946	35582	49383	61324	26572	84503	03496	60449	17962
26017	65651	40400	83246	80056	75306	75147	41863	25581	87530
33193	43294	05065	99644	62771	75986	79005	44924	18703	40889
04403	05862	02571	82500	74200	36170	46836	74642	65471	26815
30937	64946	10160	15544	31962	54015	28853	66533	14573	79398
47391	73165	47805	77589	16881	13423	89452	76992	62509	09796
57540	13486	48855	25546	47589	21012	47388	78428	70196	84413
81026	87597	22445	83769	85937	38321	85485	87359	09839	67228
71179	94372	04446	62801	50775	96179	40646	44272	12417	47199
39701	30665	32775	66525	53558	78882	31939	67209	38906	34533
99914	27719	00216	99225	96537	03843	90564	91110	51838	30300
09559	37795	94880	11325	44979	89696	28129	29931	89971	46292
92710	11036	74760	75307	12291	49618	16293	92408	67928	80823
32872	25460	66819	35374	04035	99087	61129	11341	39118	10891
37217	63638	75477	30068	42334	57570	06890	59353	89939	37692
15232	20033	32202	22348	02766	96791	58448	92248	05769	96684

TABLE **B**

WILCOXON, MANN-WHITNEY DISTRIBUTIONS*

Table B gives the distribution of the sum of the ranks, X, for a randomly chosen n scores when a total of $n + m$ scores, without ties, are converted to ranks. The table is cumulative from each extreme to, but not beyond, the mean. That is, the relation between the table and the distribution is as for the following example for $n = 2$, $m = 3$.

Distribution

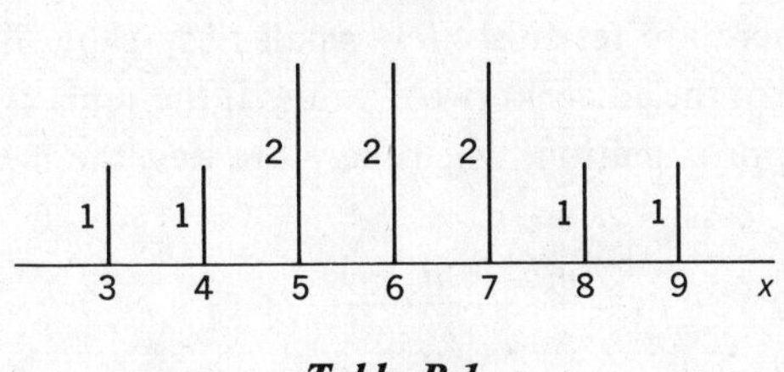

Table B.1

	x	P
Lower tail	3	$.1 = 1/10$
	4	.2
	5	$.4 = (1 + 1 + 2)/10$
	6	.6
Upper tail	6	$.6 = (2 + 2 + 1 + 1)/10$
	7	.4
	8	$.2 = (1 + 1)/10$
	9	.1

The ranges for m and n are $1 \leq n \leq m$, $3 \leq m \leq 10$, and $1 \leq n \leq 4$, $11 \leq m \leq 20$.

* Adapted from pp. 26–34 of "Handleiding voor de Toets van Wilcoxon," *Report S176(M65), Mathematical Center, Amsterdam* (1955), for $1 \leq n \leq m$, $3 \leq m \leq 10$. Computed at the Centre de Calcul de l'Université de Montréal for $1 \leq n \leq 4$, $11 \leq m \leq 20$.

If $m > 10$, and $n \geq 5$, the normal approximation can be used for the distribution of the sum of the n ranks. In particular, $P(X \leq k)$ is approximately the area, from a unit normal curve (Table E) below $[(k + 1/2) - \mu]/\sigma$, where

$$\mu = \frac{n(n + m + 1)}{2},$$

$$\sigma = \sqrt{\frac{n \cdot m \cdot (n + m + 1)}{12}}.$$

Experiments with one sample over 20 and the other less than 5 are not usually conducted. In such cases, if $n = 1$, the distribution is uniform from 1 to $n + m$. For $n = 2$, 3, and 4, the normal approximation will give a rough guess. If an exact value is desired, it can be computed by enumeration.

If there are ties among the scores, a choice must be made between an approximation and the exact computation. For the exact computation, see Exercise 5.8. If there are relatively few small ties, Table B can be used by taking the average of the adjacent two P values if the sum, x, is not an integer. For the normal approximation, when there are ties, the mean and standard deviation are

$$\mu = \frac{n(n + m + 1)}{2},$$

$$\sigma = \sqrt{\frac{n \cdot m[(n + m)^3 - D]}{12(n + m)(n + m - 1)}},$$

where D is the sum of cubes of the total number of scores within each tie (untied scores are counted as "ties" containing one observation).

Example (for σ, not for normal approximation). The two groups of scores (13, 12, 10, 16), (13, 13, 10), arranged in order, are

Ranks	1.5	1.5	3	5	5	5	7
Scores	10	10	12	13	13	13	16
	2		1	3			1

so that

$$D = 2^3 + 1^3 + 3^3 + 1^3 = 8 + 1 + 27 + 1 = 37,$$

$$\sigma = \sqrt{\frac{3 \cdot 4 \cdot (7^3 - 37)}{12 \cdot 7 \cdot 6}} = 2.70.$$

If σ is computed as though there were no ties, the value obtained will be higher.

Table B. Wilcoxon, Mann-Whitney Distributions

Larger Sample Size 3

Smaller Sample Size 1		2		3	
x	P	x	P	x	P
1	.250	3	.100	6	.050
2	.500	4	.200	7	.100
		5	.400	8	.200
3	.500	6	.600	9	.350
4	.250			10	.500
		6	.600		
		7	.400	11	.500
		8	.200	12	.350
		9	.100	13	.200
				14	.100
				15	.050

Larger Sample Size 4

Smaller Sample Size 1		2		3		4	
x	P	x	P	x	P	x	P
1	.200	3	.067	6	.029	10	.014
2	.400	4	.133	7	.057	11	.029
3	.600	5	.267	8	.114	12	.057
		6	.400	9	.200	13	.100
3	.600	7	.600	10	.314	14	.171
4	.400			11	.429	15	.243
5	.200	7	.600	12	.571	16	.343
		8	.400			17	.443
		9	.267	12	.571	18	.557
		10	.133	13	.429		
		11	.067	14	.314	18	.557
				15	.200	19	.443
				16	.114	20	.343
				17	.057	21	.243
				18	.029	22	.171
						23	.100
						24	.057
						25	.029
						26	.014

Table B. Wilcoxon, Mann–Whitney Distributions

Larger Sample Size 5

Smaller Sample Size									
1		2		3		4		5	
x	P	x	P	x	P	x	P	x	P
1	.167	3	.048	6	.018	10	.008	15	.004
2	.333	4	.095	7	.036	11	.016	16	.008
3	.500	5	.190	8	.071	12	.032	17	.016
		6	.286	9	.125	13	.056	18	.028
4	.500	7	.429	10	.196	14	.095	19	.048
5	.333	8	.571	11	.286	15	.143	20	.075
6	.167			12	.393	16	.206	21	.111
		8	.571	13	.500	17	.278	22	.155
		9	.429			18	.365	23	.210
		10	.286	14	.500	19	.452	24	.274
		11	.190	15	.393	20	.548	25	.345
		12	.095	16	.286			26	.421
		13	.048	17	.196	20	.548	27	.500
				18	.125	21	.452		
				19	.071	22	.365	28	.500
				20	.036	23	.278	29	.421
				21	.018	24	.206	30	.345
						25	.143	31	.274
						26	.095	32	.210
						27	.056	33	.155
						28	.032	34	.111
						29	.016	35	.075
						30	.008	36	.048
								37	.028
								38	.016
								39	.008
								40	.004

Larger Sample Size 6

Smaller Sample Size											
1		2		3		4		5		6	
x	P	x	P	x	P	x	P	x	P	x	P
1	.143	3	.036	6	.012	10	.005	15	.002	21	.001
2	.286	4	.071	7	.024	11	.010	16	.004	22	.002
3	.429	5	.143	8	.048	12	.019	17	.009	23	.004
4	.571	6	.214	9	.083	13	.033	18	.015	24	.008
		7	.321	10	.131	14	.057	19	.026	25	.013
4	.571	8	.429	11	.190	15	.086	20	.041	26	.021
5	.429	9	.571	12	.274	16	.129	21	.063	27	.032
6	.286			13	.357	17	.176	22	.089	28	.047
7	.143	9	.571	14	.452	18	.238	23	.123	29	.066
		10	.429	15	.548	19	.305	24	.165	30	.090
		11	.321			20	.381	25	.214	31	.120
		12	.214	15	.548	21	.457	26	.268	32	.155
		13	.143	16	.452	22	.543	27	.331	33	.197
		14	.071	17	.357			28	.396	34	.242
		15	.036	18	.274	22	.543	29	.465	35	.294
				19	.190	23	.457	30	.535	36	.350
				20	.131	24	.381			37	.409
				21	.083	25	.305	30	.535	38	.469
				22	.048	26	.238	31	.465	39	.531
				23	.024	27	.176	32	.396		
				24	.012	28	.129	33	.331	39	.531
						29	.086	34	.268	40	.469
						30	.057	35	.214	41	.409
						31	.033	36	.165	42	.350
						32	.019	37	.123	43	.294
						33	.010	38	.089	44	.242
						34	.005	39	.063	45	.197
								40	.041	46	.155
								41	.026	47	.120
								42	.015	48	.090
								43	.009	49	.066
								44	.004	50	.047
								45	.002	51	.032
										52	.021
										53	.013
										54	.008
										55	.004
										56	.002
										57	.001

Table B. Wilcoxon, Mann-Whitney Distributions

Larger Sample Size 7

Smaller Sample Size													
1		2		3		4		5		6		7	
x	P	x	P	x	P	x	P	x	P	x	P	x	P
1	.125	3	.028	6	.008	10	.003	15	.001	21	.001	28	.000
2	.250	4	.056	7	.017	11	.006	16	.003	22	.001	29	.001
3	.375	5	.111	8	.033	12	.012	17	.005	23	.002	30	.001
4	.500	6	.167	9	.058	13	.021	18	.009	24	.004	31	.002
		7	.250	10	.092	14	.036	19	.015	25	.007	32	.003
5	.500	8	.333	11	.133	15	.055	20	.024	26	.011	33	.006
6	.375	9	.444	12	.192	16	.082	21	.037	27	.017	34	.009
7	.250	10	.556	13	.258	17	.115	22	.053	28	.026	35	.013
8	.125			14	.333	18	.158	23	.074	29	.037	36	.019
		10	.556	15	.417	19	.206	24	.101	30	.051	37	.027
		11	.444	16	.500	20	.264	25	.134	31	.069	38	.036
		12	.333			21	.324	26	.172	32	.090	39	.049
		13	.250	17	.500	22	.394	27	.216	33	.117	40	.064
		14	.167	18	.417	23	.464	28	.265	34	.147	41	.082
		15	.111	19	.333	24	.536	29	.319	35	.183	42	.104
		16	.056	20	.258			30	.378	36	.223	43	.130
		17	.028	21	.192	24	.536	31	.438	37	.267	44	.159
				22	.133	25	.464	32	.500	38	.314	45	.191
				23	.092	26	.394			39	.365	46	.228
				24	.058	27	.324	33	.500	40	.418	47	.267
				25	.033	28	.264	34	.438	41	.473	48	.310
				26	.017	29	.206	35	.378	42	.527	49	.355
				27	.008	30	.158	36	.319			50	.402
						31	.115	37	.265	42	.527	51	.451
						32	.082	38	.216	43	.473	52	.500
						33	.055	39	.172	44	.418		
						34	.036	40	.134	45	.365	53	.500
						35	.021	41	.101	46	.314	54	.451
						36	.012	42	.074	47	.267	55	.402
						37	.006	43	.053	48	.223	56	.355
						38	.003	44	.037	49	.183	57	.310
								45	.024	50	.147	58	.267
								46	.015	51	.117	59	.228
								47	.009	52	.090	60	.191
								48	.005	53	.069	61	.159
								49	.003	54	.051	62	.130
								50	.001	55	.037	63	.104
										56	.026	64	.082
										57	.017	65	.064
										58	.011	66	.049
										59	.007	67	.036
										60	.004	68	.027
										61	.002	69	.019
										62	.001	70	.013
										63	.001	71	.009
												72	.006
												73	.003
												74	.002
												75	.001
												76	.001
												77	.000

Table B. Wilcoxon, Mann-Whitney Distributions

Larger Sample Size 8, (Lower Tail)

Smaller Sample Size															
1		2		3		4		5		6		7		8	
x	P	x	P	x	P	x	P	x	P	x	P	x	P	x	P
1	.111	3	.022	6	.006	10	.002	15	.001	21	.000	28	.000	36	.000
2	.222	4	.044	7	.012	11	.004	16	.002	22	.001	29	.000	37	.000
3	.333	5	.089	8	.024	12	.008	17	.003	23	.001	30	.001	38	.000
4	.444	6	.133	9	.042	13	.014	18	.005	24	.002	31	.001	39	.001
5	.556	7	.200	10	.067	14	.024	19	.009	25	.004	32	.002	40	.001
		8	.267	11	.097	15	.036	20	.015	26	.006	33	.003	41	.001
		9	.356	12	.139	16	.055	21	.023	27	.010	34	.005	42	.002
		10	.444	13	.188	17	.077	22	.033	28	.015	35	.007	43	.003
		11	.556	14	.248	18	.107	23	.047	29	.021	36	.010	44	.005
				15	.315	19	.141	24	.064	30	.030	37	.014	45	.007
				16	.388	20	.184	25	.085	31	.041	38	.020	46	.010
				17	.461	21	.230	26	.111	32	.054	39	.027	47	.014
				18	.539	22	.285	27	.142	33	.071	40	.036	48	.019
						23	.341	28	.177	34	.091	41	.047	49	.025
						24	.404	29	.218	35	.114	42	.060	50	.032
						25	.467	30	.262	36	.141	43	.076	51	.041
						26	.533	31	.311	37	.172	44	.095	52	.052
								32	.362	38	.207	45	.116	53	.065
								33	.416	39	.245	46	.140	54	.080
								34	.472	40	.286	47	.168	55	.097
								35	.528	41	.331	48	.198	56	.117
										42	.377	49	.232	57	.139
										43	.426	50	.268	58	.164
										44	.475	51	.306	59	.191
										45	.525	52	.347	60	.221
												53	.389	61	.253
												54	.433	62	.287
												55	.478	63	.323
												56	.522	64	.360
														65	.399
														66	.439
														67	.480
														68	.520

Table B. Wilcoxon, Mann-Whitney Distributions

Larger Sample Size 8, (Upper Tail)

Smaller Sample Size															
1		2		3		4		5		6		7		8	
x	P	x	P	x	P	x	P	x	P	x	P	x	P	x	P
5	.556	11	.556	18	.539	26	.533	35	.528	45	.525	56	.522	68	.520
6	.444	12	.444	19	.461	27	.467	36	.472	46	.475	57	.478	69	.480
7	.333	13	.356	20	.388	28	.404	37	.416	47	.426	58	.433	70	.439
8	.222	14	.267	21	.315	29	.341	38	.362	48	.377	59	.389	71	.399
9	.111	15	.200	22	.248	30	.285	39	.311	49	.331	60	.347	72	.360
		16	.133	23	.188	31	.230	40	.262	50	.286	61	.306	73	.323
		17	.089	24	.139	32	.184	41	.218	51	.245	62	.268	74	.287
		18	.044	25	.097	33	.141	42	.177	52	.207	63	.232	75	.253
		19	.022	26	.067	34	.107	43	.142	53	.172	64	.198	76	.221
				27	.042	35	.077	44	.111	54	.141	65	.168	77	.191
				28	.024	36	.055	45	.085	55	.114	66	.140	78	.164
				29	.012	37	.036	46	.064	56	.091	67	.116	79	.139
				30	.006	38	.024	47	.047	57	.071	68	.095	80	.117
						39	.014	48	.033	58	.054	69	.076	81	.097
						40	.008	49	.023	59	.041	70	.060	82	.080
						41	.004	50	.015	60	.030	71	.047	83	.065
						42	.002	51	.009	61	.021	72	.036	84	.052
								52	.005	62	.015	73	.027	85	.041
								53	.003	63	.010	74	.020	86	.032
								54	.002	64	.006	75	.014	87	.025
								55	.001	65	.004	76	.010	88	.019
										66	.002	77	.007	89	.014
										67	.001	78	.005	90	.010
										68	.001	79	.003	91	.007
										69	.000	80	.002	92	.005
												81	.001	93	.003
												82	.001	94	.002
												83	.000	95	.001
												84	.000	96	.001
														97	.001
														98	.000
														99	.000
														100	.000

Table B. Wilcoxon, Mann-Whitney Distributions

Larger Sample Size 9, (Lower Tail)

Smaller Sample Size																	
1		2		3		4		5		6		7		8		9	
x	P	x	P	x	P	x	P	x	P	x	P	x	P	x	P	x	P
1	.100	3	.018	6	.005	10	.001	15	.000	21	.000	28	.000	36	.000	45	.000
2	.200	4	.036	7	.009	11	.003	16	.001	22	.000	29	.000	37	.000	46	.000
3	.300	5	.073	8	.018	12	.006	17	.002	23	.001	30	.000	38	.000	47	.000
4	.400	6	.109	9	.032	13	.010	18	.003	24	.001	31	.001	39	.000	48	.000
5	.500	7	.164	10	.050	14	.017	19	.006	25	.002	32	.001	40	.000	49	.000
		8	.218	11	.073	15	.025	20	.009	26	.004	33	.002	41	.001	50	.000
		9	.291	12	.105	16	.038	21	.014	27	.006	34	.003	42	.001	51	.001
		10	.364	13	.141	17	.053	22	.021	28	.009	35	.004	43	.002	52	.001
		11	.455	14	.186	18	.074	23	.030	29	.013	36	.006	44	.003	53	.001
		12	.545	15	.241	19	.099	24	.041	30	.018	37	.008	45	.004	54	.002
				16	.300	20	.130	25	.056	31	.025	38	.011	46	.006	55	.003
				17	.364	21	.165	26	.073	32	.033	39	.016	47	.008	56	.004
				18	.432	22	.207	27	.095	33	.044	40	.021	48	.010	57	.005
				19	.500	23	.252	28	.120	34	.057	41	.027	49	.014	58	.007
						24	.302	29	.149	35	.072	42	.036	50	.018	59	.009
						25	.355	30	.182	36	.091	43	.045	51	.023	60	.012
						26	.413	31	.219	37	.112	44	.057	52	.030	61	.016
						27	.470	32	.259	38	.136	45	.071	53	.037	62	.020
						28	.530	33	.303	39	.164	46	.087	54	.046	63	.025
								34	.350	40	.194	47	.105	55	.057	64	.031
								35	.399	41	.228	48	.126	56	.069	65	.039
								36	.449	42	.264	49	.150	57	.084	66	.047
								37	.500	43	.303	50	.176	58	.100	67	.057
										44	.344	51	.204	59	.118	68	.068
										45	.388	52	.235	60	.138	69	.081
										46	.432	53	.268	61	.161	70	.095
										47	.477	54	.303	62	.185	71	.111
										48	.523	55	.340	63	.212	72	.129
												56	.379	64	.240	73	.149
												57	.419	65	.271	74	.170
												58	.459	66	.303	75	.193
												59	.500	67	.336	76	.218
														68	.371	77	.245
														69	.407	78	.273
														70	.444	79	.302
														71	.481	80	.333
														72	.519	81	.365
																82	.398
																83	.432
																84	.466
																85	.500

Table B. Wilcoxon, Mann-Whitney Distributions

Larger Sample Size 9, (Upper Tail)

Smaller Sample Size																	
1		2		3		4		5		6		7		8		9	
x	P	x	P	x	P	x	P	x	P	x	P	x	P	x	P	x	P
6	.500	12	.545	20	.500	28	.530	38	.500	48	.523	60	.500	72	.519	86	.500
7	.400	13	.455	21	.432	29	.470	39	.449	49	.477	61	.459	73	.481	87	.466
8	.300	14	.364	22	.364	30	.413	40	.399	50	.432	62	.419	74	.444	88	.432
9	.200	15	.291	23	.300	31	.355	41	.350	51	.388	63	.379	75	.407	89	.398
10	.100	16	.218	24	.241	32	.302	42	.303	52	.344	64	.340	76	.371	90	.365
		17	.164	25	.186	33	.252	43	.259	53	.303	65	.303	77	.336	91	.333
		18	.109	26	.141	34	.207	44	.219	54	.264	66	.268	78	.303	92	.302
		19	.073	27	.105	35	.165	45	.182	55	.228	67	.235	79	.271	93	.273
		20	.036	28	.073	36	.130	46	.149	56	.194	68	.204	80	.240	94	.245
		21	.018	29	.050	37	.099	47	.120	57	.164	69	.176	81	.212	95	.218
				30	.032	38	.074	48	.095	58	.136	70	.150	82	.185	96	.193
				31	.018	39	.053	49	.073	59	.112	71	.126	83	.161	97	.170
				32	.009	40	.038	50	.056	60	.091	72	.105	84	.138	98	.149
				33	.005	41	.025	51	.041	61	.072	73	.087	85	.118	99	.129
						42	.017	52	.030	62	.057	74	.071	86	.100	100	.111
						43	.010	53	.021	63	.044	75	.057	87	.084	101	.095
						44	.006	54	.014	64	.033	76	.045	88	.069	102	.081
						45	.003	55	.009	65	.025	77	.036	89	.057	103	.068
						46	.001	56	.006	66	.018	78	.027	90	.046	104	.057
								57	.003	67	.013	79	.021	91	.037	105	.047
								58	.002	68	.009	80	.016	92	.030	106	.039
								59	.001	69	.006	81	.011	93	.023	107	.031
								60	.000	70	.004	82	.008	94	.018	108	.025
										71	.002	83	.006	95	.014	109	.020
										72	.001	84	.004	96	.010	110	.016
										73	.001	85	.003	97	.008	111	.012
										74	.000	86	.002	98	.006	112	.009
										75	.000	87	.001	99	.004	113	.007
												88	.001	100	.003	114	.005
												89	.000	101	.002	115	.004
												90	.000	102	.001	116	.003
												91	.000	103	.001	117	.002
														104	.000	118	.001
														105	.000	119	.001
														106	.000	120	.001
														107	.000	121	.000
														108	.000	122	.000
																123	.000
																124	.000
																125	.000
																126	.000

Table B. Wilcoxon, Mann-Whitney Distributions

Larger Sample Size 10, (Lower Tail)

Smaller Sample Size																			
1		2		3		4		5		6		7		8		9		10	
x	*P*	*x*	*P*	*x*	*P*	*x*	*P*	*x*	*P*	*x*	*P*	*x*	*P*	*x*	*P*	*x*	*P*	*x*	*P*
1	.091	3	.015	6	.003	10	.001	15	.000	21	.000	28	.000	36	.000	45	.000	55	.000
2	.182	4	.030	7	.007	11	.002	16	.001	22	.000	29	.000	37	.000	46	.000	56	.000
3	.273	5	.061	8	.014	12	.004	17	.001	23	.000	30	.000	38	.000	47	.000	57	.000
4	.364	6	.091	9	.024	13	.007	18	.002	24	.001	31	.000	39	.000	48	.000	58	.000
5	.455	7	.136	10	.038	14	.012	19	.004	25	.001	32	.001	40	.000	49	.000	59	.000
6	.545	8	.182	11	.056	15	.018	20	.006	26	.002	33	.001	41	.000	50	.000	60	.000
		9	.242	12	.080	16	.027	21	.010	27	.004	34	.002	42	.001	51	.000	61	.000
		10	.303	13	.108	17	.038	22	.014	28	.005	35	.002	43	.001	52	.000	62	.000
		11	.379	14	.143	18	.053	23	.020	29	.008	36	.003	44	.002	53	.001	63	.000
		12	.455	15	.185	19	.071	24	.028	30	.011	37	.005	45	.002	54	.001	64	.001
		13	.545	16	.234	20	.094	25	.038	31	.016	38	.007	46	.003	55	.001	65	.001
				17	.287	21	.120	26	.050	32	.021	39	.009	47	.004	56	.002	66	.001
				18	.346	22	.152	27	.065	33	.028	40	.012	48	.006	57	.003	67	.001
				19	.406	23	.187	28	.082	34	.036	41	.017	49	.008	58	.004	68	.002
				20	.469	24	.227	29	.103	35	.047	42	.022	50	.010	59	.005	69	.003
				21	.531	25	.270	30	.127	36	.059	43	.028	51	.013	60	.007	70	.003
						26	.318	31	.155	37	.074	44	.035	52	.017	61	.009	71	.004
						27	.367	32	.185	38	.090	45	.044	53	.022	62	.011	72	.006
						28	.420	33	.220	39	.110	46	.054	54	.027	63	.014	73	.007
						29	.473	34	.257	40	.132	47	.067	55	.034	64	.017	74	.009
						30	.527	35	.297	41	.157	48	.081	56	.042	65	.022	75	.012
								36	.339	42	.184	49	.097	57	.051	66	.027	76	.014
								37	.384	43	.214	50	.115	58	.061	67	.033	77	.018
								38	.430	44	.246	51	.135	59	.073	68	.039	78	.022
								39	.477	45	.281	52	.157	60	.086	69	.047	79	.026
								40	.523	46	.318	53	.182	61	.102	70	.056	80	.032
										47	.356	54	.209	62	.118	71	.067	81	.038
										48	.396	55	.237	63	.137	72	.078	82	.045
										49	.437	56	.268	64	.158	73	.091	83	.053
										50	.479	57	.300	65	.180	74	.106	84	.062
										51	.521	58	.335	66	.204	75	.121	85	.072
												59	.370	67	.230	76	.139	86	.083
												60	.406	68	.257	77	.158	87	.095
												61	.443	69	.286	78	.178	88	.109
												62	.481	70	.317	79	.200	89	.124
												63	.519	71	.348	80	.223	90	.140
														72	.381	81	.248	91	.157
														73	.414	82	.274	92	.176
														74	.448	83	.302	93	.197
														75	.483	84	.330	94	.218
														76	.517	85	.360	95	.241
																86	.390	96	.264
																87	.421	97	.289
																88	.452	98	.315
																89	.484	99	.342
																90	.516	100	.370
																		101	.398
																		102	.427
																		103	.456
																		104	.485
																		105	.515

Table B. Wilcoxon, Mann-Whitney Distributions

Larger Sample Size 10, (Upper Tail)

Smaller Sample Size																			
1		2		3		4		5		6		7		8		9		10	
x	P	x	P	x	P	x	P	x	P	x	P	x	P	x	P	x	P	x	P
6	.545	13	.545	21	.531	30	.527	40	.523	51	.521	63	.519	76	.517	90	.516	105	.515
7	.455	14	.455	22	.469	31	.473	41	.477	52	.479	64	.481	77	.483	91	.484	106	.485
8	.364	15	.379	23	.406	32	.420	42	.430	53	.437	65	.443	78	.448	92	.452	107	.456
9	.273	16	.303	24	.346	33	.367	43	.384	54	.396	66	.406	79	.414	93	.421	108	.427
10	.182	17	.242	25	.287	34	.318	44	.339	55	.356	67	.370	80	.381	94	.390	109	.398
11	.091	18	.182	26	.234	35	.270	45	.297	56	.318	68	.335	81	.348	95	.360	110	.370
		19	.136	27	.185	36	.227	46	.257	57	.281	69	.300	82	.317	96	.330	111	.342
		20	.091	28	.143	37	.187	47	.220	58	.246	70	.268	83	.286	97	.302	112	.315
		21	.061	29	.108	38	.152	48	.185	59	.214	71	.237	84	.257	98	.274	113	.289
		22	.030	30	.080	39	.120	49	.155	60	.184	72	.209	85	.230	99	.248	114	.264
		23	.015	31	.056	40	.094	50	.127	61	.157	73	.182	86	.204	100	.223	115	.241
				32	.038	41	.071	51	.103	62	.132	74	.157	87	.180	101	.200	116	.218
				33	.024	42	.053	52	.082	63	.110	75	.135	88	.158	102	.178	117	.197
				34	.014	43	.038	53	.065	64	.090	76	.115	89	.137	103	.158	118	.176
				35	.007	44	.027	54	.050	65	.074	77	.097	90	.118	104	.139	119	.157
				36	.003	45	.018	55	.038	66	.059	78	.081	91	.102	105	.121	120	.140
						46	.012	56	.028	67	.047	79	.067	92	.086	106	.106	121	.124
						47	.007	57	.020	68	.036	80	.054	93	.073	107	.091	122	.109
						48	.004	58	.014	69	.028	81	.044	94	.061	108	.078	123	.095
						49	.002	59	.010	70	.021	82	.035	95	.051	109	.067	124	.083
						50	.001	60	.006	71	.016	83	.028	96	.042	110	.056	125	.072
								61	.004	72	.011	84	.022	97	.034	111	.047	126	.062
								62	.002	73	.008	85	.017	98	.027	112	.039	127	.053
								63	.001	74	.005	86	.012	99	.022	113	.033	128	.045
								64	.001	75	.004	87	.009	100	.017	114	.027	129	.038
								65	.000	76	.002	88	.007	101	.013	115	.022	130	.032
										77	.001	89	.005	102	.010	116	.017	131	.026
										78	.001	90	.003	103	.008	117	.014	132	.022
										79	.000	91	.002	104	.006	118	.011	133	.018
										80	.000	92	.002	105	.004	119	.009	134	.014
										81	.000	93	.001	106	.003	120	.007	135	.012
												94	.001	107	.002	121	.005	136	.009
												95	.000	108	.002	122	.004	137	.007
												96	.000	109	.001	123	.003	138	.006
												97	.000	110	.001	124	.002	139	.004
												98	.000	111	.000	125	.001	140	.003
														112	.000	126	.001	141	.003
														113	.000	127	.001	142	.002
														114	.000	128	.000	143	.001
														115	.000	129	.000	144	.001
														116	.000	130	.000	145	.001
																131	.000	146	.001
																132	.000	147	.000
																133	.000	148	.000
																134	.000	149	.000
																135	.000	150	.000
																		151	.000
																		152	.000
																		153	.000
																		154	.000
																		155	.000

Table B. Wilcoxon, Mann-Whitney Distributions

Larger Sample Size 11

Smaller Sample Size							
1		2		3		4	
x	P	x	P	x	P	x	P
1	.083	3	.013	6	.003	10	.001
2	.167	4	.026	7	.005	11	.001
3	.250	5	.051	8	.011	12	.003
4	.333	6	.077	9	.019	13	.005
5	.417	7	.115	10	.030	14	.009
6	.500	8	.154	11	.044	15	.013
		9	.205	12	.063	16	.020
7	.500	10	.256	13	.085	17	.028
8	.417	11	.321	14	.113	18	.039
9	.333	12	.385	15	.146	19	.052
10	.250	13	.462	16	.184	20	.069
11	.167	14	.538	17	.228	21	.089
12	.083			18	.277	22	.113
		14	.538	19	.330	23	.140
		15	.462	20	.385	24	.171
		16	.385	21	.442	25	.206
		17	.321	22	.500	26	.245
		18	.256			27	.286
		19	.205	23	.500	28	.330
		20	.154	24	.442	29	.377
		21	.115	25	.385	30	.426
		22	.077	26	.330	31	.475
		23	.051	27	.277	32	.525
		24	.026	28	.228		
		25	.013	29	.184	32	.525
				30	.146	33	.475
				31	.113	34	.426
				32	.085	35	.377
				33	.063	36	.330
				34	.044	37	.286
				35	.030	38	.245
				36	.019	39	.206
				37	.011	40	.171
				38	.005	41	.140
				39	.003	42	.113
						43	.089
						44	.069
						45	.052
						46	.039
						47	.028
						48	.020
						49	.013
						50	.009
						51	.005
						52	.003
						53	.001
						54	.001

Larger Sample Size 12

Smaller Sample Size							
1		2		3		4	
x	P	x	P	x	P	x	P
1	.077	3	.011	6	.002	10	.001
2	.154	4	.022	7	.004	11	.001
3	.231	5	.044	8	.009	12	.002
4	.308	6	.066	9	.015	13	.004
5	.385	7	.099	10	.024	14	.007
6	.462	8	.132	11	.035	15	.010
7	.538	9	.176	12	.051	16	.015
		10	.220	13	.068	17	.021
7	.538	11	.275	14	.090	18	.029
8	.462	12	.330	15	.116	19	.039
9	.385	13	.396	16	.147	20	.052
10	.308	14	.462	17	.182	21	.066
11	.231	15	.538	18	.224	22	.085
12	.154			19	.268	23	.106
13	.077	15	.538	20	.316	24	.131
		16	.462	21	.367	25	.158
		17	.396	22	.420	26	.190
		18	.330	23	.473	27	.223
		19	.275	24	.527	28	.260
		20	.220			29	.299
		21	.176	24	.527	30	.342
		22	.132	25	.473	31	.385
		23	.099	26	.420	32	.431
		24	.066	27	.367	33	.476
		25	.044	28	.316	34	.524
		26	.022	29	.268		
		27	.011	30	.224	34	.524
				31	.182	35	.476
				32	.147	36	.431
				33	.116	37	.385
				34	.090	38	.342
				35	.068	39	.299
				36	.051	40	.260
				37	.035	41	.223
				38	.024	42	.190
				39	.015	43	.158
				40	.009	44	.131
				41	.004	45	.106
				42	.002	46	.085
						47	.066
						48	.052
						49	.039
						50	.029
						51	.021
						52	.015
						53	.010
						54	.007
						55	.004
						56	.002
						57	.001
						58	.001

Table B. Wilcoxon, Mann-Whitney Distributions

Larger Sample Size 13

Smaller Sample Size									
1		2		3		4			
x	*P*	*x*	*P*	*x*	*P*	*x*	*P*	*x*	*P*
1	.071	3	.010	6	.002	10	.000	36	.522
2	.143	4	.019	7	.004	11	.001	37	.478
3	.214	5	.038	8	.007	12	.002	38	.435
4	.286	6	.057	9	.012	13	.003	39	.392
5	.357	7	.086	10	.020	14	.005	40	.352
6	.429	8	.114	11	.029	15	.008	41	.312
7	.500	9	.152	12	.041	16	.011	42	.274
		10	.190	13	.055	17	.016	43	.239
8	.500	11	.238	14	.073	18	.022	44	.206
9	.429	12	.286	15	.095	19	.030	45	.175
10	.357	13	.343	16	.120	20	.039	46	.148
11	.286	14	.400	17	.148	21	.051	47	.123
12	.214	15	.467	18	.182	22	.065	48	.101
13	.143	16	.533	19	.220	23	.082	49	.082
14	.071			20	.261	24	.101	50	.065
		16	.533	21	.305	25	.123	51	.051
		17	.467	22	.352	26	.148	52	.039
		18	.400	23	.400	27	.175	53	.030
		19	.343	24	.450	28	.206	54	.022
		20	.286	25	.500	29	.239	55	.016
		21	.238			30	.274	56	.011
		22	.190	26	.500	31	.312	57	.008
		23	.152	27	.450	32	.352	58	.005
		24	.114	28	.400	33	.392	59	.003
		25	.086	29	.352	34	.435	60	.002
		26	.057	30	.305	35	.478	61	.001
		27	.038	31	.261	36	.522	62	.000
		28	.019	32	.220				
		29	.010	33	.182				
				34	.148				
				35	.120				
				36	.095				
				37	.073				
				38	.055				
				39	.041				
				40	.029				
				41	.020				
				42	.012				
				43	.007				
				44	.004				
				45	.002				

Larger Sample Size 14

Smaller Sample Size									
1		2		3		4			
x	*P*	*x*	*P*	*x*	*P*	*x*	*P*	*x*	*P*
1	.067	3	.008	6	.001	10	.000	38	.521
2	.133	4	.017	7	.003	11	.001	39	.479
3	.200	5	.033	8	.006	12	.001	40	.439
4	.267	6	.050	9	.010	13	.002	41	.399
5	.333	7	.075	10	.016	14	.004	42	.360
6	.400	8	.100	11	.024	15	.006	43	.323
7	.467	9	.133	12	.034	16	.009	44	.287
8	.533	10	.167	13	.046	17	.012	45	.253
		11	.208	14	.060	18	.017	46	.221
8	.533	12	.250	15	.078	19	.023	47	.191
9	.467	13	.300	16	.099	20	.031	48	.164
10	.400	14	.350	17	.122	21	.040	49	.139
11	.333	15	.408	18	.150	22	.051	50	.116
12	.267	16	.467	19	.181	23	.063	51	.096
13	.200	17	.533	20	.216	24	.079	52	.079
14	.133			21	.254	25	.096	53	.063
15	.067	17	.533	22	.296	26	.116	54	.051
		18	.467	23	.338	27	.139	55	.040
		19	.408	24	.384	28	.164	56	.031
		20	.350	25	.429	29	.191	57	.023
		21	.300	26	.476	30	.221	58	.017
		22	.250	27	.524	31	.253	59	.012
		23	.208			32	.287	60	.009
		24	.167	27	.524	33	.323	61	.006
		25	.133	28	.476	34	.360	62	.004
		26	.100	29	.429	35	.399	63	.002
		27	.075	30	.384	36	.439	64	.001
		28	.050	31	.338	37	.479	65	.001
		29	.033	32	.296	38	.521	66	.000
		30	.017	33	.254				
		31	.008	34	.216				
				35	.181				
				36	.150				
				37	.122				
				38	.099				
				39	.078				
				40	.060				
				41	.046				
				42	.034				
				43	.024				
				44	.016				
				45	.010				
				46	.006				
				47	.003				
				48	.001				

Table B. Wilcoxon, Mann-Whitney Distributions

Larger Sample Size 15

(Lower Tail)

Smaller Sample Size							
1		2		3		4	
x	P	x	P	x	P	x	P
1	.062	3	.007	6	.001	10	.000
2	.125	4	.015	7	.002	11	.001
3	.188	5	.029	8	.005	12	.001
4	.250	6	.044	9	.009	13	.002
5	.312	7	.066	10	.013	14	.003
6	.375	8	.088	11	.020	15	.005
7	.438	9	.118	12	.028	16	.007
8	.500	10	.147	13	.038	17	.010
		11	.184	14	.050	18	.014
		12	.221	15	.065	19	.018
		13	.265	16	.082	20	.024
		14	.309	17	.102	21	.031
		15	.360	18	.125	22	.040
		16	.412	19	.151	23	.050
		17	.471	20	.180	24	.062
		18	.529	21	.213	25	.076
				22	.249	26	.092
				23	.287	27	.110
				24	.327	28	.131
				25	.369	29	.154
				26	.412	30	.179
				27	.456	31	.205
				28	.500	32	.235
						33	.265
						34	.298
						35	.332
						36	.368
						37	.405
						38	.443
						39	.481
						40	.519

(Upper Tail)

Smaller Sample Size							
1		2		3		4	
x	P	x	P	x	P	x	P
9	.500	18	.529	29	.500	40	.519
10	.438	19	.471	30	.456	41	.481
11	.375	20	.412	31	.412	42	.443
12	.312	21	.360	32	.369	43	.405
13	.250	22	.309	33	.327	44	.368
14	.188	23	.265	34	.287	45	.332
15	.125	24	.221	35	.249	46	.298
16	.062	25	.184	36	.213	47	.265
		26	.147	37	.180	48	.235
		27	.118	38	.151	49	.205
		28	.088	39	.125	50	.179
		29	.066	40	.102	51	.154
		30	.044	41	.082	52	.131
		31	.029	42	.065	53	.110
		32	.015	43	.050	54	.092
		33	.007	44	.038	55	.076
				45	.028	56	.062
				46	.020	57	.050
				47	.013	58	.040
				48	.009	59	.031
				49	.005	60	.024
				50	.002	61	.018
				51	.001	62	.014
						63	.010
						64	.007
						65	.005
						66	.003
						67	.002
						68	.001
						69	.001
						70	.000

Table B. Wilcoxon, Mann-Whitney Distributions

Larger Sample Size 16

(Lower Tail)

Smaller Sample Size							
1		2		3		4	
x	P	x	P	x	P	x	P
1	.059	3	.007	6	.001	10	.000
2	.118	4	.013	7	.002	11	.000
3	.176	5	.026	8	.004	12	.001
4	.235	6	.039	9	.007	13	.001
5	.294	7	.059	10	.011	14	.002
6	.353	8	.078	11	.017	15	.004
7	.412	9	.105	12	.024	16	.006
8	.471	10	.131	13	.032	17	.008
9	.529	11	.163	14	.042	18	.011
		12	.196	15	.055	19	.015
		13	.235	16	.069	20	.019
		14	.275	17	.086	21	.025
		15	.320	18	.105	22	.032
		16	.366	19	.127	23	.040
		17	.418	20	.152	24	.050
		18	.471	21	.180	25	.061
		19	.529	22	.211	26	.074
				23	.244	27	.089
				24	.280	28	.106
				25	.317	29	.124
				26	.356	30	.145
				27	.396	31	.168
				28	.438	32	.192
				29	.479	33	.219
				30	.521	34	.247
						35	.277
						36	.308
						37	.341
						38	.375
						39	.410
						40	.446
						41	.482
						42	.518

(Upper Tail)

Smaller Sample Size							
1		2		3		4	
x	P	x	P	x	P	x	P
9	.529	19	.529	30	.521	42	.518
10	.471	20	.471	31	.479	43	.482
11	.412	21	.418	32	.438	44	.446
12	.353	22	.366	33	.396	45	.410
13	.294	23	.320	34	.356	46	.375
14	.235	24	.275	35	.317	47	.341
15	.176	25	.235	36	.280	48	.308
16	.118	26	.196	37	.244	49	.277
17	.059	27	.163	38	.211	50	.247
		28	.131	39	.180	51	.219
		29	.105	40	.152	52	.192
		30	.078	41	.127	53	.168
		31	.059	42	.105	54	.145
		32	.039	43	.086	55	.124
		33	.026	44	.069	56	.106
		34	.013	45	.055	57	.089
		35	.007	46	.042	58	.074
				47	.032	59	.061
				48	.024	60	.050
				49	.017	61	.040
				50	.011	62	.032
				51	.007	63	.025
				52	.004	64	.019
				53	.002	65	.015
				54	.001	66	.011
						67	.008
						68	.006
						69	.004
						70	.002
						71	.001
						72	.001
						73	.000
						74	.000

Table B. Wilcoxon, Mann-Whitney Distributions

Larger Sample Size 17

(Lower Tail)

Smaller Sample Size							
1		2		3		4	
x	P	x	P	x	P	x	P
1	.056	3	.006	6	.001	10	.000
2	.111	4	.012	7	.002	11	.000
3	.167	5	.023	8	.004	12	.001
4	.222	6	.035	9	.006	13	.001
5	.278	7	.053	10	.010	14	.002
6	.333	8	.070	11	.014	15	.003
7	.389	9	.094	12	.020	16	.005
8	.444	10	.117	13	.027	17	.006
9	.500	11	.146	14	.036	18	.009
		12	.175	15	.046	19	.012
		13	.211	16	.059	20	.016
		14	.246	17	.073	21	.020
		15	.287	18	.089	22	.026
		16	.327	19	.108	23	.032
		17	.374	20	.129	24	.040
		18	.421	21	.153	25	.049
		19	.474	22	.179	26	.060
		20	.526	23	.208	27	.072
				24	.239	28	.086
				25	.273	29	.101
				26	.308	30	.119
				27	.345	31	.138
				28	.382	32	.158
				29	.421	33	.181
				30	.461	34	.205
				31	.500	35	.231
						36	.258
						37	.287
						38	.318
						39	.349
						40	.381
						41	.415
						42	.449
						43	.483
						44	.517

(Upper Tail)

Smaller Sample Size							
1		2		3		4	
x	P	x	P	x	P	x	P
10	.500	20	.526	32	.500	44	.517
11	.444	21	.474	33	.461	45	.483
12	.389	22	.421	34	.421	46	.449
13	.333	23	.374	35	.382	47	.415
14	.278	24	.327	36	.345	48	.381
15	.222	25	.287	37	.308	49	.349
16	.167	26	.246	38	.273	50	.318
17	.111	27	.211	39	.239	51	.287
18	.056	28	.175	40	.208	52	.258
		29	.146	41	.179	53	.231
		30	.117	42	.153	54	.205
		31	.094	43	.129	55	.181
		32	.070	44	.108	56	.158
		33	.053	45	.089	57	.138
		34	.035	46	.073	58	.119
		35	.023	47	.059	59	.101
		36	.012	48	.046	60	.086
		37	.006	49	.036	61	.072
				50	.027	62	.060
				51	.020	63	.049
				52	.014	64	.040
				53	.010	65	.032
				54	.006	66	.026
				55	.004	67	.020
				56	.002	68	.016
				57	.001	69	.012
						70	.009
						71	.006
						72	.005
						73	.003
						74	.002
						75	.001
						76	.001
						77	.000
						78	.000

Table B. Wilcoxon, Mann-Whitney Distributions

Larger Sample Size 18

(Lower Tail)

Smaller Sample Size							
1		2		3		4	
x	P	x	P	x	P	x	P
1	.053	3	.005	6	.001	10	.000
2	.105	4	.011	7	.002	11	.000
3	.158	5	.021	8	.003	12	.001
4	.211	6	.032	9	.005	13	.001
5	.263	7	.047	10	.008	14	.002
6	.316	8	.063	11	.012	15	.002
7	.368	9	.084	12	.017	16	.004
8	.421	10	.105	13	.023	17	.005
9	.474	11	.132	14	.031	18	.007
10	.526	12	.158	15	.040	19	.010
		13	.189	16	.050	20	.013
		14	.221	17	.062	21	.017
		15	.258	18	.077	22	.021
		16	.295	19	.092	23	.027
		17	.337	20	.111	24	.033
		18	.379	21	.131	25	.040
		19	.426	22	.153	26	.049
		20	.474	23	.178	27	.059
		21	.526	24	.206	28	.070
				25	.235	29	.083
				26	.267	30	.098
				27	.300	31	.113
				28	.335	32	.131
				29	.370	33	.150
				30	.407	34	.171
				31	.444	35	.193
				32	.481	36	.217
				33	.519	37	.242
						38	.269
						39	.297
						40	.326
						41	.356
						42	.387
						43	.419
						44	.451
						45	.484
						46	.516

(Upper Tail)

Smaller Sample Size							
1		2		3		4	
x	P	x	P	x	P	x	P
10	.526	21	.526	33	.519	46	.516
11	.474	22	.474	34	.481	47	.484
12	.421	23	.426	35	.444	48	.451
13	.368	24	.379	36	.407	49	.419
14	.316	25	.337	37	.370	50	.387
15	.263	26	.295	38	.335	51	.356
16	.211	27	.258	39	.300	52	.326
17	.158	28	.221	40	.267	53	.297
18	.105	29	.189	41	.235	54	.269
19	.053	30	.158	42	.206	55	.242
		31	.132	43	.178	56	.217
		32	.105	44	.153	57	.193
		33	.084	45	.131	58	.171
		34	.063	46	.111	59	.150
		35	.047	47	.092	60	.131
		36	.032	48	.077	61	.113
		37	.021	49	.062	62	.098
		38	.011	50	.050	63	.083
		39	.005	51	.040	64	.070
				52	.031	65	.059
				53	.023	66	.049
				54	.017	67	.040
				55	.012	68	.033
				56	.008	69	.027
				57	.005	70	.021
				58	.003	71	.017
				59	.002	72	.013
				60	.001	73	.010
						74	.007
						75	.005
						76	.004
						77	.002
						78	.002
						79	.001
						80	.001
						81	.000
						82	.000

Table B. Wilcoxon, Mann-Whitney Distributions

Larger Sample Size 19

(Lower Tail)

Smaller Sample Size							
1		2		3		4	
x	P	x	P	x	P	x	P
1	.050	3	.005	6	.001	10	.000
2	.100	4	.010	7	.001	11	.000
3	.150	5	.019	8	.003	12	.000
4	.200	6	.029	9	.005	13	.001
5	.250	7	.043	10	.007	14	.001
6	.300	8	.057	11	.010	15	.002
7	.350	9	.076	12	.015	16	.003
8	.400	10	.095	13	.020	17	.004
9	.450	11	.119	14	.027	18	.006
10	.500	12	.143	15	.034	19	.008
		13	.171	16	.044	20	.011
		14	.200	17	.054	21	.014
		15	.233	18	.066	22	.018
		16	.267	19	.080	23	.022
		17	.305	20	.095	24	.027
		18	.343	21	.113	25	.033
		19	.386	22	.132	26	.041
		20	.429	23	.154	27	.049
		21	.476	24	.178	28	.058
		22	.524	25	.204	29	.069
				26	.232	30	.081
				27	.262	31	.094
				28	.293	32	.109
				29	.325	33	.125
				30	.359	34	.143
				31	.394	35	.162
				32	.429	36	.183
				33	.464	37	.205
				34	.500	38	.228
						39	.253
						40	.279
						41	.306
						42	.334
						43	.363
						44	.392
						45	.422
						46	.453
						47	.484
						48	.516

(Upper Tail)

Smaller Sample Size							
1		2		3		4	
x	P	x	P	x	P	x	P
11	.500	22	.524	35	.500	48	.516
12	.450	23	.476	36	.464	49	.484
13	.400	24	.429	37	.429	50	.453
14	.350	25	.386	38	.394	51	.422
15	.300	26	.343	39	.359	52	.392
16	.250	27	.305	40	.325	53	.363
17	.200	28	.267	41	.293	54	.334
18	.150	29	.233	42	.262	55	.306
19	.100	30	.200	43	.232	56	.279
20	.050	31	.171	44	.204	57	.253
		32	.143	45	.178	58	.228
		33	.119	46	.154	59	.205
		34	.095	47	.132	60	.183
		35	.076	48	.113	61	.162
		36	.057	49	.095	62	.143
		37	.043	50	.080	63	.125
		38	.029	51	.066	64	.109
		39	.019	52	.054	65	.094
		40	.010	53	.044	66	.081
		41	.005	54	.034	67	.069
				55	.027	68	.058
				56	.020	69	.049
				57	.015	70	.041
				58	.010	71	.033
				59	.007	72	.027
				60	.005	73	.022
				61	.003	74	.018
				62	.001	75	.014
				63	.001	76	.011
						77	.008
						78	.006
						79	.004
						80	.003
						81	.002
						82	.001
						83	.001
						84	.000
						85	.000
						86	.000

Table B. Wilcoxon, Mann-Whitney Distributions

Larger Sample Size 20

(Lower Tail)

Smaller Sample Size							
1		2		3		4	
x	P	x	P	x	P	x	P
1	.048	3	.004	6	.001	10	.000
2	.095	4	.009	7	.001	11	.000
3	.143	5	.017	8	.002	12	.000
4	.190	6	.026	9	.004	13	.001
5	.238	7	.039	10	.006	14	.001
6	.286	8	.052	11	.009	15	.002
7	.333	9	.069	12	.013	16	.003
8	.381	10	.087	13	.018	17	.004
9	.429	11	.108	14	.023	18	.005
10	.476	12	.130	15	.030	19	.007
11	.524	13	.156	16	.038	20	.009
		14	.182	17	.047	21	.011
		15	.212	18	.058	22	.015
		16	.242	19	.069	23	.018
		17	.277	20	.083	24	.023
		18	.312	21	.098	25	.028
		19	.351	22	.115	26	.034
		20	.390	23	.134	27	.041
		21	.433	24	.155	28	.048
		22	.476	25	.177	29	.057
		23	.524	26	.202	30	.067
				27	.229	31	.079
				28	.257	32	.091
				29	.286	33	.105
				30	.317	34	.120
				31	.349	35	.137
				32	.382	36	.155
				33	.415	37	.174
				34	.449	38	.194
				35	.483	39	.216
				36	.517	40	.239
						41	.262
						42	.288
						43	.314
						44	.341
						45	.368
						46	.397
						47	.426
						48	.455
						49	.485
						50	.515

(Upper Tail)

Smaller Sample Size							
1		2		3		4	
x	P	x	P	x	P	x	P
11	.524	23	.524	36	.517	50	.515
12	.476	24	.476	37	.483	51	.485
13	.429	25	.433	38	.449	52	.455
14	.381	26	.390	39	.415	53	.426
15	.333	27	.351	40	.382	54	.397
16	.286	28	.312	41	.349	55	.368
17	.238	29	.277	42	.317	56	.341
18	.190	30	.242	43	.286	57	.314
19	.143	31	.212	44	.257	58	.288
20	.095	32	.182	45	.229	59	.262
21	.048	33	.156	46	.202	60	.239
		34	.130	47	.177	61	.216
		35	.108	48	.155	62	.194
		36	.087	49	.134	63	.174
		37	.069	50	.115	64	.155
		38	.052	51	.098	65	.137
		39	.039	52	.083	66	.120
		40	.026	53	.069	67	.105
		41	.017	54	.058	68	.091
		42	.009	55	.047	69	.079
		43	.004	56	.038	70	.067
				57	.030	71	.057
				58	.023	72	.048
				59	.018	73	.041
				60	.013	74	.034
				61	.009	75	.028
				62	.006	76	.023
				63	.004	77	.018
				64	.002	78	.015
				65	.001	79	.011
				66	.001	80	.009
						81	.007
						82	.005
						83	.004
						84	.003
						85	.002
						86	.001
						87	.001
						88	.000
						89	.000
						90	.000

TABLE **C**

WILCOXON SIGNED-RANK DISTRIBUTIONS*

Table C gives the distribution of the sum of the ranks, X, of the positive scores, among the absolute values of all the scores, when + or − signs are assigned at random to a set of n nonzero scores without ties. ($P = 1/2^n$ for each of the 2^n possible assignments.) The table is cumulative from each extreme to, but not beyond, the mean. That is, the relation between the table and the distribution is as for the following example for $n = 3$.

Distribution

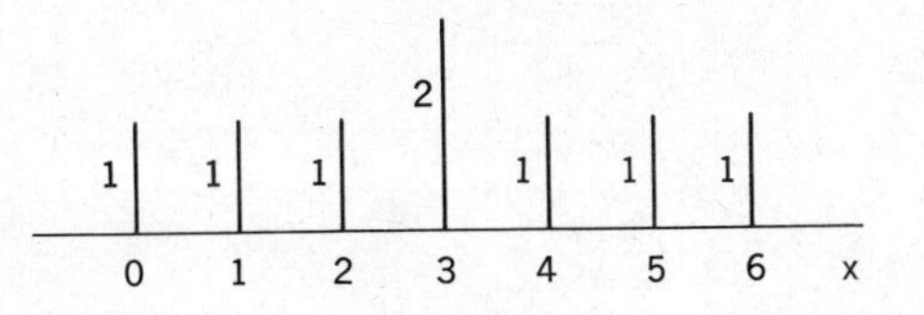

Table C.1.

	x	P
Lower tail	0	.125 = 1/8
	1	.250
	2	.375 = (1 + 1 + 1)/8
	3	.625
Upper tail	3	.625 = (2 + 1 + 1 + 1)/8
	4	.375
	5	.250 = (1 + 1)/8
	6	.125

The range for n is $3 \leq n \leq 15$.

* Adapted from pp. 26–25 of "Handleiding voor de Symmetrie Toets van Wilcoxon," *Report S208(M76), Mathematical Center, Amsterdam* (1956).

If $n > 15$, the normal approximation can be used for the distribution of X. In particular, $P\{X \leq k\}$ is approximately the area from a unit normal curve (Table E) below $[(k + 1/2) - \mu]/\sigma$, where

$$\mu = \frac{n(n + 1)}{4},$$

$$\sigma = \sqrt{\frac{n(n + 1)(2n + 1)}{24}}.$$

If there are zeros, the usual practice is to discard the zeros and proceed with the number of nonzero observations as n.

If there are ties among the absolute values, a choice must be made between an approximation and the exact computation. For the exact computation see Exercise 9.6. If there are relatively few small ties, Table C can be used by taking the average of the two adjacent P values if the sum x is not an integer. For the normal approximation, when there are ties, the mean and standard deviation are

$$\mu = \frac{n(n + 1)}{4},$$

$$\sigma = \sqrt{\frac{3n(n + 1)^2 + n^3 - D}{48}},$$

where D is the sum of cubes of the total number of scores within each tie among the absolute values. (Scores, untied among the absolute values, are counted as "ties" of size 1.)

Example (for σ, not for normal approximation). The scores $(-6, -3, 6, 6, 7, 3)$ arranged in order of their absolute values are

Ranks	1.5	1.5	4	4	4	6
Scores	−3	3	−6	6	6	7
	2			3		1

so that

$$D = 2^3 + 3^3 + 1^3 = 8 + 27 + 1 = 36,$$

$$\sigma = \sqrt{\frac{3 \cdot 6 \cdot 7^2 + 7^3 - 36}{48}} = 4.98.$$

If σ is computed as though there were no ties, the value will be higher.

Table C. Wilcoxon Signed-Rank Distributions

Sample Size													
3		4		5		6		7		8		9	
x	P	x	P	x	P	x	P	x	P	x	P	x	P
0	.125	0	.062	0	.031	0	.016	0	.008	0	.004	0	.002
1	.250	1	.125	1	.062	1	.031	1	.016	1	.008	1	.004
2	.375	2	.188	2	.094	2	.047	2	.023	2	.012	2	.006
3	.625	3	.312	3	.156	3	.078	3	.039	3	.020	3	.010
		4	.438	4	.219	4	.109	4	.055	4	.027	4	.014
3	.625	5	.562	5	.312	5	.156	5	.078	5	.039	5	.020
4	.375			6	.406	6	.219	6	.109	6	.055	6	.027
5	.250	5	.562	7	.500	7	.281	7	.148	7	.074	7	.037
6	.125	6	.438			8	.344	8	.188	8	.098	8	.049
		7	.312	8	.500	9	.422	9	.234	9	.125	9	.064
		8	.188	9	.406	10	.500	10	.289	10	.156	10	.082
		9	.125	10	.312			11	.344	11	.191	11	.102
		10	.062	11	.219	11	.500	12	.406	12	.230	12	.125
				12	.156	12	.422	13	.469	13	.273	13	.150
				13	.094	13	.344	14	.531	14	.320	14	.180
				14	.062	14	.281			15	.371	15	.213
				15	.031	15	.219	14	.531	16	.422	16	.248
						16	.156	15	.469	17	.473	17	.285
						17	.109	16	.406	18	.527	18	.326
						18	.078	17	.344			19	.367
						19	.047	18	.289	18	.527	20	.410
						20	.031	19	.234	19	.473	21	.455
						21	.016	20	.188	20	.422	22	.500
								21	.148	21	.371		
								22	.109	22	.320	23	.500
								23	.078	23	.273	24	.455
								24	.055	24	.230	25	.410
								25	.039	25	.191	26	.367
								26	.023	26	.156	27	.326
								27	.016	27	.125	28	.285
								28	.008	28	.098	29	.248
										29	.074	30	.213
										30	.055	31	.180
										31	.039	32	.150
										32	.027	33	.125
										33	.020	34	.102
										34	.012	35	.082
										35	.008	36	.064
										36	.004	37	.049
												38	.037
												39	.027
												40	.020
												41	.014
												42	.010
												43	.006
												44	.004
												45	.002

Table C. Wilcoxon Signed-Rank Distributions

(Lower Tail)

Sample Size													
10		11		12		13		14		15			
x	P	x	P	x	P	x	P	x	P	x	P	x	P
0	.001	0	.000	0	.000	0	.000	0	.000	0	.000	31	.053
1	.002	1	.001	1	.000	1	.000	1	.000	1	.000	32	.060
2	.003	2	.001	2	.001	2	.000	2	.000	2	.000	33	.068
3	.005	3	.002	3	.001	3	.001	3	.000	3	.000	34	.076
4	.007	4	.003	4	.002	4	.001	4	.000	4	.000	35	.084
5	.010	5	.005	5	.002	5	.001	5	.001	5	.000	36	.094
6	.014	6	.007	6	.003	6	.002	6	.001	6	.000	37	.104
7	.019	7	.009	7	.005	7	.002	7	.001	7	.001	38	.115
8	.024	8	.012	8	.006	8	.003	8	.002	8	.001	39	.126
9	.032	9	.016	9	.008	9	.004	9	.002	9	.001	40	.138
10	.042	10	.021	10	.010	10	.005	10	.003	10	.001	41	.151
11	.053	11	.027	11	.013	11	.007	11	.003	11	.002	42	.165
12	.065	12	.034	12	.017	12	.009	12	.004	12	.002	43	.180
13	.080	13	.042	13	.021	13	.011	13	.005	13	.003	44	.195
14	.097	14	.051	14	.026	14	.013	14	.007	14	.003	45	.211
15	.116	15	.062	15	.032	15	.016	15	.008	15	.004	46	.227
16	.138	16	.074	16	.039	16	.020	16	.010	16	.005	47	.244
17	.161	17	.087	17	.046	17	.024	17	.012	17	.006	48	.262
18	.188	18	.103	18	.055	18	.029	18	.015	18	.008	49	.281
19	.216	19	.120	19	.065	19	.034	19	.018	19	.009	50	.300
20	.246	20	.139	20	.076	20	.040	20	.021	20	.011	51	.319
21	.278	21	.160	21	.088	21	.047	21	.025	21	.013	52	.339
22	.312	22	.183	22	.102	22	.055	22	.029	22	.015	53	.360
23	.348	23	.207	23	.117	23	.064	23	.034	23	.018	54	.381
24	.385	24	.232	24	.133	24	.073	24	.039	24	.021	55	.402
25	.423	25	.260	25	.151	25	.084	25	.045	25	.024	56	.423
26	.461	26	.289	26	.170	26	.095	26	.052	26	.028	57	.445
27	.500	27	.319	27	.190	27	.108	27	.059	27	.032	58	.467
		28	.350	28	.212	28	.122	28	.068	28	.036	59	.489
		29	.382	29	.235	29	.137	29	.077	29	.042	60	.511
		30	.416	30	.259	30	.153	30	.086	30	.047		
		31	.449	31	.285	31	.170	31	.097				
		32	.483	32	.311	32	.188	32	.108				
		33	.517	33	.339	33	.207	33	.121				
				34	.367	34	.227	34	.134				
				35	.396	35	.249	35	.148				
				36	.425	36	.271	36	.163				
				37	.455	37	.294	37	.179				
				38	.485	38	.318	38	.196				
				39	.515	39	.342	39	.213				
						40	.368	40	.232				
						41	.393	41	.251				
						42	.420	42	.271				
						43	.446	43	.292				
						44	.473	44	.313				
						45	.500	45	.335				
								46	.357				
								47	.380				
								48	.404				
								49	.428				
								50	.452				
								51	.476				
								52	.500				

Table C. Wilcoxon Signed-Rank Distributions

(Upper Tail)

Sample Size													
10		11		12		13		14		15			
x	P	x	P	x	P	x	P	x	P	x	P	x	P
28	.500	33	.517	39	.515	46	.500	53	.500	60	.511	91	.042
29	.461	34	.483	40	.485	47	.473	54	.476	61	.489	92	.036
30	.423	35	.449	41	.455	48	.446	55	.452	62	.467	93	.032
31	.385	36	.416	42	.425	49	.420	56	.428	63	.445	94	.028
32	.348	37	.382	43	.396	50	.393	57	.404	64	.423	95	.024
33	.312	38	.350	44	.367	51	.368	58	.380	65	.402	96	.021
34	.278	39	.319	45	.339	52	.342	59	.357	66	.381	97	.018
35	.246	40	.289	46	.311	53	.318	60	.335	67	.360	98	.015
36	.216	41	.260	47	.285	54	.294	61	.313	68	.339	99	.013
37	.188	42	.232	48	.259	55	.271	62	.292	69	.319	100	.011
38	.161	43	.207	49	.235	56	.249	63	.271	70	.300	101	.009
39	.138	44	.183	50	.212	57	.227	64	.251	71	.281	102	.008
40	.116	45	.160	51	.190	58	.207	65	.232	72	.262	103	.006
41	.097	46	.139	52	.170	59	.188	66	.213	73	.244	104	.005
42	.080	47	.120	53	.151	60	.170	67	.196	74	.227	105	.004
43	.065	48	.103	54	.133	61	.153	68	.179	75	.211	106	.003
44	.053	49	.087	55	.117	62	.137	69	.163	76	.195	107	.003
45	.042	50	.074	56	.102	63	.122	70	.148	77	.180	108	.002
46	.032	51	.062	57	.088	64	.108	71	.134	78	.165	109	.002
47	.024	52	.051	58	.076	65	.095	72	.121	79	.151	110	.001
48	.019	53	.042	59	.065	66	.084	73	.108	80	.138	111	.001
49	.014	54	.034	60	.055	67	.073	74	.097	81	.126	112	.001
50	.010	55	.027	61	.046	68	.064	75	.086	82	.115	113	.001
51	.007	56	.021	62	.039	69	.055	76	.077	83	.104	114	.000
52	.005	57	.016	63	.032	70	.047	77	.068	84	.094	115	.000
53	.003	58	.012	64	.026	71	.040	78	.059	85	.084	116	.000
54	.002	59	.009	65	.021	72	.034	79	.052	86	.076	117	.000
55	.001	60	.007	66	.017	73	.029	80	.045	87	.068	118	.000
		61	.005	67	.013	74	.024	81	.039	88	.060	119	.000
		62	.003	68	.010	75	.020	82	.034	89	.053	120	.000
		63	.002	69	.008	76	.016	83	.029	90	.047		
		64	.001	70	.006	77	.013	84	.025				
		65	.001	71	.005	78	.011	85	.021				
		66	.000	72	.003	79	.009	86	.018				
				73	.002	80	.007	87	.015				
				74	.002	81	.005	88	.012				
				75	.001	82	.004	89	.010				
				76	.001	83	.003	90	.008				
				77	.000	84	.002	91	.007				
				78	.000	85	.002	92	.005				
						86	.001	93	.004				
						87	.001	94	.003				
						88	.001	95	.003				
						89	.000	96	.002				
						90	.000	97	.002				
						91	.000	98	.001				
								99	.001				
								100	.001				
								101	.000				
								102	.000				
								103	.000				
								104	.000				
								105	.000				

TABLE D

BINOMIAL DISTRIBUTIONS*

Table D gives the distribution of the number of successes, X, in n independent trials for which p = (probability of a success on a single trial) is constant. The table is cumulative from each extreme to, but not beyond, the mean, that is, the relation between the table and the distribution is, as for the following example for $n = 3$ and $p = .40$ (or $p = .60$).

Distribution

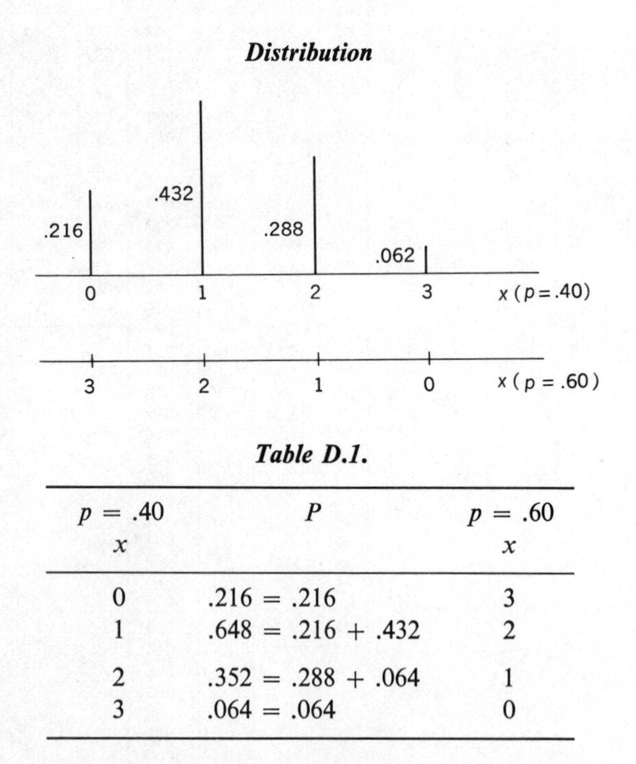

Table D.1.

$p = .40$ x	P	$p = .60$ x
0	.216 = .216	3
1	.648 = .216 + .432	2
2	.352 = .288 + .064	1
3	.064 = .064	0

* Adapted from "Tables of the Binomial Probability Distribution," *Applied Mathematics Series 6, National Bureau of Standards* (1950).

The range for n is $2 \leq n \leq 12$. For each n the values of p are .01, .05, .10 (by .05 to .90), .95, and .99. For values of p not included, linear interpolation gives an approximation. However, for small values of the tabled probability P, the relative error may be large. If the exact value is important, it can be obtained from the formula $\binom{n}{k} p^k(1 - p)^{n-k}$ for the probability associated with k, or from the National Bureau of Standards table (from which this table is an excerpt) in which $2 \leq n \leq 50$ and $p = .01$ and .02 (by .01 to .99).

For $n \geq 12$, the normal approximation or the Poisson approximation can be used. The mean and standard deviation for the normal approximation are

$$\mu = np,$$
$$\sigma = \sqrt{np(1 - p)},$$

and $P\{\text{number of successes} \leq k\}$ is approximately the area below $[(k + 1/2) - \mu]/\sigma$ from a unit normal curve (Table E). For np^2 small [see W. Feller, *An Introduction to Probability Theory and its Applications*, John Wiley and Sons, Inc., New York (1950) for a discussion of the Poisson approximation], the Poisson approximation can be used. Then $P\{\text{number of successes} \leq k\}$ is approximately the corresponding probability from a Poisson distribution (Table L) for $\lambda = np$. If $n(1 - p)^2$ is small (p is large), then $P\{\text{number of failures} \leq k\}$ is approximately the corresponding probability from a Poisson distribution (Table L) for $\lambda = n(1 - p)$.

Table D. Binomial Distributions

n = 2

$p = .01$		$p = .99$	$p = .30$		$p = .70$
x	P	x	x	P	x
0	.980	2	0	.490	2
1	.020	1	1	.510	1
2	.000	0	2	.090	0
$p = .05$		$p = .95$	$p = .35$		$p = .65$
x	P	x	x	P	x
0	.902	2	0	.422	2
1	.098	1	1	.578	1
2	.002	0	2	.122	0
$p = .10$		$p = .90$	$p = .40$		$p = .60$
x	P	x	x	P	x
0	.810	2	0	.360	2
1	.190	1	1	.640	1
2	.010	0	2	.160	0
$p = .15$		$p = .85$	$p = .45$		$p = .55$
x	P	x	x	P	x
0	.722	2	0	.302	2
1	.278	1	1	.698	1
2	.022	0	2	.202	0
$p = .20$		$p = .80$	$p = .50$		
x	P	x	x	P	
0	.640	2	0	.250	
			1	.750	
1	.360	1	1	.750	
2	.040	0	2	.250	
$p = .25$		$p = .75$			
x	P	x			
0	.562	2			
1	.438	1			
2	.062	0			

n = 3

$p = .01$		$p = .99$	$p = .20$		$p = .80$	$p = .40$		$p = .60$
x	P	x	x	P	x	x	P	x
0	.970	3	0	.512	3	0	.216	3
						1	.648	2
1	.030	2	1	.488	2			
2	.000	1	2	.104	1	2	.352	1
3	.000	0	3	.008	0	3	.064	0
$p = .05$		$p = .95$	$p = .25$		$p = .75$	$p = .45$		$p = .55$
x	P	x	x	P	x	x	P	x
0	.857	3	0	.422	3	0	.166	3
						1	.575	2
1	.143	2	1	.578	2			
2	.007	1	2	.156	1	2	.425	1
3	.000	0	3	.016	0	3	.091	0
$p = .10$		$p = .90$	$p = .30$		$p = .70$	$p = .50$		
x	P	x	x	P	x	x	P	
0	.729	3	0	.343	3	0	.125	
						1	.500	
1	.271	2	1	.657	2	2	.500	
2	.028	1	2	.216	1	3	.125	
3	.001	0	3	.027	0			
$p = .15$		$p = .85$	$p = .35$		$p = .65$			
x	P	x	x	P	x			
0	.614	3	0	.275	3			
			1	.725	2			
1	.386	2						
2	.061	1	2	.282	1			
3	.003	0	3	.043	0			

Table D. Binomial Distributions

$n = 4$

$p = .01$ x	P	$p = .99$ x	$p = .20$ x	P	$p = .80$ x	$p = .40$ x	P	$p = .60$ x
0	.961	4	0	.410	4	0	.130	4
						1	.475	3
1	.039	3	1	.590	3			
2	.001	2	2	.181	2	2	.525	2
3	.000	1	3	.027	1	3	.179	1
4	.000	0	4	.002	0	4	.026	0
$p = .05$ x	**P**	**$p = .95$ x**	**$p = .25$ x**	**P**	**$p = .75$ x**	**$p = .45$ x**	**P**	**$p = .55$ x**
0	.815	4	0	.316	4	0	.092	4
			1	.738	3	1	.391	3
1	.185	3	1	.684	3			
2	.014	2	2	.262	2	2	.609	2
3	.000	1	3	.051	1	3	.241	1
4	.000	0	4	.004	0	4	.041	0
$p = .10$ x	**P**	**$p = .90$ x**	**$p = .30$ x**	**P**	**$p = .70$ x**	**$p = .50$ x**	**P**	
0	.656	4	0	.240	4	0	.062	
			1	.652	3	1	.312	
						2	.688	
1	.344	3						
2	.052	2	2	.348	2	2	.688	
3	.004	1	3	.084	1	3	.312	
4	.000	0	4	.008	0	4	.062	
$p = .15$ x	**P**	**$p = .85$ x**	**$p = .35$ x**	**P**	**$p = .65$ x**			
0	.522	4	0	.179	4			
			1	.563	3			
1	.478	3						
2	.110	2	2	.437	2			
3	.012	1	3	.126	1			
4	.001	0	4	.015	0			

$n = 5$

$p = .01$ x	P	$p = .99$ x	$p = .20$ x	P	$p = .80$ x	$p = .40$ x	P	$p = .60$ x
0	.951	5	0	.328	5	0	.078	5
			1	.737	4	1	.337	4
						2	.683	3
1	.049	4	1	.672	4			
2	.001	3	2	.263	3	2	.663	3
3	.000	2	3	.058	2	3	.317	2
4	.000	1	4	.007	1	4	.087	1
5	.000	0	5	.000	0	5	.010	0
$p = .05$ x	**P**	**$p = .95$ x**	**$p = .25$ x**	**P**	**$p = .75$ x**	**$p = .45$ x**	**P**	**$p = .55$ x**
0	.774	5	0	.237	5	0	.050	5
			1	.633	4	1	.256	4
						2	.593	3
1	.226	4						
2	.023	3	2	.367	3			
3	.001	2	3	.104	2	3	.407	2
4	.000	1	4	.016	1	4	.131	1
5	.000	0	5	.001	0	5	.018	0
$p = .10$ x	**P**	**$p = .90$ x**	**$p = .30$ x**	**P**	**$p = .70$ x**	**$p = .50$ x**	**P**	
0	.590	5	0	.168	5	0	.031	
			1	.528	4	1	.188	
						2	.500	
1	.410	4						
2	.081	3	2	.472	3	3	.500	
3	.009	2	3	.163	2	4	.188	
4	.000	1	4	.031	1	5	.031	
5	.000	0	5	.002	0			
$p = .15$ x	**P**	**$p = .85$ x**	**$p = .35$ x**	**P**	**$p = .65$ x**			
0	.444	5	0	.116	5			
			1	.428	4			
1	.556	4						
2	.165	3	2	.572	3			
3	.027	2	3	.235	2			
4	.002	1	4	.054	1			
5	.000	0	5	.005	0			

Table D. Binomial Distributions

$n = 6$

p = .01 x	P	p = .99 x	p = .15 x	P	p = .85 x	p = .30 x	P	p = .70 x	p = .45 x	P	p = .55 x
0	.941	6	0	.377	6	0	.118	6	0	.028	6
						1	.420	5	1	.164	5
									2	.442	4
1	.059	5	1	.623	5						
2	.001	4	2	.224	4	2	.580	4			
3	.000	3	3	.047	3	3	.256	3	3	.558	3
4	.000	2	4	.006	2	4	.070	2	4	.255	2
5	.000	1	5	.000	1	5	.011	1	5	.069	1
6	.000	0	6	.000	0	6	.001	0	6	.008	0

p = .05 x	P	p = .95 x	p = .20 x	P	p = .80 x	p = .35 x	P	p = .65 x	p = .50 x	P
0	.735	6	0	.262	6	0	.075	6	0	.016
			1	.655	5	1	.319	5	1	.109
						2	.647	4	2	.344
									3	.656
1	.265	5								
2	.033	4	2	.345	4					
3	.002	3	3	.099	3	3	.353	3	3	.656
4	.000	2	4	.017	2	4	.117	2	4	.344
5	.000	1	5	.002	1	5	.022	1	5	.109
6	.000	0	6	.000	0	6	.002	0	6	.016

p = .10 x	P	p = .90 x	p = .25 x	P	p = .75 x	p = .40 x	P	p = .60 x
0	.531	6	0	.178	6	0	.047	6
			1	.534	5	1	.233	5
						2	.544	4
1	.469	5						
2	.114	4	2	.466	4			
3	.016	3	3	.169	3	3	.456	3
4	.001	2	4	.038	2	4	.179	2
5	.000	1	5	.005	1	5	.041	1
6	.000	0	6	.000	0	6	.004	0

Table D. Binomial Distributions

$n = 7$

p = .01 x	P	p = .99 x	p = .15 x	P	p = .85 x	p = .30 x	P	p = .70 x	p = .45 x	P	p = .55 x
0	.932	7	0	.321	7	0	.082	7	0	.015	7
			1	.717	6	1	.329	6	1	.102	6
						2	.647	5	2	.316	5
1	.068	6							3	.608	4
2	.002	5	2	.283	5						
3	.000	4	3	.074	4	3	.353	4			
4	.000	3	4	.012	3	4	.126	3	4	.392	3
5	.000	2	5	.001	2	5	.029	2	5	.153	2
6	.000	1	6	.000	1	6	.004	1	6	.036	1
7	.000	0	7	.000	0	7	.000	0	7	.004	0

p = .05 x	P	p = .95 x	p = .20 x	P	p = .80 x	p = .35 x	P	p = .65 x	p = .50 x	P
0	.698	7	0	.210	7	0	.049	7	0	.008
			1	.577	6	1	.234	6	1	.062
						2	.532	5	2	.227
1	.302	6							3	.500
2	.044	5	2	.423	5					
3	.004	4	3	.148	4	3	.468	4	4	.500
4	.000	3	4	.033	3	4	.200	3	5	.227
5	.000	2	5	.005	2	5	.056	2	6	.062
6	.000	1	6	.000	1	6	.009	1	7	.008
7	.000	0	7	.000	0	7	.001	0		

p = .10 x	P	p = .90 x	p = .25 x	P	p = .75 x	p = .40 x	P	p = .60 x
0	.478	7	0	.133	7	0	.028	7
			1	.445	6	1	.159	6
						2	.420	5
1	.522	6						
2	.150	5	2	.555	5			
3	.026	4	3	.244	4	3	.580	4
4	.003	3	4	.071	3	4	.290	3
5	.000	2	5	.013	2	5	.096	2
6	.000	1	6	.001	1	6	.019	1
7	.000	0	7	.000	0	7	.002	0

Table D. Binomial Distributions

$n = 8$

$p = .01$ x	P	$p = .99$ x	$p = .15$ x	P	$p = .85$ x	$p = .30$ x	P	$p = .70$ x	$p = .45$ x	P	$p = .55$ x
0	.923	8	0	.272	8	0	.058	8	0	.008	8
			1	.657	7	1	.255	7	1	.063	7
						2	.552	6	2	.220	6
1	.077	7							3	.477	5
2	.003	6	2	.343	6						
3	.000	5	3	.105	5	3	.448	5			
4	.000	4	4	.021	4	4	.194	4	4	.523	4
5	.000	3	5	.003	3	5	.058	3	5	.260	3
6	.000	2	6	.000	2	6	.011	2	6	.088	2
7	.000	1	7	.000	1	7	.001	1	7	.018	1
8	.000	0	8	.000	0	8	.000	0	8	.002	0

$p = .05$ x	P	$p = .95$ x	$p = .20$ x	P	$p = .80$ x	$p = .35$ x	P	$p = .65$ x	$p = .50$ x	P
0	.663	8	0	.168	8	0	.032	8	0	.004
			1	.503	7	1	.169	7	1	.035
						2	.428	6	2	.145
1	.337	7							3	.363
2	.057	6	2	.497	6				4	.637
3	.006	5	3	.203	5	3	.572	5		
4	.000	4	4	.056	4	4	.294	4	4	.637
5	.000	3	5	.010	3	5	.106	3	5	.363
6	.000	2	6	.001	2	6	.025	2	6	.145
7	.000	1	7	.000	1	7	.004	1	7	.035
8	.000	0	8	.000	0	8	.000	0	8	.004

$p = .10$ x	P	$p = .90$ x	$p = .25$ x	P	$p = .75$ x	$p = .40$ x	P	$p = .60$ x
0	.430	8	0	.100	8	0	.017	8
			1	.367	7	1	.106	7
			2	.679	6	2	.315	6
1	.570	7				3	.594	5
2	.187	6	2	.633	6			
3	.038	5	3	.321	5			
4	.005	4	4	.114	4	4	.406	4
5	.000	3	5	.027	3	5	.174	3
6	.000	2	6	.004	2	6	.050	2
7	.000	1	7	.000	1	7	.009	1
8	.000	0	8	.000	0	8	.001	0

Table D. Binomial Distributions

$n = 9$

$p = .01$		$p = .99$	$p = .15$		$p = .85$	$p = .30$		$p = .70$	$p = .45$		$p = .55$
x	P	x	x	P	x	x	P	x	x	P	x
0	.914	9	0	.232	9	0	.040	9	0	.005	9
			1	.599	8	1	.196	8	1	.039	8
						2	.463	7	2	.150	7
1	.086	8							3	.361	6
2	.003	7	2	.401	7				4	.621	5
3	.000	6	3	.141	6	3	.537	6			
4	.000	5	4	.034	5	4	.270	5			
5	.000	4	5	.006	4	5	.099	4	5	.379	4
6	.000	3	6	.001	3	6	.025	3	6	.166	3
7	.000	2	7	.000	2	7	.004	2	7	.050	2
8	.000	1	8	.000	1	8	.000	1	8	.009	1
9	.000	0	9	.000	0	9	.000	0	9	.001	0

$p = .05$		$p = .95$	$p = .20$		$p = .80$	$p = .35$		$p = .65$	$p = .50$	
x	P	x	x	P	x	x	P	x	x	P
0	.630	9	0	.134	9	0	.021	9	0	.002
			1	.436	8	1	.121	8	1	.020
						2	.337	7	2	.090
1	.370	8				3	.609	6	3	.254
2	.071	7	2	.564	7				4	.500
3	.008	6	3	.262	6					
4	.001	5	4	.086	5	4	.391	5	5	.500
5	.000	4	5	.020	4	5	.172	4	6	.254
6	.000	3	6	.003	3	6	.054	3	7	.090
7	.000	2	7	.000	2	7	.011	2	8	.020
8	.000	1	8	.000	1	8	.001	1	9	.002
9	.000	0	9	.000	0	9	.000	0		

$p = .10$		$p = .90$	$p = .25$		$p = .75$	$p = .40$		$p = .60$
x	P	x	x	P	x	x	P	x
0	.387	9	0	.075	9	0	.010	9
			1	.300	8	1	.071	8
			2	.601	7	2	.232	7
1	.613	8				3	.483	6
2	.225	7						
3	.053	6	3	.399	6			
4	.008	5	4	.166	5	4	.517	5
5	.001	4	5	.049	4	5	.267	4
6	.000	3	6	.010	3	6	.099	3
7	.000	2	7	.001	2	7	.025	2
8	.000	1	8	.000	1	8	.004	1
9	.000	0	9	.000	0	9	.000	0

Table D. Binomial Distributions

$n = 10$

$p = .01$ x	P	$p = .99$ x	$p = .15$ x	P	$p = .85$ x	$p = .30$ x	P	$p = .70$ x	$p = .45$ x	P	$p = .55$ x
0	.904	10	0	.197	10	0	.028	10	0	.003	10
			1	.544	9	1	.149	9	1	.023	9
						2	.383	8	2	.100	8
1	.096	9				3	.650	7	3	.266	7
2	.004	8	2	.456	8				4	.504	6
3	.000	7	3	.180	7	3	.617	7			
4	.000	6	4	.050	6	4	.350	6			
5	.000	5	5	.010	5	5	.150	5	5	.496	5
6	.000	4	6	.001	4	6	.047	4	6	.262	4
7	.000	3	7	.000	3	7	.011	3	7	.102	3
8	.000	2	8	.000	2	8	.002	2	8	.027	2
9	.000	1	9	.000	1	9	.000	1	9	.005	1
10	.000	0	10	.000	0	10	.000	0	10	.000	0

$p = .05$ x	P	$p = .95$ x	$p = .20$ x	P	$p = .80$ x	$p = .35$ x	P	$p = .65$ x	$p = .50$ x	P
0	.599	10	0	.107	10	0	.013	10	0	.001
			1	.376	9	1	.086	9	1	.011
			2	.678	8	2	.262	8	2	.055
1	.401	9				3	.514	7	3	.172
2	.086	8	2	.624	8				4	.377
3	.012	7	3	.322	7				5	.623
4	.001	6	4	.121	6	4	.486	6		
5	.000	5	5	.033	5	5	.249	5	5	.623
6	.000	4	6	.006	4	6	.095	4	6	.377
7	.000	3	7	.001	3	7	.026	3	7	.172
8	.000	2	8	.000	2	8	.005	2	8	.055
9	.000	1	9	.000	1	9	.001	1	9	.011
10	.000	0	10	.000	0	10	.000	0	10	.001

$p = .10$ x	P	$p = .90$ x	$p = .25$ x	P	$p = .75$ x	$p = .40$ x	P	$p = .60$ x
0	.349	10	0	.056	10	0	.006	10
1	.736	9	1	.244	9	1	.046	9
			2	.526	8	2	.167	8
1	.651	9				3	.382	7
2	.264	8				4	.633	6
3	.070	7	3	.474	7			
4	.013	6	4	.224	6	4	.618	6
5	.002	5	5	.078	5	5	.367	5
6	.000	4	6	.020	4	6	.166	4
7	.000	3	7	.004	3	7	.055	3
8	.000	2	8	.000	2	8	.012	2
9	.000	1	9	.000	1	9	.002	1
10	.000	0	10	.000	0	10	.000	0

Table D. Binomial Distributions

$n = 11$

$p = .01$ x	P	$p = .99$ x
0	.895	11
1	.105	10
2	.005	9
3	.000	8
4	.000	7
5	.000	6
6	.000	5
7	.000	4
8	.000	3
9	.000	2
10	.000	1
11	.000	0

$p = .15$ x	P	$p = .85$ x
0	.167	11
1	.492	10
2	.508	9
3	.221	8
4	.069	7
5	.016	6
6	.003	5
7	.000	4
8	.000	3
9	.000	2
10	.000	1
11	.000	0

$p = .30$ x	P	$p = .70$ x
0	.020	11
1	.113	10
2	.313	9
3	.570	8
4	.430	7
5	.210	6
6	.078	5
7	.022	4
8	.004	3
9	.001	2
10	.000	1
11	.000	0

$p = .45$ x	P	$p = .55$ x
0	.001	11
1	.014	10
2	.065	9
3	.191	8
4	.397	7
5	.603	6
6	.367	5
7	.174	4
8	.061	3
9	.015	2
10	.002	1
11	.000	0

$p = .05$ x	P	$p = .95$ x
0	.569	11
1	.431	10
2	.102	9
3	.015	8
4	.002	7
5	.000	6
6	.000	5
7	.000	4
8	.000	3
9	.000	2
10	.000	1
11	.000	0

$p = .20$ x	P	$p = .80$ x
0	.086	11
1	.322	10
2	.617	9
3	.383	8
4	.161	7
5	.050	6
6	.012	5
7	.002	4
8	.000	3
9	.000	2
10	.000	1
11	.000	0

$p = .35$ x	P	$p = .65$ x
0	.009	11
1	.061	10
2	.200	9
3	.426	8
4	.574	7
5	.332	6
6	.149	5
7	.050	4
8	.012	3
9	.002	2
10	.000	1
11	.000	0

$p = .50$ x	P
0	.000
1	.006
2	.033
3	.113
4	.274
5	.500
6	.500
7	.274
8	.113
9	.033
10	.006
11	.000

$p = .10$ x	P	$p = .90$ x
0	.314	11
1	.697	10
2	.303	9
3	.090	8
4	.019	7
5	.003	6
6	.000	5
7	.000	4
8	.000	3
9	.000	2
10	.000	1
11	.000	0

$p = .25$ x	P	$p = .75$ x
0	.042	11
1	.197	10
2	.455	9
3	.545	8
4	.287	7
5	.115	6
6	.034	5
7	.008	4
8	.001	3
9	.000	2
10	.000	1
11	.000	0

$p = .40$ x	P	$p = .60$ x
0	.004	11
1	.030	10
2	.119	9
3	.296	8
4	.533	7
5	.467	6
6	.247	5
7	.099	4
8	.029	3
9	.006	2
10	.001	1
11	.000	0

Table D. Binomial Distributions

$n = 12$

$p = .01$ x	P	$p = .99$ x	$p = .15$ x	P	$p = .85$ x	$p = .30$ x	P	$p = .70$ x	$p = .45$ x	P	$p = .55$ x
0	.886	12	0	.142	12	0	.014	12	0	.001	12
			1	.443	11	1	.085	11	1	.008	11
						2	.253	10	2	.042	10
1	.114	11				3	.493	9	3	.134	9
2	.006	10	2	.557	10				4	.304	8
3	.000	9	3	.264	9				5	.527	7
4	.000	8	4	.092	8	4	.507	8			
5	.000	7	5	.024	7	5	.276	7			
6	.000	6	6	.005	6	6	.118	6	6	.473	6
7	.000	5	7	.001	5	7	.039	5	7	.261	5
8	.000	4	8	.000	4	8	.009	4	8	.112	4
9	.000	3	9	.000	3	9	.002	3	9	.036	3
10	.000	2	10	.000	2	10	.000	2	10	.008	2
11	.000	1	11	.000	1	11	.000	1	11	.001	1
12	.000	0	12	.000	0	12	.000	0	12	.000	0

$p = .05$ x	P	$p = .95$ x	$p = .20$ x	P	$p = .80$ x	$p = .35$ x	P	$p = .65$ x	$p = .50$ x	P
0	.540	12	0	.069	12	0	.006	12	0	.000
			1	.275	11	1	.042	11	1	.003
			2	.558	10	2	.151	10	2	.019
1	.460	11				3	.347	9	3	.073
2	.118	10				4	.583	8	4	.194
3	.020	9	3	.442	9				5	.387
4	.002	8	4	.205	8				6	.613
5	.000	7	5	.073	7	5	.417	7		
6	.000	6	6	.019	6	6	.213	6	6	.613
7	.000	5	7	.004	5	7	.085	5	7	.387
8	.000	4	8	.001	4	8	.026	4	8	.194
9	.000	3	9	.000	3	9	.006	3	9	.073
10	.000	2	10	.000	2	10	.001	2	10	.019
11	.000	1	11	.000	1	11	.000	1	11	.003
12	.000	0	12	.000	0	12	.000	0	12	.000

$p = .10$ x	P	$p = .90$ x	$p = .25$ x	P	$p = .75$ x	$p = .40$ x	P	$p = .60$ x
0	.282	12	0	.032	12	0	.002	12
1	.659	11	1	.158	11	1	.020	11
			2	.391	10	2	.083	10
			3	.649	9	3	.225	9
2	.341	10				4	.438	8
3	.111	9	3	.609	9			
4	.026	8	4	.351	8			
5	.004	7	5	.158	7	5	.562	7
6	.001	6	6	.054	6	6	.335	6
7	.000	5	7	.014	5	7	.158	5
8	.000	4	8	.003	4	8	.057	4
9	.000	3	9	.000	3	9	.015	3
10	.000	2	10	.000	2	10	.003	2
11	.000	1	11	.000	1	11	.000	1
12	.000	0	12	.000	0	12	.000	0

TABLE E

UNIT NORMAL DISTRIBUTION*

Table E gives the area under the unit normal curve, $(1/\sqrt{2\pi})e^{-x^2/2}$, with mean $\mu = 0$ and standard deviation $\sigma = 1$. The table is cumulative from each extreme to the mean. The relation between the table and areas under the curve is as for the following figure.

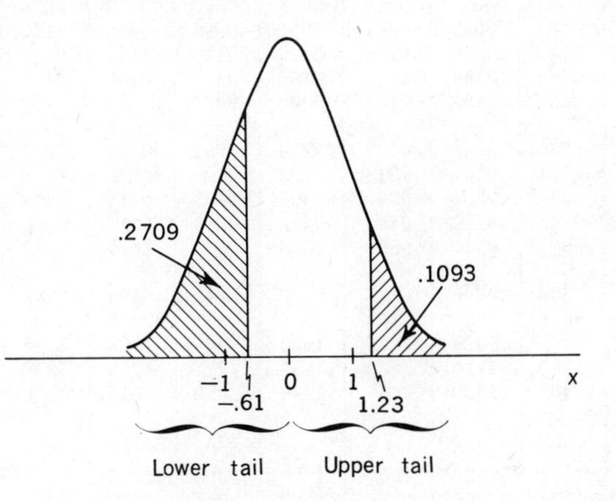

For $\mu \neq 0$ or $\sigma \neq 1$, areas for a number y_0 are found by entering the table with $x_0 = (y_0 - \mu)/\sigma$ as shown below.

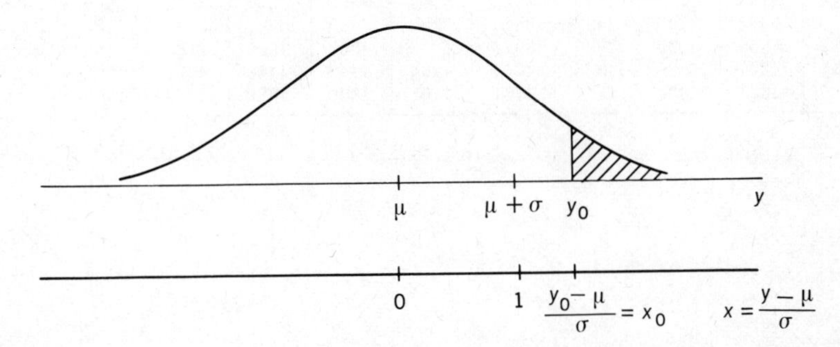

* With kind permission of the publisher, adapted from Table E of *Basic Concepts of Probability and Statistics*, by J. L. Hodges, Jr., and E. L. Lehmann, Holden-Day, Inc. (1964).

Table E. Unit Normal Distribution

(Lower Tail)

x	.09	.08	.07	.06	.05	.04	.03	.02	.01	.00
−3.4	.0002	.0003	.0003	.0003	.0003	.0003	.0003	.0003	.0003	.0003
−3.3	.0003	.0004	.0004	.0004	.0004	.0004	.0004	.0005	.0005	.0005
−3.2	.0005	.0005	.0005	.0006	.0006	.0006	.0006	.0006	.0007	.0007
−3.1	.0007	.0007	.0008	.0008	.0008	.0008	.0009	.0009	.0009	.0010
−3.0	.0010	.0010	.0011	.0011	.0011	.0012	.0012	.0013	.0013	.0013
−2.9	.0014	.0014	.0015	.0015	.0016	.0016	.0017	.0018	.0018	.0019
−2.8	.0019	.0020	.0021	.0021	.0022	.0023	.0023	.0024	.0025	.0026
−2.7	.0026	.0027	.0028	.0029	.0030	.0031	.0032	.0033	.0034	.0035
−2.6	.0036	.0037	.0038	.0039	.0040	.0041	.0043	.0044	.0045	.0047
−2.5	.0048	.0049	.0051	.0052	.0054	.0055	.0057	.0059	.0060	.0062
−2.4	.0064	.0066	.0068	.0069	.0071	.0073	.0075	.0078	.0080	.0082
−2.3	.0084	.0087	.0089	.0091	.0094	.0096	.0099	.0102	.0104	.0107
−2.2	.0110	.0113	.0116	.0119	.0122	.0125	.0129	.0132	.0136	.0139
−2.1	.0143	.0146	.0150	.0154	.0158	.0162	.0166	.0170	.0174	.0179
−2.0	.0183	.0188	.0192	.0197	.0202	.0207	.0212	.0217	.0222	.0228
−1.9	.0233	.0239	.0244	.0250	.0256	.0262	.0268	.0274	.0281	.0287
−1.8	.0294	.0301	.0307	.0314	.0322	.0329	.0336	.0344	.0351	.0359
−1.7	.0367	.0375	.0384	.0392	.0401	.0409	.0418	.0427	.0436	.0446
−1.6	.0455	.0465	.0475	.0485	.0495	.0505	.0516	.0526	.0537	.0548
−1.5	.0559	.0571	.0582	.0594	.0606	.0618	.0630	.0643	.0655	.0668
−1.4	.0681	.0694	.0708	.0721	.0735	.0749	.0764	.0778	.0793	.0808
−1.3	.0823	.0838	.0853	.0869	.0885	.0901	.0918	.0934	.0951	.0968
−1.2	.0985	.1003	.1020	.1038	.1056	.1075	.1093	.1112	.1131	.1151
−1.1	.1170	.1190	.1210	.1230	.1251	.1271	.1292	.1314	.1335	.1357
−1.0	.1379	.1401	.1423	.1446	.1469	.1492	.1515	.1539	.1562	.1587
− .9	.1611	.1635	.1660	.1685	.1711	.1736	.1762	.1788	.1814	.1841
− .8	.1867	.1894	.1922	.1949	.1977	.2005	.2033	.2061	.2090	.2119
− .7	.2148	.2177	.2206	.2236	.2266	.2296	.2327	.2358	.2389	.2420
− .6	.2451	.2483	.2514	.2546	.2578	.2611	.2643	.2676	.2709	.2743
− .5	.2776	.2810	.2843	.2877	.2912	.2946	.2981	.3015	.3050	.3085
− .4	.3121	.3156	.3192	.3228	.3264	.3300	.3336	.3372	.3409	.3446
− .3	.3483	.3520	.3557	.3594	.3632	.3669	.3707	.3745	.3783	.3821
− .2	.3859	.3897	.3936	.3974	.4013	.4052	.4090	.4129	.4168	.4207
− .1	.4247	.4286	.4325	.4364	.4404	.4443	.4483	.4522	.4562	.4602
− .0	.4641	.4681	.4721	.4761	.4801	.4840	.4880	.4920	.4960	.5000

Table E. Unit Normal Distribution

(Upper Tail)

x	.00	.01	.02	.03	.04	.05	.06	.07	.08	.09
.0	.5000	.4960	.4920	.4880	.4840	.4801	.4761	.4721	.4681	.4641
.1	.4602	.4562	.4522	.4483	.4443	.4404	.4364	.4325	.4286	.4247
.2	.4207	.4168	.4129	.4090	.4052	.4013	.3974	.3936	.3897	.3859
.3	.3821	.3783	.3745	.3707	.3669	.3632	.3594	.3557	.3520	.3483
.4	.3446	.3409	.3372	.3336	.3300	.3264	.3228	.3192	.3156	.3121
.5	.3085	.3050	.3015	.2981	.2946	.2912	.2877	.2843	.2810	.2776
.6	.2743	.2709	.2676	.2643	.2611	.2578	.2546	.2514	.2483	.2451
.7	.2420	.2389	.2358	.2327	.2296	.2266	.2236	.2206	.2177	.2148
.8	.2119	.2090	.2061	.2033	.2005	.1977	.1949	.1922	.1894	.1867
.9	.1841	.1814	.1788	.1762	.1736	.1711	.1685	.1660	.1635	.1611
1.0	.1587	.1562	.1539	.1515	.1492	.1469	.1446	.1423	.1401	.1379
1.1	.1357	.1335	.1314	.1292	.1271	.1251	.1230	.1210	.1190	.1170
1.2	.1151	.1131	.1112	.1093	.1075	.1056	.1038	.1020	.1003	.0985
1.3	.0968	.0951	.0934	.0918	.0901	.0885	.0869	.0853	.0838	.0823
1.4	.0808	.0793	.0778	.0764	.0749	.0735	.0721	.0708	.0694	.0681
1.5	.0668	.0655	.0643	.0630	.0618	.0606	.0594	.0582	.0571	.0559
1.6	.0548	.0537	.0526	.0516	.0505	.0495	.0485	.0475	.0465	.0455
1.7	.0446	.0436	.0427	.0418	.0409	.0401	.0392	.0384	.0375	.0367
1.8	.0359	.0351	.0344	.0336	.0329	.0322	.0314	.0307	.0301	.0294
1.9	.0287	.0281	.0274	.0268	.0262	.0256	.0250	.0244	.0239	.0233
2.0	.0228	.0222	.0217	.0212	.0207	.0202	.0197	.0192	.0188	.0183
2.1	.0179	.0174	.0170	.0166	.0162	.0158	.0154	.0150	.0146	.0143
2.2	.0139	.0136	.0132	.0129	.0125	.0122	.0119	.0116	.0113	.0110
2.3	.0107	.0104	.0102	.0099	.0096	.0094	.0091	.0089	.0087	.0084
2.4	.0082	.0080	.0078	.0075	.0073	.0071	.0069	.0068	.0066	.0064
2.5	.0062	.0060	.0059	.0057	.0055	.0054	.0052	.0051	.0049	.0048
2.6	.0047	.0045	.0044	.0043	.0041	.0040	.0039	.0038	.0037	.0036
2.7	.0035	.0034	.0033	.0032	.0031	.0030	.0029	.0028	.0027	.0026
2.8	.0026	.0025	.0024	.0023	.0023	.0022	.0021	.0021	.0020	.0019
2.9	.0019	.0018	.0018	.0017	.0016	.0016	.0015	.0015	.0014	.0014
3.0	.0013	.0013	.0013	.0012	.0012	.0011	.0011	.0011	.0010	.0010
3.1	.0010	.0009	.0009	.0009	.0008	.0008	.0008	.0008	.0007	.0007
3.2	.0007	.0007	.0006	.0006	.0006	.0006	.0006	.0005	.0005	.0005
3.3	.0005	.0005	.0005	.0004	.0004	.0004	.0004	.0004	.0004	.0003
3.4	.0003	.0003	.0003	.0003	.0003	.0003	.0003	.0003	.0003	.0002

TABLE F

KRUSKAL-WALLIS, RIJKOORT k-SAMPLE DISTRIBUTIONS*

Table F gives the distribution of

$$\frac{R_1^2}{n_1} + \frac{R_2^2}{n_2} + \cdots + \frac{R_k^2}{n_k}$$

$(= X)$, where $R_1, R_2, \ldots, R_k$ are the sums of the ranks for randomly chosen groups of sizes $n_1, n_2, \ldots, n_k$ from a set of $N = \sum n_i$ scores. The table is cumulative from the right-hand extreme to zero. That is, the relation between the table and the distribution is as for the following example, where $k = 3$ and $n_1 = 1$, $n_2 = 1$, $n_3 = 4$. Table F also gives the distribution of the equivalent function

$$H = \frac{12}{N(N+1)} \sum \frac{(R_i - n_i\bar{R})^2}{n_i},$$

which is sometimes computed instead of X.

Distribution

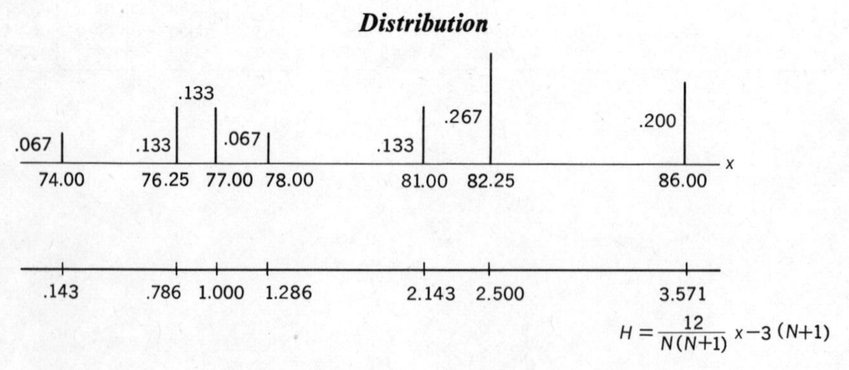

* Computed at the Centre de Calcul de l'Université de Montréal.

Table F.1

H	x	P
.143	74.00	1.000
.786	76.25	.933
1.000	77.00	.800
1.286	78.00	.667 = .200 + .267 + .133 + .067
2.143	81.00	.600
2.500	82.25	.467 = .200 + .267
3.571	86.00	.200

The ranges for k and $n_1, n_2, \ldots, n_k$ are $k = 3$, $1 \leq n_1 \leq n_2 \leq n_3 \leq 5$ (for $k = 2$, this test can be carried out as a two-sided Wilcoxon, Mann–Whitney test).

If all sample sizes are reasonably large, a χ^2 or an F approximation can be used. The distribution of H can be approximated by a χ^2 distribution with $k - 1$ degrees of freedom; that is, $P\{H \leq t\}$ is approximately the area below t from the χ^2 distribution (Table H) with $k - 1$ degrees of freedom. The F approximation is an approximation of the distribution of $[(M - k + 1)/(k - 1)][H/(M - H)]$ by an F distribution with

$$\nu_1 = 2(k - 1)\frac{(k - 1)(M - k + 1) - V}{MV} \quad \text{and} \quad \nu_2 = \frac{M - k + 1}{k - 1}\nu_1$$

degrees of freedom, where

$$M = \frac{N^3 - \sum n_i^3}{N(N + 1)}$$

and

$$V = 2(k - 1) - \frac{2[3k^2 - 6k + N(2k^2 - 6k + 1)]}{5N(N + 1)} - \frac{6}{5}\sum \frac{1}{n_i}.$$

In particular, $P\{H \leq t\}$ is approximately the area below t from an F distribution (Table I) with ν_1 and ν_2 degrees of freedom. For intermediate sample sizes, the F approximation will, in general, give a little better approximation, especially for small P values.

If there are ties, the above approximations, with H replaced by

$$H' = \frac{12(N-1)}{N^3 - D}\left[X - \frac{N(N+1)^2}{4}\right],$$

can be used if all sample sizes are reasonably large and the sizes of the ties not too disparate. (See the introduction to Table B for a definition of ranks, sizes of ties, and D.) For $k = 3$ and $1 \leq n_1 \leq n_2 \leq n_3 \leq 5$ and a few small ties, interpolation in Table F gives an approximation. If there are a few large ties, the distribution can be computed exactly by enumerating all the divisions of the (tied) ranks into groups of sizes $n_1, n_2, \ldots, n_k$ and evaluating X for each.

Table F. Kruskal-Wallis, Rijkoort k-Sample Distributions

(Upper Tail)

$n_1 = 1$	$n_2 = 1$	$n_3 = 2$
H	x	P
.300	25.50	1.000
1.800	28.00	.833
2.700	29.50	.500

$n_1 = 1$	$n_2 = 1$	$n_3 = 3$
H	x	P
.533	46.33	1.000
.800	47.00	.800
2.133	50.33	.700
3.200	53.00	.300

$n_1 = 1$	$n_2 = 1$	$n_3 = 4$
H	x	P
.143	74.00	1.000
.786	76.25	.933
1.000	77.00	.800
1.286	78.00	.667
2.143	81.00	.600
2.500	82.25	.467
3.571	86.00	.200

$n_1 = 1$	$n_2 = 1$	$n_3 = 5$
H	x	P
.257	113.20	1.000
.429	114.00	.905
1.029	116.80	.857
1.114	117.20	.762
1.457	118.80	.667
1.714	120.00	.571
2.314	122.80	.524
2.829	125.20	.333
3.857	130.00	.143

$n_1 = 1$	$n_2 = 2$	$n_3 = 2$
H	x	P
.000	45.00	1.000
.400	46.00	.933
.600	46.50	.867
1.400	48.50	.733
2.000	50.00	.600
2.400	51.00	.467
3.000	52.50	.333
3.600	54.00	.200

$n_1 = 1$	$n_2 = 2$	$n_3 = 3$
H	x	P
.095	73.83	1.000
.238	74.33	.933
.429	75.00	.900
.810	76.33	.833
.857	76.50	.800
1.238	77.83	.700
1.381	78.33	.600
1.952	80.33	.567
2.143	81.00	.533
2.381	81.83	.433
3.095	84.33	.267
3.524	85.83	.200
3.857	87.00	.133
4.286	88.50	.100

$n_1 = 1$	$n_2 = 2$	$n_3 = 4$
H	x	P
.000	112.00	1.000
.161	112.75	.971
.268	113.25	.933
.321	113.50	.895
.536	114.50	.857
.643	115.00	.819
.696	115.25	.800
1.018	116.75	.781
1.071	117.00	.743
1.125	117.25	.705
1.286	118.00	.667
1.393	118.50	.629
1.446	118.75	.590
1.875	120.75	.533
2.036	121.50	.495
2.143	122.00	.476
2.250	122.50	.457
2.411	123.25	.400
2.571	124.00	.305
2.786	125.00	.286
2.893	125.50	.267
3.161	126.75	.190
3.696	129.25	.171
3.750	129.50	.133
4.018	130.75	.114
4.500	133.00	.076
4.821	134.50	.057

$n_1 = 1$	$n_2 = 2$	$n_3 = 5$
H	x	P
.050	162.30	1.000
.133	162.80	.964
.200	163.20	.940
.450	164.70	.905
.467	164.80	.845
.583	165.50	.821
.667	166.00	.798
.717	166.30	.774
1.000	168.00	.750
1.117	168.70	.738
1.200	169.20	.714
1.250	169.50	.655
1.383	170.30	.619
1.533	171.20	.583
1.783	172.70	.560
1.800	172.80	.536
1.917	173.50	.488
2.050	174.30	.464
2.333	176.00	.429
2.450	176.70	.393
2.717	178.30	.298
2.800	178.80	.286
2.867	179.20	.214
3.133	180.80	.202
3.333	182.00	.190
3.383	182.30	.179
3.783	184.70	.131
4.050	186.30	.119
4.200	187.20	.095
4.450	188.70	.071
5.000	192.00	.048
5.250	193.50	.036

Table F. Kruskal-Wallis, Rijkoort k-Sample Distributions

(Upper Tail)

$n_1 = 1$	$n_2 = 3$	$n_3 = 3$
H	x	P
.000	112.00	1.000
.143	112.67	.986
.286	113.33	.957
.571	114.67	.871
1.000	116.67	.771
1.143	117.33	.743
1.286	118.00	.600
1.571	119.33	.571
2.000	121.33	.514
2.286	122.67	.486
2.571	124.00	.329
3.143	126.67	.243
3.286	127.33	.157
4.000	130.67	.129
4.571	133.33	.100
5.143	136.00	.043

$n_1 = 1$	$n_2 = 3$	$n_3 = 4$
H	x	P
.056	162.33	1.000
.097	162.58	.971
.208	163.25	.950
.333	164.00	.921
.431	164.58	.900
.500	165.00	.871
.556	165.33	.843
.764	166.58	.786
.875	167.25	.743
1.097	168.58	.721
1.208	169.25	.707
1.222	169.33	.679
1.389	170.33	.629
1.431	170.58	.557
1.764	172.58	.536
1.833	173.00	.514
1.875	173.25	.471
2.097	174.58	.457
2.208	175.25	.443
2.333	176.00	.429
2.431	176.58	.371
2.722	178.33	.300
2.764	178.58	.229
3.000	180.00	.221
3.097	180.58	.214
3.208	181.25	.200
3.222	181.33	.157
3.764	184.58	.136
3.889	185.33	.129
4.056	186.33	.093
4.097	186.58	.086
4.208	187.25	.079
4.764	190.58	.071
5.000	192.00	.057
5.208	193.25	.050
5.389	194.33	.036
5.833	197.00	.021

$n_1 = 1$	$n_2 = 3$	$n_3 = 5$
H	x	P
.000	225.00	1.000
.071	225.53	.992
.160	226.20	.972
.178	226.33	.952
.284	227.13	.929
.338	227.53	.889
.551	229.13	.869
.604	229.53	.853
.640	229.80	.833
.711	230.33	.770
.818	231.13	.750
.960	232.20	.730
1.084	233.13	.694
1.138	233.53	.683
1.351	235.13	.651
1.404	235.53	.611
1.440	235.80	.591
1.511	236.33	.571
1.600	237.00	.560
1.671	237.53	.520
1.778	238.33	.488
1.884	239.13	.480
1.938	239.53	.468
2.044	240.33	.452
2.204	241.53	.437
2.400	243.00	.413
2.418	243.13	.405
2.560	244.20	.341
2.844	246.33	.258
2.951	247.13	.218
3.040	247.80	.210
3.218	249.13	.190
3.271	249.53	.183
3.378	250.33	.143
3.484	251.13	.135
3.804	253.53	.131
3.840	253.80	.123
4.018	255.13	.095
4.284	257.13	.083
4.338	257.53	.079
4.551	259.13	.075
4.711	260.33	.056
4.871	261.53	.052
4.960	262.20	.048
5.404	265.53	.044
5.440	265.80	.036
5.760	268.20	.028
6.044	270.33	.020
6.400	273.00	.012

Table F. Kruskal-Wallis, Rijkoort k-Sample Distributions

(Upper Tail)

$n_1 = 1$	$n_2 = 4$	$n_3 = 4$
H	x	P
.000	225.00	1.000
.067	225.50	.987
.167	226.25	.968
.267	227.00	.930
.300	227.25	.911
.567	229.25	.873
.600	229.50	.835
.667	230.00	.803
.867	231.50	.759
.967	232.25	.721
1.067	233.00	.689
1.200	234.00	.676
1.367	235.25	.644
1.500	236.25	.600
1.667	237.50	.537
1.767	238.25	.498
2.167	241.25	.460
2.267	242.00	.410
2.400	243.00	.384
2.467	243.50	.349
2.667	245.00	.305
2.700	245.25	.260
2.967	247.25	.235
3.000	247.50	.222
3.267	249.50	.178
3.367	250.25	.171
3.467	251.00	.152
3.867	254.00	.121
3.900	254.25	.108
4.067	255.50	.102
4.167	256.25	.083
4.267	257.00	.070
4.800	261.00	.067
4.867	261.50	.054
4.967	262.25	.048
5.100	263.25	.041
5.667	267.50	.035
6.000	270.00	.029
6.167	271.25	.022
6.667	275.00	.010

$n_1 = 1$ $n_2 = 4$ $n_3 = 5$					
H	x	P	H	x	P
.033	302.80	1.000	2.591	326.25	.300
.060	303.05	.983	2.651	326.80	.286
.104	303.45	.968	2.896	329.05	.251
.186	304.20	.952	2.913	329.20	.222
.273	305.00	.938	2.940	329.45	.216
.278	305.05	.922	3.000	330.00	.208
.295	305.20	.906	3.087	330.80	.194
.360	305.80	.890	3.158	331.45	.187
.409	306.25	.875	3.240	332.20	.183
.540	307.45	.848	3.349	333.20	.151
.622	308.20	.821	3.524	334.80	.146
.731	309.20	.806	3.595	335.45	.138
.758	309.45	.794	3.682	336.25	.132
.796	309.80	.778	3.813	337.45	.110
.818	310.00	.762	3.960	338.80	.102
.906	310.80	.730	3.987	339.05	.098
.933	311.05	.719	4.206	341.05	.095
.976	311.45	.690	4.222	341.20	.087
1.151	313.05	.676	4.287	341.80	.071
1.167	313.20	.665	4.549	344.20	.067
1.195	313.45	.651	4.636	345.00	.063
1.233	313.80	.640	4.724	345.80	.060
1.342	314.80	.625	4.833	346.80	.059
1.369	315.05	.614	4.860	347.05	.056
1.495	316.20	.606	4.986	348.20	.044
1.500	316.25	.589	5.078	349.05	.041
1.587	317.05	.562	5.160	349.80	.038
1.604	317.20	.535	5.515	353.05	.037
1.669	317.80	.517	5.558	353.45	.035
1.778	318.80	.498	5.596	353.80	.033
1.806	319.05	.483	5.733	355.05	.027
1.849	319.45	.468	5.776	355.45	.025
1.931	320.20	.460	5.858	356.20	.024
2.040	321.20	.441	5.864	356.25	.022
2.067	321.45	.432	5.967	357.20	.021
2.106	321.80	.419	6.431	361.45	.019
2.242	323.05	.406	6.578	362.80	.016
2.286	323.45	.400	6.818	365.00	.013
2.455	325.00	.394	6.840	365.20	.011
2.460	325.05	.354	6.954	366.25	.008
2.504	325.45	.346	7.364	370.00	.005

Table F. Kruskal-Wallis, Rijkoort k-Sample Distributions

(Upper Tail)

$n_1 = 1 \quad n_2 = 5 \quad n_3 = 5$					
H	x	P	H	x	P
.000	396.00	1.000	2.909	428.00	.242
.036	396.40	.994	2.946	428.40	.227
.109	397.20	.982	3.236	431.60	.188
.146	397.60	.956	3.346	432.80	.168
.182	398.00	.944	3.382	433.20	.161
.327	399.60	.920	3.527	434.80	.141
.400	400.40	.885	3.600	435.60	.132
.436	400.80	.872	3.636	436.00	.116
.546	402.00	.847	3.927	439.20	.113
.582	402.40	.802	4.036	440.40	.105
.727	404.00	.792	4.109	441.20	.086
.836	405.20	.771	4.182	442.00	.082
.909	406.00	.752	4.400	444.40	.076
.982	406.80	.716	4.546	446.00	.074
1.127	408.40	.669	4.800	448.80	.056
1.200	409.20	.646	4.909	450.00	.053
1.309	410.40	.630	5.127	452.40	.046
1.346	410.80	.605	5.236	453.60	.039
1.600	413.60	.584	5.636	458.00	.033
1.636	414.00	.571	5.709	458.80	.030
1.709	414.80	.509	5.782	459.60	.027
1.746	415.20	.493	6.000	462.00	.022
1.782	415.60	.468	6.146	463.60	.019
1.927	417.20	.462	6.509	467.60	.018
2.000	418.00	.438	6.546	468.00	.015
2.146	419.60	.422	6.582	468.40	.014
2.182	420.00	.411	6.727	470.00	.012
2.327	421.60	.379	6.836	471.20	.011
2.436	422.80	.374	7.309	476.40	.009
2.509	423.60	.361	7.527	478.80	.008
2.582	424.40	.314	7.746	481.20	.005
2.727	426.00	.286	8.182	486.00	.002

$n_1 = 2 \quad n_2 = 2 \quad n_3 = 2$		
H	x	P
.000	73.50	1.000
.286	74.50	.933
.857	76.50	.800
1.143	77.50	.667
2.000	80.50	.533
2.571	82.50	.400
3.429	85.50	.333
3.714	86.50	.200
4.571	89.50	.067

$n_1 = 2 \quad n_2 = 2 \quad n_3 = 3$		
H	x	P
.000	112.00	1.000
.179	112.83	.971
.214	113.00	.895
.500	114.33	.857
.607	114.83	.800
.714	115.33	.743
.857	116.00	.686
1.179	117.50	.657
1.357	118.33	.619
1.464	118.83	.562
1.607	119.50	.524
1.929	121.00	.467
2.000	121.33	.438
2.214	122.33	.419
2.429	123.33	.381
2.464	123.50	.362
2.750	124.83	.324
2.857	125.33	.286
3.179	126.83	.267
3.429	128.00	.248
3.607	128.83	.238
3.750	129.50	.219
3.929	130.33	.181
4.464	132.83	.105
4.500	133.00	.067
4.714	134.00	.048
5.357	137.00	.029

Table F. Kruskal-Wallis, Rijkoort k-Sample Distributions

(Upper Tail)

$n_1 = 2$	$n_2 = 2$	$n_3 = 4$
H	x	P
.000	162.00	1.000
.125	162.75	.971
.167	163.00	.914
.333	164.00	.890
.458	164.75	.862
.500	165.00	.814
.667	166.00	.757
.792	166.75	.733
1.000	168.00	.695
1.125	168.75	.657
1.333	170.00	.581
1.500	171.00	.552
1.792	172.75	.514
1.833	173.00	.486
2.000	174.00	.448
2.125	174.75	.410
2.458	176.75	.362
2.667	178.00	.333
2.792	178.75	.314
2.833	179.00	.295
3.000	180.00	.276
3.125	180.75	.248
3.167	181.00	.229
3.458	182.75	.210
3.667	184.00	.190
4.000	186.00	.181
4.125	186.75	.152
4.167	187.00	.105
4.458	188.75	.100
4.500	189.00	.090
5.125	192.75	.052
5.333	194.00	.033
5.500	195.00	.024
6.000	198.00	.014

$n_1 = 2$	$n_2 = 2$	$n_3 = 5$
H	x	P
.000	225.00	1.000
.093	225.70	.984
.133	226.00	.937
.240	226.80	.913
.360	227.70	.881
.373	227.80	.844
.533	229.00	.807
.573	229.30	.791
.773	230.80	.759
.840	231.30	.722
.893	231.70	.685
.960	232.20	.653
1.093	233.20	.638
1.200	234.00	.606
1.373	235.30	.590
1.440	235.80	.563
1.493	236.20	.542
1.533	236.50	.516
1.693	237.70	.495
1.800	238.50	.474
2.133	241.00	.452
2.160	241.20	.444
2.173	241.30	.402
2.293	242.20	.381
2.333	242.50	.365
2.373	242.80	.344
2.693	245.20	.317
2.760	245.70	.296
2.973	247.30	.275
3.093	248.20	.265
3.133	248.50	.254
3.240	249.30	.238
3.333	250.00	.206
3.360	250.20	.196
3.573	251.80	.185
3.773	253.30	.175
3.840	253.80	.164
3.973	254.80	.159
4.093	255.70	.148
4.200	256.50	.138
4.293	257.20	.122
4.373	257.80	.090
4.573	259.30	.085
4.800	261.00	.063
4.893	261.70	.061
5.040	262.80	.056
5.160	263.70	.034
5.693	267.70	.029
6.000	270.00	.019
6.133	271.00	.013
6.533	274.00	.008

$n_1 = 2$	$n_2 = 3$	$n_3 = 3$
H	x	P
.028	162.17	1.000
.111	162.67	.968
.222	163.33	.946
.250	163.50	.896
.472	164.83	.864
.556	165.33	.807
.694	166.17	.757
1.000	168.00	.686
1.111	168.67	.671
1.139	168.83	.600
1.361	170.17	.564
1.444	170.67	.539
1.806	172.83	.511
1.889	173.33	.446
2.000	174.00	.425
2.028	174.17	.396
2.250	175.50	.368
2.472	176.83	.357
2.694	178.17	.329
2.778	178.67	.307
2.889	179.33	.286
3.139	180.83	.243
3.222	181.33	.221
3.361	182.17	.207
3.778	184.67	.200
3.806	184.83	.179
4.028	186.17	.164
4.111	186.67	.129
4.250	187.50	.121
4.556	189.33	.100
4.694	190.17	.093
5.000	192.00	.075
5.139	192.83	.061
5.361	194.17	.032
5.556	195.33	.025
6.250	199.50	.011

Table F. Kruskal-Wallis, Rijkoort k-Sample Distributions

(Upper Tail)

$n_1 = 2$ $n_2 = 3$ $n_3 = 4$					
H	x	P	H	x	P
.000	225.00	1.000	2.911	246.83	.271
.078	225.58	.987	2.944	247.08	.262
.100	225.75	.965	3.011	247.58	.256
.111	225.83	.944	3.100	248.25	.251
.244	226.83	.922	3.111	248.33	.238
.278	227.08	.902	3.244	249.33	.232
.311	227.33	.881	3.278	249.58	.225
.344	227.58	.862	3.300	249.75	.216
.400	228.00	.844	3.311	249.83	.203
.444	228.33	.829	3.444	250.83	.197
.544	229.08	.811	3.478	251.08	.190
.600	229.50	.794	3.544	251.58	.184
.611	229.58	.770	3.600	252.00	.175
.700	230.25	.756	3.811	253.58	.168
.778	230.83	.722	3.844	253.83	.163
.811	231.08	.703	3.911	254.33	.159
.900	231.75	.689	3.978	254.83	.156
.978	232.33	.673	4.000	255.00	.149
1.000	232.50	.660	4.078	255.58	.140
1.078	233.08	.627	4.200	256.50	.137
1.111	233.33	.614	4.278	257.08	.124
1.178	233.83	.602	4.311	257.33	.108
1.244	234.33	.586	4.378	257.83	.105
1.344	235.08	.571	4.444	258.33	.102
1.378	235.33	.559	4.511	258.83	.098
1.411	235.58	.548	4.544	259.08	.086
1.500	236.25	.537	4.611	259.58	.083
1.600	237.00	.511	4.711	260.33	.079
1.611	237.08	.502	4.811	261.08	.076
1.678	237.58	.478	4.878	261.58	.073
1.711	237.83	.468	4.900	261.75	.071
1.778	238.33	.457	4.978	262.33	.059
1.844	238.83	.448	5.078	263.08	.057
1.944	239.58	.437	5.144	263.58	.054
2.144	241.08	.417	5.378	265.33	.052
2.178	241.33	.406	5.400	265.50	.051
2.200	241.50	.398	5.444	265.83	.046
2.211	241.58	.376	5.500	266.25	.040
2.244	241.83	.368	5.611	267.08	.032
2.378	242.83	.357	5.800	268.50	.030
2.400	243.00	.346	6.000	270.00	.024
2.411	243.08	.338	6.111	270.83	.021
2.444	243.33	.329	6.144	271.08	.014
2.500	243.75	.321	6.300	272.25	.011
2.778	245.83	.294	6.444	273.33	.008
2.800	246.00	.284	7.000	277.50	.005

Table F. Kruskal-Wallis, Rijkoort k-Sample Distributions

(Upper Tail)

	$n_1 = 2$			$n_2 = 3$			$n_3 = 5$	
H	x	P	H	x	P	H	x	P
.014	302.63	1.000	2.076	321.53	.396	4.214	341.13	.125
.069	303.13	.981	2.106	321.80	.389	4.233	341.30	.122
.113	303.53	.966	2.196	322.63	.382	4.258	341.53	.120
.131	303.70	.951	2.251	323.13	.375	4.331	342.20	.117
.142	303.80	.932	2.294	323.53	.368	4.378	342.63	.113
.273	305.00	.917	2.367	324.20	.362	4.494	343.70	.101
.276	305.03	.901	2.454	325.00	.356	4.651	345.13	.091
.306	305.30	.886	2.458	325.03	.350	4.694	345.53	.089
.331	305.53	.869	2.469	325.13	.336	4.724	345.80	.087
.364	305.83	.855	2.487	325.30	.330	4.727	345.83	.085
.451	306.63	.823	2.546	325.83	.321	4.814	346.63	.071
.549	307.53	.807	2.633	326.63	.294	4.869	347.13	.067
.567	307.70	.794	2.749	327.70	.287	4.913	347.53	.063
.622	308.20	.781	2.818	328.33	.279	4.942	347.80	.062
.636	308.33	.769	2.894	329.03	.269	5.076	349.03	.060
.713	309.03	.743	2.924	329.30	.263	5.087	349.13	.053
.724	309.13	.714	2.949	329.53	.257	5.106	349.30	.052
.767	309.53	.703	2.978	329.80	.252	5.251	350.63	.049
.887	310.63	.692	3.022	330.20	.248	5.349	351.53	.046
.942	311.13	.680	3.069	330.63	.243	5.513	353.03	.044
1.014	311.80	.659	3.167	331.53	.237	5.524	353.13	.043
1.058	312.20	.648	3.186	331.70	.233	5.542	353.30	.041
1.091	312.50	.638	3.273	332.50	.222	5.727	355.00	.037
1.149	313.03	.616	3.331	333.03	.211	5.742	355.13	.034
1.178	313.30	.593	3.342	333.13	.206	5.786	355.53	.033
1.276	314.20	.579	3.386	333.53	.201	5.804	355.70	.033
1.324	314.63	.569	3.414	333.80	.193	5.949	357.03	.026
1.378	315.13	.537	3.506	334.63	.189	6.004	357.53	.025
1.451	315.80	.529	3.546	335.00	.183	6.033	357.80	.024
1.586	317.03	.519	3.604	335.53	.175	6.091	358.33	.021
1.596	317.13	.510	3.676	336.20	.171	6.124	358.63	.020
1.614	317.30	.502	3.767	337.03	.167	6.294	360.20	.017
1.713	318.20	.483	3.778	337.13	.159	6.386	361.03	.016
1.727	318.33	.474	3.822	337.53	.156	6.414	361.30	.015
1.760	318.63	.459	3.909	338.33	.152	6.818	365.00	.012
1.814	319.13	.451	3.942	338.63	.146	6.822	365.03	.010
1.858	319.53	.444	3.996	339.13	.139	6.909	365.83	.009
1.876	319.70	.429	4.058	339.70	.137	6.949	366.20	.006
2.022	321.03	.420	4.069	339.80	.132	7.182	368.33	.004
2.033	321.13	.403	4.204	341.03	.129	7.636	372.50	.002

Table F. Kruskal-Wallis, Rijkoort k-Sample Distributions

(Upper Tail)

$n_1 = 2$ $n_2 = 4$ $n_3 = 4$					
H	x	P	H	x	P
.000	302.50	1.000	3.136	331.25	.228
.054	303.00	.988	3.327	333.00	.220
.082	303.25	.970	3.354	333.25	.210
.191	304.25	.940	3.464	334.25	.192
.218	304.50	.910	3.491	334.50	.185
.273	305.00	.893	3.682	336.25	.180
.327	305.50	.879	3.764	337.00	.166
.409	306.25	.848	3.818	337.50	.152
.491	307.00	.820	4.009	339.25	.142
.627	308.25	.779	4.364	342.50	.125
.736	309.25	.757	4.418	343.00	.120
.764	309.50	.712	4.446	343.25	.103
.873	310.50	.685	4.554	344.25	.098
.954	311.25	.671	4.582	344.50	.094
1.091	312.50	.651	4.691	345.50	.080
1.146	313.00	.638	4.773	346.25	.075
1.173	313.25	.596	4.854	347.00	.071
1.282	314.25	.577	4.991	348.25	.065
1.309	314.50	.559	5.127	349.50	.057
1.364	315.00	.537	5.236	350.50	.052
1.582	317.00	.526	5.454	352.50	.046
1.636	317.50	.510	5.509	353.00	.044
1.718	318.25	.488	5.536	353.25	.042
1.827	319.25	.441	5.646	354.25	.039
1.964	320.50	.426	5.727	355.00	.034
2.046	321.25	.400	5.946	357.00	.028
2.236	323.00	.386	6.082	358.25	.025
2.264	323.25	.375	6.327	360.50	.024
2.373	324.25	.363	6.409	361.25	.022
2.454	325.00	.338	6.546	362.50	.020
2.509	325.50	.317	6.600	363.00	.017
2.673	327.00	.301	6.627	363.25	.016
2.809	328.25	.281	6.873	365.50	.011
2.918	329.25	.272	7.036	367.00	.006
2.946	329.50	.263	7.282	369.25	.004
3.054	330.50	.239	7.854	374.50	.002

Table F. Kruskal-Wallis, Rijkoort k-Sample Distributions

(Upper Tail)

$n_1 = 2$ $n_2 = 4$ $n_3 = 5$

H	x	P	H	x	P	H	x	P	H	x	P
.000	396.00	1.000	1.618	413.80	.491	3.454	434.00	.193	5.300	454.30	.048
.041	396.45	.992	1.641	414.05	.485	3.523	434.75	.190	5.314	454.45	.046
.064	396.70	.979	1.664	414.30	.479	3.564	435.20	.187	5.414	455.55	.045
.068	396.75	.965	1.704	414.75	.472	3.568	435.25	.184	5.518	456.70	.043
.141	397.55	.952	1.750	415.25	.465	3.573	435.30	.181	5.523	456.75	.042
.154	397.70	.939	1.754	415.30	.459	3.618	435.80	.178	5.564	457.20	.038
.164	397.80	.926	1.814	415.95	.452	3.641	436.05	.175	5.641	458.05	.037
.223	398.45	.913	1.823	416.05	.432	3.654	436.20	.170	5.664	458.30	.036
.254	398.80	.902	1.973	417.70	.427	3.700	436.70	.164	5.754	459.30	.035
.273	399.00	.891	2.004	418.05	.420	3.704	436.75	.160	5.823	460.05	.034
.300	399.30	.880	2.018	418.20	.403	3.791	437.70	.157	5.891	460.80	.032
.323	399.55	.866	2.073	418.80	.398	3.800	437.80	.151	5.954	461.50	.030
.368	400.05	.855	2.114	419.25	.392	3.818	438.00	.148	5.973	461.70	.029
.404	400.45	.832	2.118	419.30	.387	3.823	438.05	.145	6.004	462.05	.026
.504	401.55	.823	2.141	419.55	.381	3.864	438.50	.143	6.041	462.45	.025
.518	401.70	.812	2.164	419.80	.375	4.041	440.45	.139	6.068	462.75	.025
.541	401.95	.801	2.223	420.45	.371	4.064	440.70	.135	6.118	463.30	.024
.564	402.20	.791	2.254	420.80	.366	4.073	440.80	.133	6.141	463.55	.023
.573	402.30	.781	2.291	421.20	.361	4.091	441.00	.130	6.223	464.45	.022
.614	402.75	.759	2.318	421.50	.351	4.141	441.55	.128	6.368	466.05	.021
.618	402.80	.749	2.323	421.55	.346	4.154	441.70	.126	6.391	466.30	.021
.654	403.20	.740	2.391	422.30	.335	4.200	442.20	.123	6.473	467.20	.020
.723	403.95	.730	2.454	423.00	.329	4.223	442.45	.121	6.504	467.55	.020
.791	404.70	.720	2.473	423.20	.324	4.250	442.75	.119	6.541	467.95	.017
.841	405.25	.710	2.504	423.55	.320	4.323	443.55	.116	6.550	468.05	.017
.864	405.50	.701	2.550	424.05	.315	4.364	444.00	.114	6.564	468.20	.016
.891	405.80	.691	2.618	424.80	.311	4.368	444.05	.112	6.654	469.20	.016
.904	405.95	.683	2.700	425.70	.306	4.404	444.45	.110	6.723	469.95	.015
.914	406.05	.674	2.723	425.95	.301	4.500	445.50	.104	6.904	471.95	.014
.950	406.45	.657	2.754	426.30	.296	4.518	445.70	.101	6.914	472.05	.013
.954	406.50	.649	2.768	426.45	.285	4.541	445.95	.098	7.000	473.00	.013
1.018	407.20	.640	2.773	426.50	.273	4.614	446.75	.090	7.018	473.20	.012
1.023	407.25	.632	2.868	427.55	.267	4.664	447.30	.088	7.064	473.70	.012
1.050	407.55	.623	2.891	427.80	.262	4.768	448.45	.079	7.118	474.30	.010
1.091	408.00	.614	2.904	427.95	.258	4.791	448.70	.078	7.204	475.25	.009
1.200	409.20	.607	2.914	428.05	.249	4.800	448.80	.076	7.254	475.80	.009
1.204	409.25	.599	2.973	428.70	.246	4.818	449.00	.074	7.291	476.20	.008
1.268	409.95	.592	3.023	429.25	.237	4.841	449.25	.072	7.450	477.95	.007
1.291	410.20	.576	3.050	429.55	.234	4.868	449.55	.071	7.500	478.50	.007
1.314	410.45	.569	3.064	429.70	.231	4.950	450.45	.063	7.568	479.25	.006
1.318	410.50	.562	3.118	430.30	.226	5.073	451.80	.061	7.573	479.30	.005
1.391	411.30	.554	3.164	430.80	.221	5.154	452.70	.059	7.773	481.50	.004
1.414	411.55	.537	3.268	431.95	.217	5.164	452.80	.053	7.814	481.95	.003
1.450	411.95	.529	3.314	432.45	.214	5.254	453.80	.052	8.018	484.20	.002
1.473	412.20	.521	3.341	432.75	.208	5.268	453.95	.051	8.114	485.25	.001
1.518	412.70	.507	3.364	433.00	.200	5.273	454.00	.049	8.591	490.50	.001
1.591	413.50	.499	3.414	433.55	.197						

Table F. Kruskal-Wallis, Rijkoort k-Sample Distributions

(Upper Tail)

$n_1 = 2$			$n_2 = 5$			$n_3 = 5$		
H	x	P	H	x	P	H	x	P
.008	507.10	1.000	2.408	538.30	.330	5.246	575.20	.051
.046	507.60	.988	2.469	539.10	.323	5.338	576.40	.047
.069	507.90	.978	2.538	540.00	.315	5.546	579.10	.045
.077	508.00	.966	2.592	540.70	.300	5.585	579.60	.041
.169	509.20	.947	2.662	541.60	.292	5.608	579.90	.040
.192	509.50	.928	2.754	542.80	.286	5.615	580.00	.039
.254	510.30	.896	2.777	543.10	.279	5.708	581.20	.037
.323	511.20	.877	2.908	544.80	.276	5.731	581.50	.036
.377	511.90	.859	2.962	545.50	.270	5.792	582.30	.032
.415	512.40	.830	3.023	546.30	.243	5.915	583.90	.030
.446	512.80	.822	3.031	546.40	.234	5.985	584.80	.028
.538	514.00	.807	3.123	547.60	.228	6.077	586.00	.027
.562	514.30	.775	3.146	547.90	.218	6.231	588.00	.026
.623	515.10	.759	3.331	550.30	.210	6.346	589.50	.025
.692	516.00	.749	3.369	550.80	.203	6.354	589.60	.021
.746	516.70	.735	3.392	551.10	.198	6.446	590.80	.020
.808	517.50	.719	3.492	552.40	.190	6.469	591.10	.019
.815	517.60	.688	3.515	552.70	.186	6.654	593.50	.017
.908	518.80	.674	3.577	553.50	.181	6.692	594.00	.016
.931	519.10	.661	3.646	554.40	.169	6.815	595.60	.015
1.115	521.50	.638	3.738	555.60	.165	6.838	595.90	.014
1.154	522.00	.611	3.769	556.00	.163	6.969	597.60	.013
1.185	522.40	.593	3.862	557.20	.150	7.023	598.30	.013
1.277	523.60	.569	3.885	557.50	.146	7.185	600.40	.012
1.300	523.90	.558	4.015	559.20	.136	7.208	600.70	.011
1.362	524.70	.552	4.069	559.90	.132	7.269	601.50	.010
1.431	525.60	.539	4.131	560.70	.130	7.338	602.40	.010
1.485	526.30	.528	4.138	560.80	.127	7.392	603.10	.009
1.523	526.80	.516	4.231	562.00	.124	7.462	604.00	.008
1.554	527.20	.506	4.254	562.30	.114	7.577	605.50	.007
1.646	528.40	.496	4.438	564.70	.106	7.762	607.90	.007
1.669	528.70	.486	4.477	565.20	.103	7.923	610.00	.006
1.731	529.50	.463	4.508	565.60	.100	8.008	611.10	.006
1.854	531.10	.445	4.623	567.10	.097	8.077	612.00	.006
1.915	531.90	.434	4.685	567.90	.092	8.131	612.70	.005
1.923	532.00	.424	4.754	568.80	.084	8.169	613.20	.003
2.015	533.20	.407	4.808	569.50	.081	8.292	614.80	.003
2.038	533.50	.398	4.846	570.00	.073	8.377	615.90	.002
2.223	535.90	.379	4.877	570.40	.068	8.562	618.30	.002
2.262	536.40	.374	4.992	571.90	.066	8.685	619.90	.001
2.285	536.70	.363	5.054	572.70	.060	8.938	623.20	.001
2.292	536.80	.353	5.177	574.30	.057	9.423	629.50	.000
2.385	538.00	.345	5.238	575.10	.054			

Table F. Kruskal-Wallis, Rijkoort k-Sample Distributions

(Upper Tail)

$n_1 = 3$	$n_2 = 3$	$n_3 = 3$
H	x	P
.000	225.00	1.000
.089	225.67	.993
.267	227.00	.929
.356	227.67	.879
.622	229.67	.829
.800	231.00	.721
1.067	233.00	.664
1.156	233.67	.629
1.422	235.67	.543
1.689	237.67	.511
1.867	239.00	.439
2.222	241.67	.382
2.400	243.00	.361
2.489	243.67	.339
2.756	245.67	.296
3.200	249.00	.254
3.289	249.67	.232
3.467	251.00	.196
3.822	253.67	.168
4.267	257.00	.139
4.356	257.67	.132
4.622	259.67	.100
5.067	263.00	.086
5.422	265.67	.071
5.600	267.00	.050
5.689	267.67	.029
5.956	269.67	.025
6.489	273.67	.011
7.200	279.00	.004

$n_1 = 3$		$n_2 = 3$		$n_3 = 4$	
H	x	P	H	x	P
.018	302.67	1.000	3.254	332.33	.212
.046	302.92	.984	3.364	333.33	.203
.118	303.58	.970	3.391	333.58	.196
.164	304.00	.941	3.609	335.58	.188
.200	304.33	.925	3.682	336.25	.180
.336	305.58	.895	3.754	336.92	.178
.346	305.67	.869	3.800	337.33	.165
.409	306.25	.842	3.836	337.67	.150
.454	306.67	.830	3.973	338.92	.143
.482	306.92	.817	4.046	339.58	.132
.636	308.33	.791	4.091	340.00	.126
.700	308.92	.764	4.273	341.67	.123
.746	309.33	.717	4.336	342.25	.117
.891	310.67	.690	4.382	342.67	.111
1.064	312.25	.656	4.564	344.33	.106
1.073	312.33	.633	4.700	345.58	.101
1.136	312.92	.611	4.709	345.67	.092
1.182	313.33	.602	4.818	346.67	.085
1.209	313.58	.582	4.846	346.92	.081
1.427	315.58	.541	5.000	348.33	.074
1.473	316.00	.523	5.064	348.92	.070
1.573	316.92	.513	5.109	349.33	.068
1.618	317.33	.497	5.254	350.67	.064
1.654	317.67	.481	5.436	352.33	.062
1.791	318.92	.447	5.500	352.92	.056
1.800	319.00	.433	5.573	353.58	.053
1.864	319.58	.415	5.727	355.00	.050
2.091	321.67	.402	5.791	355.58	.046
2.200	322.67	.389	5.936	356.92	.036
2.227	322.92	.368	5.982	357.33	.034
2.300	323.58	.351	6.018	357.67	.027
2.382	324.33	.326	6.154	358.92	.025
2.518	325.58	.314	6.300	360.25	.023
2.527	325.67	.303	6.564	362.67	.017
2.664	326.92	.291	6.664	363.58	.014
2.882	328.92	.281	6.709	364.00	.013
2.927	329.33	.273	6.746	364.33	.010
2.954	329.58	.253	7.000	366.67	.006
3.027	330.25	.244	7.318	369.58	.004
3.073	330.67	.234	7.436	370.67	.002
3.109	331.00	.220	8.018	376.00	.001

Table F. Kruskal-Wallis, Rijkoort k-Sample Distributions

(Upper Tail)

$n_1 = 3$			$n_2 = 3$			$n_3 = 5$		
H	x	P	H	x	P	H	x	P
.000	396.00	1.000	2.182	420.00	.358	4.909	450.00	.079
.048	396.53	.994	2.194	420.13	.352	5.042	451.47	.077
.061	396.67	.970	2.315	421.47	.342	5.079	451.87	.069
.133	397.47	.958	2.376	422.13	.334	5.103	452.13	.067
.170	397.87	.948	2.594	424.53	.315	5.212	453.33	.065
.194	398.13	.926	2.667	425.33	.306	5.261	453.87	.062
.242	398.67	.902	2.679	425.47	.298	5.346	454.80	.058
.315	399.47	.890	2.715	425.87	.291	5.442	455.87	.055
.376	400.13	.868	2.836	427.20	.267	5.503	456.53	.053
.412	400.53	.847	2.861	427.47	.258	5.515	456.67	.051
.436	400.80	.826	2.970	428.67	.242	5.648	458.13	.049
.533	401.87	.804	3.079	429.87	.239	5.770	459.47	.047
.546	402.00	.794	3.103	430.13	.232	5.867	460.53	.042
.594	402.53	.783	3.333	432.67	.218	6.012	462.13	.040
.679	403.47	.765	3.382	433.20	.215	6.061	462.67	.033
.776	404.53	.725	3.394	433.33	.209	6.109	463.20	.032
.848	405.33	.686	3.442	433.87	.196	6.194	464.13	.027
.970	406.67	.668	3.467	434.13	.184	6.303	465.33	.026
1.042	407.47	.641	3.503	434.53	.179	6.315	465.47	.021
1.079	407.87	.624	3.576	435.33	.173	6.376	466.13	.020
1.103	408.13	.609	3.648	436.13	.167	6.533	467.87	.019
1.200	409.20	.594	3.709	436.80	.162	6.594	468.53	.019
1.212	409.33	.587	3.879	438.67	.156	6.715	469.87	.014
1.261	409.87	.571	3.927	439.20	.149	6.776	470.53	.013
1.442	411.87	.539	4.012	440.13	.144	6.861	471.47	.012
1.503	412.53	.526	4.048	440.53	.139	6.982	472.80	.011
1.515	412.67	.512	4.170	441.87	.135	7.079	473.87	.009
1.527	412.80	.505	4.194	442.13	.126	7.333	476.67	.008
1.576	413.33	.491	4.242	442.67	.122	7.467	478.13	.008
1.648	414.13	.478	4.303	443.33	.117	7.503	478.53	.006
1.746	415.20	.450	4.315	443.47	.113	7.515	478.67	.005
1.770	415.47	.437	4.412	444.53	.109	7.636	480.00	.004
1.867	416.53	.425	4.533	445.87	.097	7.879	482.67	.003
2.012	418.13	.414	4.679	447.47	.094	8.048	484.53	.002
2.048	418.53	.403	4.776	448.53	.090	8.242	486.67	.001
2.061	418.67	.393	4.800	448.80	.087	8.727	492.00	.001
2.133	419.47	.382	4.848	449.33	.085			
2.170	419.87	.367	4.861	449.47	.082			

Table F. Kruskal-Wallis, Rijkoort k-Sample Distributions

(Upper Tail)

	$n_1 = 3$			$n_2 = 4$			$n_3 = 4$	
H	x	P	H	x	P	H	x	P
.000	396.00	1.000	2.326	421.58	.334	5.144	452.58	.073
.046	396.50	.993	2.394	422.33	.325	5.182	453.00	.068
.053	396.58	.981	2.417	422.58	.315	5.212	453.33	.066
.144	397.58	.959	2.598	424.58	.306	5.296	454.25	.063
.167	397.83	.937	2.636	425.00	.290	5.303	454.33	.061
.182	398.00	.925	2.667	425.33	.281	5.326	454.58	.058
.212	398.33	.913	2.712	425.83	.276	5.386	455.25	.054
.326	399.58	.890	2.848	427.33	.269	5.500	456.50	.052
.348	399.83	.870	2.894	427.83	.261	5.576	457.33	.051
.386	400.25	.850	2.909	428.00	.254	5.598	457.58	.049
.409	400.50	.829	2.932	428.25	.250	5.667	458.33	.047
.477	401.25	.819	2.962	428.58	.243	5.803	459.83	.045
.576	402.33	.799	3.076	429.83	.230	5.932	461.25	.043
.598	402.58	.779	3.136	430.50	.218	5.962	461.58	.041
.659	403.25	.761	3.326	432.58	.212	6.000	462.00	.040
.667	403.33	.742	3.386	433.25	.207	6.046	462.50	.039
.712	403.83	.731	3.394	433.33	.201	6.053	462.58	.035
.727	404.00	.713	3.417	433.58	.195	6.144	463.58	.032
.848	405.33	.704	3.477	434.25	.190	6.167	463.83	.031
.894	405.83	.685	3.576	435.33	.184	6.182	464.00	.030
.932	406.25	.668	3.598	435.58	.178	6.348	465.83	.027
.962	406.58	.651	3.659	436.25	.173	6.386	466.25	.026
1.053	407.58	.635	3.682	436.50	.162	6.394	466.33	.025
1.076	407.83	.620	3.727	437.00	.160	6.409	466.50	.023
1.136	408.50	.604	3.803	437.83	.154	6.417	466.58	.022
1.144	408.58	.597	3.848	438.33	.150	6.546	468.00	.021
1.296	410.25	.582	3.932	439.25	.145	6.659	469.25	.020
1.303	410.33	.568	3.962	439.58	.140	6.712	469.83	.019
1.326	410.58	.553	4.144	441.58	.135	6.727	470.00	.018
1.394	411.33	.539	4.167	441.83	.131	6.962	472.58	.017
1.417	411.58	.524	4.212	442.33	.129	7.000	473.00	.016
1.500	412.50	.510	4.296	443.25	.125	7.053	473.58	.014
1.546	413.00	.503	4.303	443.33	.121	7.076	473.83	.011
1.598	413.58	.490	4.326	443.58	.116	7.136	474.50	.011
1.636	414.00	.477	4.348	443.83	.113	7.144	474.58	.010
1.682	414.50	.470	4.409	444.50	.106	7.212	475.33	.009
1.750	415.25	.457	4.477	445.25	.102	7.477	478.25	.006
1.803	415.83	.444	4.546	446.00	.099	7.598	479.58	.004
1.909	417.00	.421	4.576	446.33	.097	7.636	480.00	.004
1.962	417.58	.409	4.598	446.58	.093	7.682	480.50	.003
2.053	418.58	.388	4.712	447.83	.090	7.848	482.33	.003
2.144	419.58	.378	4.750	448.25	.087	8.227	486.50	.002
2.227	420.50	.368	4.894	449.83	.084	8.326	487.58	.001
2.296	421.25	.354	5.053	451.58	.078	8.909	494.00	.001
2.303	421.33	.344						

Table F. Kruskal-Wallis, Rijkoort k-Sample Distributions

(Upper Tail)

$n_1 = 3$			$n_2 = 4$			$n_3 = 5$		
H	x	P	H	x	P	H	x	P
.010	507.13	1.000	1.241	523.13	.572	2.580	540.53	.291
.030	507.38	.990	1.246	523.20	.566	2.641	541.33	.288
.060	507.78	.981	1.260	523.38	.553	2.645	541.38	.284
.081	508.05	.972	1.349	524.53	.548	2.676	541.78	.281
.092	508.20	.963	1.414	525.38	.542	2.677	541.80	.278
.118	508.53	.953	1.445	525.78	.537	2.737	542.58	.271
.138	508.80	.944	1.465	526.05	.522	2.830	543.78	.266
.173	509.25	.935	1.472	526.13	.516	2.887	544.53	.263
.180	509.33	.926	1.487	526.33	.506	2.908	544.80	.260
.214	509.78	.917	1.506	526.58	.495	2.949	545.33	.251
.241	510.13	.908	1.558	527.25	.490	2.953	545.38	.248
.256	510.33	.900	1.568	527.38	.479	2.964	545.53	.240
.265	510.45	.891	1.599	527.78	.475	3.010	546.13	.238
.276	510.58	.882	1.615	528.00	.465	3.035	546.45	.235
.323	511.20	.874	1.718	529.33	.460	3.087	547.13	.232
.337	511.38	.865	1.733	529.53	.455	3.092	547.20	.222
.368	511.78	.857	1.753	529.78	.450	3.106	547.38	.219
.426	512.53	.841	1.780	530.13	.446	3.137	547.78	.216
.430	512.58	.833	1.814	530.58	.441	3.195	548.53	.214
.462	513.00	.825	1.856	531.13	.437	3.256	549.33	.209
.491	513.38	.817	1.906	531.78	.427	3.260	549.38	.206
.503	513.53	.809	1.927	532.05	.423	3.312	550.05	.204
.542	514.05	.784	1.938	532.20	.418	3.318	550.13	.199
.549	514.13	.777	1.964	532.53	.400	3.353	550.58	.197
.626	515.13	.769	1.968	532.58	.396	3.414	551.38	.194
.645	515.38	.754	1.985	532.80	.391	3.445	551.78	.192
.692	516.00	.746	2.019	533.25	.387	3.462	552.00	.190
.727	516.45	.738	2.030	533.38	.383	3.496	552.45	.188
.737	516.58	.716	2.060	533.78	.379	3.503	552.53	.183
.799	517.38	.709	2.103	534.33	.375	3.506	552.58	.181
.830	517.78	.696	2.112	534.45	.366	3.568	553.38	.179
.831	517.80	.689	2.169	535.20	.358	3.580	553.53	.177
.856	518.13	.667	2.272	536.53	.354	3.599	553.78	.173
.953	519.38	.660	2.308	537.00	.350	3.626	554.13	.169
1.004	520.05	.654	2.337	537.38	.346	3.703	555.13	.165
1.041	520.53	.641	2.349	537.53	.343	3.722	555.38	.163
1.045	520.58	.628	2.368	537.78	.335	3.753	555.78	.161
1.062	520.80	.621	2.388	538.05	.332	3.773	556.05	.159
1.103	521.33	.615	2.395	538.13	.321	3.785	556.20	.156
1.106	521.38	.609	2.472	539.13	.318	3.810	556.53	.152
1.118	521.53	.602	2.481	539.25	.311	3.831	556.80	.150
1.137	521.78	.590	2.491	539.38	.307	3.865	557.25	.148
1.164	522.13	.584	2.522	539.78	.301	3.876	557.38	.146
1.188	522.45	.578	2.573	540.45	.294	3.958	558.45	.144

Table F. Kruskal-Wallis, Rijkoort k-Sample Distributions

(Upper Tail)

$n_1 = 3$			$n_2 = 4$			$n_3 = 5$	(continued)	
H	x	P	H	x	P	H	x	P
4.015	559.20	.140	5.426	577.53	.057	7.010	598.13	.015
4.030	559.38	.137	5.549	579.13	.054	7.096	599.25	.014
4.060	559.78	.134	5.568	579.38	.052	7.106	599.38	.014
4.122	560.58	.132	5.619	580.05	.051	7.188	600.45	.013
4.154	561.00	.131	5.631	580.20	.050	7.195	600.53	.012
4.180	561.33	.125	5.656	580.53	.049	7.256	601.33	.012
4.195	561.53	.124	5.660	580.58	.048	7.260	601.38	.012
4.235	562.05	.121	5.677	580.80	.047	7.272	601.53	.012
4.241	562.13	.119	5.718	581.33	.046	7.291	601.78	.011
4.276	562.58	.117	5.722	581.38	.045	7.318	602.13	.011
4.318	563.13	.115	5.753	581.78	.044	7.395	603.13	.011
4.327	563.25	.112	5.780	582.13	.043	7.445	603.78	.010
4.368	563.78	.110	5.804	582.45	.041	7.465	604.05	.010
4.419	564.45	.109	5.814	582.58	.040	7.477	604.20	.009
4.426	564.53	.107	5.862	583.20	.040	7.523	604.80	.007
4.487	565.33	.106	5.876	583.38	.039	7.568	605.38	.007
4.522	565.78	.105	5.964	584.53	.038	7.641	606.33	.007
4.523	565.80	.103	6.026	585.33	.038	7.708	607.20	.006
4.549	566.13	.099	6.030	585.38	.037	7.753	607.78	.006
4.564	566.33	.097	6.060	585.78	.037	7.810	608.53	.006
4.645	567.38	.095	6.087	586.13	.035	7.876	609.38	.006
4.676	567.78	.093	6.164	587.13	.035	7.887	609.53	.006
4.754	568.80	.091	6.173	587.25	.034	7.906	609.78	.005
4.789	569.25	.089	6.231	588.00	.033	7.927	610.05	.005
4.810	569.53	.088	6.265	588.45	.032	8.030	611.38	.005
4.830	569.78	.083	6.272	588.53	.030	8.060	611.78	.004
4.856	570.13	.082	6.337	589.38	.030	8.077	612.00	.004
4.881	570.45	.081	6.368	589.78	.029	8.118	612.53	.004
4.891	570.58	.078	6.369	589.80	.029	8.122	612.58	.004
4.939	571.20	.075	6.395	590.13	.026	8.215	613.80	.003
4.953	571.38	.074	6.410	590.33	.025	8.256	614.33	.003
4.983	571.78	.073	6.491	591.38	.025	8.430	616.58	.002
5.041	572.53	.072	6.522	591.78	.024	8.446	616.80	.002
5.045	572.58	.071	6.542	592.05	.023	8.481	617.25	.002
5.106	573.38	.070	6.580	592.53	.021	8.503	617.53	.001
5.137	573.78	.068	6.635	593.25	.020	8.573	618.45	.001
5.158	574.05	.067	6.676	593.78	.020	8.626	619.13	.001
5.180	574.33	.065	6.703	594.13	.019	8.795	621.33	.001
5.291	575.78	.063	6.780	595.13	.019	9.035	624.45	.001
5.308	576.00	.062	6.785	595.20	.018	9.118	625.53	.001
5.342	576.45	.061	6.799	595.38	.016	9.199	626.58	.000
5.349	576.53	.061	6.830	595.78	.016	9.692	633.00	.000
5.353	576.58	.059	6.891	596.58	.015			
5.414	577.38	.058	7.004	598.05	.015			

Table F. Kruskal-Wallis, Rijkoort k-Sample Distributions

(Upper Tail)

			$n_1 = 3$			$n_2 = 5$			$n_3 = 5$		
H	x	P	H	x	P	H	x	P	H	x	P
.000	637.00	1.000	1.934	666.33	.413	4.255	701.53	.117	6.655	737.93	.022
.026	637.40	.996	1.978	667.00	.393	4.308	702.33	.112	6.734	739.13	.022
.035	637.53	.989	2.066	668.33	.386	4.352	703.00	.110	6.752	739.40	.021
.088	638.33	.974	2.136	669.40	.380	4.378	703.40	.107	6.866	741.13	.019
.106	638.60	.959	2.145	669.53	.377	4.457	704.60	.105	6.892	741.53	.018
.114	638.73	.951	2.163	669.80	.370	4.466	704.73	.104	6.945	742.33	.018
.141	639.13	.944	2.198	670.33	.364	4.536	705.80	.102	6.963	742.60	.017
.193	639.93	.930	2.250	671.13	.351	4.545	705.93	.100	6.998	743.13	.015
.220	640.33	.916	2.321	672.20	.339	4.571	706.33	.098	7.050	743.93	.015
.237	640.60	.902	2.374	673.00	.327	4.694	708.20	.094	7.121	745.00	.014
.264	641.00	.895	2.409	673.53	.321	4.774	709.40	.092	7.209	746.33	.014
.316	641.80	.880	2.479	674.60	.315	4.826	710.20	.089	7.226	746.60	.012
.352	642.33	.866	2.488	674.73	.310	4.835	710.33	.088	7.288	747.53	.012
.422	643.40	.840	2.514	675.13	.305	4.888	711.13	.082	7.306	747.80	.012
.457	643.93	.819	2.593	676.33	.299	4.914	711.53	.079	7.314	747.93	.011
.484	644.33	.813	2.620	676.73	.294	4.941	711.93	.077	7.437	749.80	.011
.536	645.13	.800	2.637	677.00	.289	4.993	712.73	.075	7.543	751.40	.010
.563	645.53	.788	2.716	678.20	.276	5.020	713.13	.072	7.578	751.93	.010
.580	645.80	.763	2.752	678.73	.271	5.064	713.80	.070	7.622	752.60	.009
.659	647.00	.751	2.778	679.13	.267	5.152	715.13	.067	7.736	754.33	.009
.695	647.53	.745	2.848	680.20	.262	5.169	715.40	.065	7.763	754.73	.008
.721	647.93	.733	2.857	680.33	.257	5.222	716.20	.065	7.780	755.00	.008
.774	648.73	.721	2.884	680.73	.255	5.284	717.13	.063	7.859	756.20	.007
.791	649.00	.698	2.936	681.53	.246	5.363	718.33	.062	7.894	756.73	.007
.826	649.53	.686	2.963	681.93	.241	5.407	719.00	.059	7.912	757.00	.007
.879	650.33	.675	3.094	683.93	.237	5.486	720.20	.057	8.026	758.73	.006
.950	651.40	.653	3.112	684.20	.224	5.494	720.33	.056	8.079	759.53	.006
1.029	652.60	.648	3.121	684.33	.220	5.521	720.73	.055	8.106	759.93	.006
1.037	652.73	.643	3.165	685.00	.216	5.574	721.53	.053	8.237	761.93	.005
1.055	653.00	.632	3.191	685.40	.208	5.600	721.93	.051	8.264	762.33	.005
1.064	653.13	.611	3.279	686.73	.206	5.626	722.33	.051	8.316	763.13	.005
1.116	653.93	.602	3.306	687.13	.202	5.706	723.53	.046	8.334	763.40	.005
1.134	654.20	.592	3.429	689.00	.195	5.802	725.00	.045	8.545	766.60	.004
1.143	654.33	.583	3.464	689.53	.191	5.837	725.53	.042	8.571	767.00	.004
1.248	655.93	.573	3.516	690.33	.187	5.934	727.00	.040	8.580	767.13	.004
1.266	656.20	.563	3.622	691.93	.173	5.943	727.13	.039	8.650	768.20	.003
1.292	656.60	.554	3.648	692.33	.167	6.022	728.33	.038	8.659	768.33	.003
1.371	657.80	.550	3.666	692.60	.164	6.048	728.73	.037	8.791	770.33	.002
1.407	658.33	.541	3.745	693.80	.161	6.198	731.00	.035	8.809	770.60	.002
1.450	659.00	.514	3.780	694.33	.158	6.207	731.13	.034	8.950	772.73	.002
1.459	659.13	.506	3.798	694.60	.152	6.250	731.80	.034	9.002	773.53	.002
1.512	659.93	.497	3.807	694.73	.147	6.259	731.93	.033	9.055	774.33	.001
1.565	660.73	.480	3.912	696.33	.144	6.286	732.33	.031	9.284	777.80	.001
1.688	662.60	.472	3.965	697.13	.142	6.312	732.73	.030	9.336	778.60	.001
1.723	663.13	.460	3.991	697.53	.139	6.365	733.53	.030	9.398	779.53	.001
1.741	663.40	.453	4.114	699.40	.136	6.391	733.93	.028	9.521	781.40	.000
1.750	663.53	.445	4.141	699.80	.135	6.435	734.60	.027	9.635	783.13	.000
1.802	664.33	.438	4.150	699.93	.132	6.488	735.40	.025	9.916	787.40	.000
1.829	664.73	.431	4.202	700.73	.127	6.550	736.33	.024	10.057	789.53	.000
1.855	665.13	.420	4.220	701.00	.125	6.593	737.00	.024	10.550	797.00	.000

Table F. Kruskal-Wallis, Rijkoort k-Sample Distributions

(Upper Tail)

$n_1 = 4$		$n_2 = 4$		$n_3 = 4$	
H	x	P	H	x	P
.000	507.00	1.000	4.154	561.00	.136
.038	507.50	.994	4.192	561.50	.131
.115	508.50	.968	4.269	562.50	.122
.154	509.00	.941	4.308	563.00	.114
.269	510.50	.913	4.500	565.50	.104
.346	511.50	.864	4.654	567.50	.097
.462	513.00	.840	4.769	569.00	.094
.500	513.50	.815	4.885	570.50	.086
.615	515.00	.770	4.962	571.50	.080
.731	516.50	.746	5.115	573.50	.074
.808	517.50	.706	5.346	576.50	.063
.962	519.50	.667	5.538	579.00	.057
1.038	520.50	.648	6.654	580.50	.055
1.077	521.00	.630	5.692	581.00	.049
1.192	522.50	.592	5.808	582.50	.044
1.385	525.00	.557	6.000	585.00	.040
1.423	525.50	.540	6.038	585.50	.037
1.500	526.50	.510	6.269	588.50	.033
1.654	528.50	.480	6.500	591.50	.030
1.846	531.00	.452	6.577	592.50	.026
1.885	531.50	.436	6.615	593.00	.024
2.000	533.00	.397	6.731	594.50	.021
2.192	535.50	.370	6.962	597.50	.019
2.346	537.50	.348	7.038	598.50	.018
2.423	538.50	.327	7.269	601.50	.016
2.462	539.00	.307	7.385	603.00	.015
2.577	540.50	.296	7.423	603.50	.013
2.808	543.50	.277	7.538	605.00	.011
2.885	544.50	.260	7.654	606.50	.008
2.923	545.00	.252	7.731	607.50	.007
3.038	546.50	.234	8.000	611.00	.005
3.115	547.50	.219	8.115	612.50	.003
3.231	549.00	.212	8.346	615.50	.002
3.500	552.50	.197	8.654	619.50	.001
3.577	553.50	.173	8.769	621.00	.001
3.731	555.50	.162	9.269	627.50	.001
3.846	557.00	.151	9.846	635.00	.000
3.962	558.50	.145			

Table F. Kruskal-Wallis, Rijkoort k-Sample Distributions

(Upper Tail)

$n_1 = 4$			$n_2 = 4$			$n_3 = 5$		
H	x	P	H	x	P	H	x	P
.000	637.00	1.000	1.272	656.30	.556	2.881	680.70	.257
.030	637.45	.996	1.299	656.70	.548	2.904	681.05	.253
.033	637.50	.981	1.371	657.80	.539	2.918	681.25	.249
.086	638.30	.974	1.404	658.30	.534	2.967	682.00	.245
.096	638.45	.967	1.414	658.45	.526	2.987	682.30	.240
.119	638.80	.952	1.454	659.05	.518	2.997	682.45	.236
.132	639.00	.937	1.503	659.80	.509	3.013	682.70	.228
.201	640.05	.930	1.530	660.20	.501	3.086	683.80	.224
.218	640.30	.916	1.533	660.25	.493	3.119	684.30	.221
.228	640.45	.903	1.586	661.05	.485	3.129	684.45	.217
.267	641.05	.889	1.596	661.20	.477	3.168	685.05	.214
.297	641.50	.875	1.615	661.50	.469	3.218	685.80	.210
.343	642.20	.869	1.668	662.30	.465	3.260	686.45	.206
.376	642.70	.862	1.701	662.80	.458	3.297	687.00	.202
.382	642.80	.849	1.718	663.05	.450	3.330	687.50	.200
.399	643.05	.836	1.744	663.45	.443	3.382	688.30	.197
.425	643.45	.823	1.810	664.45	.436	3.432	689.05	.190
.475	644.20	.811	1.876	665.45	.429	3.442	689.20	.187
.528	645.00	.798	1.899	665.80	.422	3.481	689.80	.183
.544	645.25	.792	1.929	666.25	.414	3.511	690.25	.180
.597	646.05	.780	1.942	666.45	.408	3.590	691.45	.176
.610	646.25	.768	1.958	666.70	.401	3.613	691.80	.170
.613	646.30	.757	2.047	668.05	.388	3.630	692.05	.167
.640	646.70	.745	2.110	669.00	.375	3.640	692.20	.164
.689	647.45	.734	2.140	669.45	.371	3.656	692.45	.160
.742	648.25	.723	2.143	669.50	.365	3.696	693.05	.157
.771	648.70	.711	2.176	670.00	.362	3.758	694.00	.154
.804	649.20	.706	2.196	670.30	.356	3.828	696.05	.151
.824	649.50	.695	2.275	671.50	.344	3.910	696.30	.146
.860	650.05	.690	2.387	673.20	.338	3.986	697.45	.143
.870	650.20	.679	2.390	673.25	.332	3.989	697.50	.141
.903	650.70	.668	2.403	673.45	.327	4.025	698.05	.139
.910	650.80	.658	2.440	674.00	.316	4.042	698.30	.134
.940	651.25	.647	2.443	674.05	.310	4.068	698.70	.132
1.019	652.45	.637	2.453	674.20	.305	4.075	698.80	.130
1.058	653.05	.627	2.558	675.80	.299	4.118	699.45	.127
1.068	653.20	.617	2.575	676.05	.293	4.170	700.25	.125
1.124	654.05	.607	2.601	676.45	.288	4.200	700.70	.122
1.167	654.70	.598	2.667	677.45	.283	4.233	701.20	.121
1.187	655.00	.589	2.670	677.50	.279	4.253	701.50	.119
1.190	655.05	.584	2.733	678.45	.271	4.272	701.80	.117
1.203	655.25	.574	2.756	678.80	.267	4.289	702.05	.114
1.256	656.05	.565	2.799	679.45	.262	4.332	702.70	.112

Table F. Kruskal-Wallis, Rijkoort k-Sample Distributions

(Upper Tail)

$n_1 = 4$			$n_2 = 4$			$n_3 = 5$	(continued)	
H	x	P	H	x	P	H	x	P
4.381	703.45	.108	5.914	726.70	.042	7.586	752.05	.012
4.447	704.45	.106	6.003	728.05	.042	7.596	752.20	.012
4.497	705.20	.104	6.013	728.20	.041	7.714	754.00	.011
4.553	706.05	.102	6.030	728.45	.040	7.744	754.45	.011
4.619	707.05	.100	6.096	729.45	.039	7.760	754.70	.009
4.668	707.80	.098	6.119	729.80	.038	7.767	754.80	.009
4.685	708.05	.096	6.132	730.00	.037	7.797	755.25	.009
4.701	708.30	.094	6.201	731.05	.036	7.810	755.45	.009
4.711	708.45	.092	6.214	731.25	.034	7.833	755.80	.008
4.728	708.70	.091	6.228	731.45	.033	7.942	757.45	.007
4.747	709.00	.089	6.267	732.05	.032	7.981	758.05	.007
4.760	709.20	.088	6.310	732.70	.031	8.047	759.05	.006
4.813	710.00	.086	6.343	733.20	.030	8.113	760.05	.006
4.830	710.25	.084	6.382	733.80	.029	8.130	760.30	.006
4.833	710.30	.082	6.399	734.05	.028	8.140	760.45	.005
4.896	711.25	.081	6.462	735.00	.027	8.156	760.70	.005
4.975	712.45	.077	6.544	736.25	.027	8.189	761.20	.005
5.014	713.05	.076	6.547	736.30	.026	8.403	764.45	.004
5.024	713.20	.074	6.597	737.05	.026	8.440	765.00	.004
5.028	713.25	.073	6.672	738.20	.024	8.456	765.25	.004
5.090	714.20	.071	6.676	738.25	.024	8.525	766.30	.003
5.172	715.45	.069	6.804	740.20	.023	8.558	766.80	.003
5.196	715.80	.068	6.860	741.05	.022	8.571	767.00	.003
5.225	716.25	.066	6.870	741.20	.022	8.575	767.05	.003
5.344	718.05	.065	6.887	741.45	.021	8.604	767.50	.003
5.360	718.30	.063	6.890	741.50	.021	8.703	769.00	.003
5.370	718.45	.062	6.943	742.30	.020	8.733	769.45	.002
5.387	718.70	.061	6.953	742.45	.020	8.782	770.20	.002
5.410	719.05	.060	6.976	742.80	.019	8.868	771.50	.002
5.440	719.50	.059	7.058	744.05	.018	8.997	773.45	.001
5.476	720.05	.057	7.075	744.30	.017	9.053	774.30	.001
5.486	720.20	.056	7.101	744.70	.017	9.099	775.00	.001
5.489	720.25	.056	7.124	745.05	.016	9.129	775.45	.001
5.519	720.70	.054	7.190	746.05	.016	9.168	776.05	.001
5.568	721.45	.052	7.203	746.25	.015	9.396	779.50	.001
5.571	721.50	.051	7.233	746.70	.015	9.528	781.50	.001
5.618	722.20	.050	7.240	746.80	.014	9.590	782.45	.001
5.657	722.80	.049	7.256	747.05	.014	9.613	782.80	.000
5.687	723.25	.048	7.418	749.50	.014	9.758	785.00	.000
5.756	724.30	.047	7.467	750.25	.013	10.118	790.45	.000
5.782	724.70	.046	7.470	750.30	.013	10.187	791.50	.000
5.815	725.20	.045	7.497	750.70	.013	10.681	799.00	.000
5.819	725.25	.043	7.503	750.80	.012			

Table F. Kruskal-Wallis, Rijkoort k-Sample Distributions

(Upper Tail)

$n_1 = 4$			$n_2 = 5$			$n_3 = 5$		
H	x	P	H	x	P	H	x	P
.006	787.60	1.000	1.423	812.40	.512	3.023	840.40	.229
.020	787.85	.994	1.483	813.45	.505	3.083	841.45	.224
.043	788.25	.988	1.551	814.65	.498	3.103	841.80	.221
.051	788.40	.976	1.560	814.80	.492	3.160	842.80	.218
.086	789.00	.970	1.606	815.60	.485	3.240	844.20	.215
.111	789.45	.958	1.620	815.85	.479	3.243	844.25	.211
.131	789.80	.946	1.643	816.25	.470	3.266	844.65	.209
.143	790.00	.935	1.651	816.40	.458	3.286	845.00	.203
.180	790.65	.929	1.686	817.00	.455	3.311	845.45	.200
.203	791.05	.923	1.711	817.45	.449	3.343	846.00	.197
.223	791.40	.912	1.731	817.80	.443	3.380	846.65	.188
.226	791.45	.901	1.743	818.00	.437	3.403	847.05	.187
.271	792.25	.890	1.803	819.05	.431	3.471	848.25	.184
.280	792.40	.879	1.826	819.45	.425	3.540	849.45	.176
.326	793.20	.874	1.871	820.25	.420	3.571	850.00	.174
.360	793.80	.863	1.963	821.85	.414	3.586	850.25	.170
.371	794.00	.852	1.971	822.00	.409	3.651	851.40	.167
.386	794.25	.841	1.986	822.25	.398	3.743	853.00	.162
.463	795.60	.821	2.006	822.60	.393	3.746	853.05	.160
.500	796.25	.805	2.031	823.05	.382	3.791	853.85	.155
.523	796.65	.800	2.051	823.40	.377	3.800	854.00	.153
.543	797.00	.790	2.063	823.60	.372	3.846	854.80	.151
.546	797.05	.781	2.100	824.25	.369	3.883	855.45	.148
.591	797.85	.771	2.143	825.00	.364	3.891	855.60	.144
.600	798.00	.752	2.191	825.85	.354	3.906	855.85	.142
.691	799.60	.742	2.246	826.80	.349	3.926	856.20	.140
.706	799.85	.738	2.280	827.40	.344	3.951	856.65	.137
.726	800.20	.729	2.306	827.85	.339	3.971	857.00	.135
.751	800.65	.720	2.351	828.65	.335	4.043	858.25	.133
.771	801.00	.711	2.371	829.00	.330	4.063	858.60	.131
.783	801.20	.693	2.383	829.20	.326	4.166	860.40	.127
.843	802.25	.684	2.420	829.85	.322	4.200	861.00	.124
.863	802.60	.675	2.443	830.25	.319	4.203	861.05	.122
.866	802.65	.667	2.463	830.60	.307	4.246	861.80	.120
.966	804.40	.658	2.466	830.65	.302	4.271	862.25	.118
.980	804.65	.654	2.511	831.45	.298	4.291	862.60	.115
1.000	805.00	.650	2.520	831.60	.294	4.303	862.80	.113
1.003	805.05	.642	2.566	832.40	.292	4.363	863.85	.111
1.011	805.20	.626	2.600	833.00	.288	4.383	864.20	.110
1.046	805.80	.617	2.626	833.45	.284	4.386	864.25	.108
1.071	806.25	.610	2.691	834.60	.280	4.486	866.00	.106
1.140	807.45	.594	2.740	835.45	.276	4.500	866.25	.105
1.183	808.20	.587	2.783	836.20	.272	4.520	866.60	.101
1.186	808.25	.579	2.786	836.25	.268	4.523	866.65	.099
1.286	810.00	.572	2.831	837.05	.257	4.531	866.80	.098
1.300	810.25	.553	2.840	837.20	.254	4.591	867.85	.096
1.323	810.65	.547	2.886	838.00	.250	4.611	868.20	.095
1.331	810.80	.540	2.931	838.80	.246	4.660	869.05	.093
1.346	811.05	.532	2.946	839.05	.239	4.706	869.85	.092
1.366	811.40	.525	2.966	839.40	.236	4.806	871.60	.089
1.411	812.20	.518	2.991	839.85	.232	4.843	872.25	.088

Table F. Kruskal-Wallis, Rijkoort k-Sample Distributions

(Upper Tail)

$n_1 = 4$			$n_2 = 5$			$n_3 = 5$	(continued)	
H	x	P	H	x	P	H	x	P
4.851	872.40	.086	6.486	901.00	.029	8.223	931.40	.007
4.866	872.65	.084	6.531	901.80	.028	8.226	931.45	.007
4.886	873.00	.083	6.543	902.00	.028	8.271	932.25	.007
4.911	873.45	.079	6.603	903.05	.027	8.280	932.40	.006
4.943	874.00	.078	6.623	903.40	.026	8.340	933.45	.006
4.980	874.65	.076	6.626	903.45	.026	8.363	933.85	.006
5.023	875.40	.075	6.671	904.25	.025	8.371	934.00	.005
5.071	876.25	.074	6.760	905.80	.025	8.386	934.25	.005
5.126	877.20	.073	6.763	905.85	.024	8.431	935.05	.005
5.163	877.85	.070	6.771	906.00	.024	8.463	935.60	.005
5.171	878.00	.069	6.786	906.25	.023	8.523	936.65	.005
5.186	878.25	.068	6.806	906.60	.022	8.543	937.00	.005
5.206	878.60	.067	6.831	907.05	.022	8.546	937.05	.004
5.231	879.05	.066	6.900	908.25	.021	8.683	939.45	.004
5.263	879.60	.064	6.943	909.00	.020	8.691	939.60	.004
5.323	880.65	.063	7.000	910.00	.019	8.726	940.20	.004
5.400	882.00	.061	7.046	910.80	.019	8.751	940.65	.004
5.446	882.80	.059	7.080	911.40	.018	8.771	941.00	.004
5.460	883.05	.058	7.106	911.85	.018	8.969	944.40	.003
5.483	883.45	.057	7.171	913.00	.018	8.980	944.65	.003
5.491	883.60	.056	7.183	913.20	.017	9.000	945.00	.003
5.526	884.20	.056	7.220	913.85	.017	9.011	945.20	.003
5.571	885.00	.055	7.243	914.25	.017	9.026	945.45	.003
5.583	885.20	.052	7.266	914.65	.016	9.071	946.25	.002
5.620	885.85	.051	7.311	915.45	.015	9.103	946.80	.002
5.643	886.25	.050	7.320	915.60	.015	9.163	947.85	.002
5.666	886.65	.049	7.426	917.45	.015	9.231	949.05	.002
5.711	887.45	.048	7.446	917.80	.014	9.286	950.00	.002
5.780	888.65	.048	7.471	918.25	.014	9.323	950.65	.001
5.803	889.05	.047	7.491	918.60	.014	9.411	952.20	.001
5.811	889.20	.046	7.503	918.80	.013	9.503	953.80	.001
5.871	890.25	.045	7.563	919.85	.013	9.506	953.85	.001
5.903	890.80	.043	7.586	920.25	.012	9.606	955.60	.001
5.963	891.85	.042	7.631	921.05	.012	9.643	956.25	.001
5.983	892.20	.042	7.640	921.20	.011	9.651	956.40	.001
5.986	892.25	.041	7.686	922.00	.011	9.686	957.00	.001
6.031	893.05	.040	7.720	922.60	.011	9.926	961.20	.001
6.086	894.00	.040	7.766	923.40	.010	9.986	962.25	.000
6.100	894.25	.038	7.791	923.85	.010	10.051	963.40	.000
6.123	894.65	.037	7.823	924.40	.010	10.063	963.60	.000
6.146	895.05	.037	7.860	925.05	.010	10.100	964.25	.000
6.166	895.40	.035	7.903	925.80	.009	10.260	967.05	.000
6.211	896.20	.035	7.906	925.85	.009	10.511	971.45	.000
6.223	896.40	.034	8.006	927.60	.009	10.520	971.60	.000
6.283	897.45	.034	8.043	928.25	.009	10.566	972.40	.000
6.303	897.80	.033	8.051	928.40	.008	10.646	973.80	.000
6.351	898.65	.032	8.066	928.65	.008	11.023	980.40	.000
6.406	899.60	.031	8.086	929.00	.008	11.083	981.45	.000
6.440	900.20	.030	8.131	929.80	.008	11.571	990.00	.000
6.451	900.40	.029	8.143	930.00	.008			

Table F. Kruskal-Wallis, Rijkoort k-Sample Distributions

(Upper Tail)

$n_1 = 5$				$n_2 = 5$				$n_3 = 5$			
H	x	P	H	x	P	H	x	P	H	x	P
.000	960.00	1.000	2.240	1004.80	.342	5.120	1062.40	.072	8.060	1121.20	.009
.020	960.40	.998	2.340	1006.80	.330	5.180	1063.60	.070	8.180	1123.60	.008
.060	961.20	.983	2.420	1008.40	.319	5.360	1067.20	.065	8.240	1124.80	.008
.080	961.60	.968	2.480	1009.60	.314	5.420	1068.40	.063	8.340	1126.80	.007
.140	962.80	.954	2.540	1010.80	.304	5.460	1069.20	.060	8.420	1128.40	.007
.180	963.60	.925	2.580	1011.60	.294	5.540	1070.80	.055	8.540	1130.80	.006
.240	964.80	.911	2.660	1013.20	.284	5.580	1071.60	.053	8.640	1132.80	.006
.260	965.20	.898	2.780	1015.60	.265	5.660	1073.20	.051	8.660	1133.20	.006
.320	966.40	.871	2.880	1017.60	.256	5.780	1075.60	.049	8.720	1134.40	.005
.380	967.60	.858	2.940	1018.80	.252	5.820	1076.40	.048	8.780	1135.60	.005
.420	968.40	.832	2.960	1019.20	.239	5.840	1076.80	.046	8.820	1136.40	.005
.500	970.00	.807	3.020	1020.40	.231	6.000	1080.00	.044	8.880	1137.60	.004
.540	970.80	.794	3.120	1022.40	.223	6.020	1080.40	.043	8.960	1139.20	.004
.560	971.20	.783	3.140	1022.80	.216	6.080	1081.60	.040	9.060	1141.20	.004
.620	972.40	.759	3.260	1025.20	.208	6.140	1082.80	.038	9.140	1142.80	.003
.720	974.40	.736	3.380	1027.60	.201	6.180	1083.60	.036	9.260	1145.20	.003
.740	974.80	.725	3.420	1028.40	.190	6.260	1085.20	.035	9.360	1147.20	.003
.780	975.60	.703	3.440	1028.80	.184	6.320	1086.40	.033	9.380	1147.60	.003
.860	977.20	.681	3.500	1030.00	.177	6.480	1089.60	.032	9.420	1148.40	.002
.960	979.20	.660	3.620	1032.40	.171	6.500	1090.00	.031	9.500	1150.00	.002
.980	979.60	.650	3.660	1033.20	.165	6.540	1090.80	.030	9.620	1152.40	.002
1.040	980.80	.620	3.780	1035.60	.159	6.620	1092.40	.028	9.680	1153.60	.001
1.140	982.80	.601	3.840	1036.80	.153	6.660	1093.20	.027	9.740	1154.80	.001
1.220	984.40	.582	3.860	1037.20	.150	6.720	1094.40	.026	9.780	1155.60	.001
1.260	985.20	.564	3.920	1038.40	.145	6.740	1094.80	.025	9.920	1158.40	.001
1.280	985.60	.547	3.980	1039.60	.137	6.860	1097.20	.024	9.980	1159.60	.001
1.340	986.80	.538	4.020	1040.40	.132	6.980	1099.60	.021	10.140	1162.80	.001
1.460	989.20	.521	4.160	1043.20	.127	7.020	1100.40	.020	10.220	1164.40	.001
1.500	990.00	.505	4.220	1044.40	.123	7.220	1104.40	.019	10.260	1165.20	.000
1.520	990.40	.497	4.340	1046.80	.118	7.260	1105.20	.018	10.500	1170.00	.000
1.580	991.60	.481	4.380	1047.60	.110	7.280	1105.60	.018	10.580	1171.60	.000
1.620	992.40	.466	4.460	1049.20	.105	7.340	1106.80	.016	10.640	1172.80	.000
1.680	993.60	.459	4.500	1050.00	.102	7.440	1108.80	.015	10.820	1176.40	.000
1.820	996.40	.444	4.560	1051.20	.100	7.460	1109.20	.015	11.060	1181.20	.000
1.860	997.20	.416	4.580	1051.60	.096	7.580	1111.60	.014	11.180	1183.60	.000
1.940	998.80	.403	4.740	1054.80	.092	7.620	1112.40	.013	11.520	1190.40	.000
2.000	1000.00	.390	4.820	1056.40	.089	7.740	1114.80	.012	11.580	1191.60	.000
2.060	1001.20	.383	4.860	1057.20	.085	7.760	1115.20	.012	12.020	1200.40	.000
2.160	1003.20	.371	4.880	1057.60	.084	7.940	1118.80	.011	12.500	1210.00	.000
2.180	1003.60	.365	4.940	1058.80	.081	7.980	1119.60	.011			
2.220	1004.40	.353	5.040	1060.80	.075	8.000	1120.00	.009			

TABLE **G**

FRIEDMAN'S *m* RANKINGS OR KENDALL'S COEFFICIENT OF CONCORDANCE DISTRIBUTIONS*

Table G gives the distribution of X, Friedman's m-rankings statistic, or Kendall's coefficient of concordance from m independent rankings, where, within each row, all permutations of the (untied) ranks from $1, 2, \ldots, k$ are equally likely.

$$X = \frac{12S}{m^2k(k^2 - 1)},$$

where $S = \sum (R_i - \bar{R})^2$ and $R_1, \ldots, R_k$ are the sums of the ranks in each of the k columns. The table is cumulative from the right-hand extreme to zero; that is, the relation between the table and the distribution is as for the following example, where $k = 3$ and $m = 2$. The table also contains the distribution of S. (See Table G.1.)

Distribution

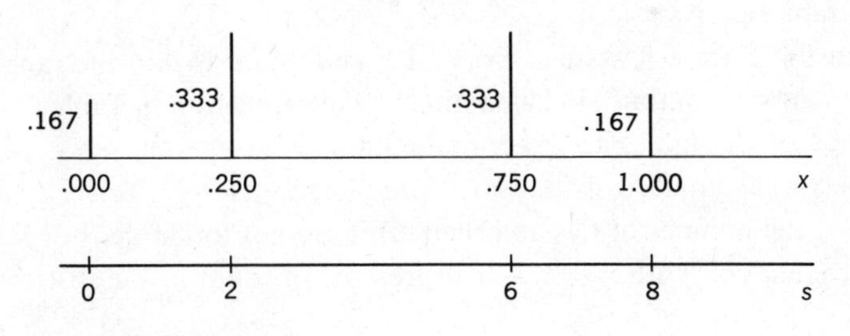

The ranges for m and k are

$$k = 3 \qquad 2 \le m \le 15$$
$$k = 4 \qquad 2 \le m \le 8$$
$$k = 5 \qquad m = 3$$

* With kind permission of the publishers; adapted from Table 14 of *Handbook of Statistical Tables*, by D. B. Owen, Addison-Wesley Publishing Company (1962), for number of columns = 3 and 4; from Table 5D of *Rank Correlation Methods*, by M. G. Kendall, Charles Griffin and Company (1962), for number of columns = 5.

Table G.1

x	S	P
.000	0	1.000
.250	2	.833 = .167 + .333 + .333
.750	6	.500 = .167 + .333
1.000	8	.167

Outside the range of the table the following approximations can be used. The distribution of $[(m-1)X]/(1-X)$ can be approximated by an F distribution (Table I) with $\nu_1 = k - 1 - (2/m)$ and $\nu_2 = (m-1)\nu_1$ degrees of freedom; somewhat more simply, if m is large, the distribution of $m(k-1)X = 12S/mk(k+1)$ can be approximated by a χ^2 distribution (Table H) with $\nu = k - 1$ degrees of freedom.

When there are ties in one or more of the rankings, the ranks within each ranking are found by averaging within ties (see the introduction to Table B) and X is replaced by

$$X' = \frac{12S}{m^2k(k^2-1) - m\sum(D_j - k)},$$

where, for $j = 1, \ldots, m$, D_j is the sum of the cubes of the sizes of the ties in the jth ranking.

When there are a few small ties and k and m are within the range of the table, an approximation can be obtained by interpolation in Table G. Outside the range of the table, an F approximation, with $\nu_1 = k - 1 - (2/m)$ and $\nu_2 = (m-1)\nu_1$, to the distribution of $[(m-1)X']/(1-X')$ gives an approximation if the number of ties and their sizes are not too large. For large m, a χ^2 approximation with $\nu = k - 1$ degrees of freedom to the distribution of

$$m(k-1)X' = \frac{12S}{mk(k+1) - [1/(k-1)]\sum(D_j - k)}$$

can be used.

The exact distribution of S, or X', can always be found by enumerating the $(k!)^m$ possible permutations of the k (tied) ranks in the m rankings, and computing S, or X', for each.

Note that, for $m = 2$, the distribution of X (or S) can be found from the distribution of Spearman's rank correlation coefficient r for k pairs of ranks (Table J). The relation between X' and r is given by

$$X' = \frac{1}{2}\left[1 + \frac{r\sqrt{(k^3 - D_1)(k^3 - D_2)}}{k^3 - \frac{1}{2}(D_1 + D_2)}\right],$$

which, in the case where none of the rankings contains ties, reduces to $X = (1 + r)/2$.

Table G. Friedman's *m* rankings or Kendall's Coefficient of Concordance Distributions

(Upper Tail)

Number of Columns = 3

Number of Rows

2			3			4			5			6		
x	S	P	x	S	P	x	S	P	x	S	P	x	S	P
.000	0	1.000	.000	0	1.000	.000	0	1.000	.000	0	1.000	.000	0	1.000
.250	2	.833	.111	2	.944	.062	2	.931	.040	2	.954	.028	2	.956
.750	6	.500	.333	6	.528	.188	6	.653	.120	6	.691	.083	6	.740
1.000	8	.167	.444	8	.361	.250	8	.431	.160	8	.522	.111	8	.570
			.778	14	.194	.438	14	.273	.280	14	.367	.194	14	.430
			1.000	18	.028	.562	18	.125	.360	18	.182	.250	18	.252
						.750	24	.069	.480	24	.124	.333	24	.184
						.812	26	.042	.520	26	.093	.361	26	.142
						1.000	32	.005	.640	32	.039	.444	32	.072
									.760	38	.024	.528	38	.052
									.840	42	.008	.583	42	.029
									1.000	50	.001	.694	50	.012
												.750	54	.008
												.778	56	.006
												.861	62	.002
												1.000	72	.001

Table G. Friedman's m rankings or Kendall's Coefficient of Concordance Distributions

(Upper Tail)

Number of Columns = 3

Number of Rows

7			8			9			10			11		
x	S	P	x	S	P	x	S	P	x	S	P	x	S	P
.000	0	1.000	.000	0	1.000	.000	0	1.000	.000	0	1.000	.000	0	1.000
.020	2	.964	.016	2	.967	.012	2	.971	.010	2	.974	.008	2	.976
.061	6	.768	.047	6	.794	.037	6	.814	.030	6	.830	.025	6	.844
.082	8	.620	.062	8	.654	.049	8	.685	.040	8	.710	.033	8	.732
.143	14	.486	.109	14	.531	.086	14	.569	.070	14	.601	.058	14	.629
.184	18	.305	.141	18	.355	.111	18	.398	.090	18	.436	.074	18	.470
.245	24	.237	.188	24	.285	.148	24	.328	.120	24	.368	.099	24	.403
.265	26	.192	.203	26	.236	.160	26	.278	.130	26	.316	.107	26	.351
.326	32	.112	.250	32	.149	.198	32	.187	.160	32	.222	.132	32	.256
.388	38	.085	.297	38	.120	.235	38	.154	.190	38	.187	.157	38	.219
.429	42	.051	.328	42	.079	.259	42	.107	.210	42	.135	.174	42	.163
.510	50	.027	.391	50	.047	.309	50	.069	.250	50	.092	.207	50	.116
.551	54	.021	.422	54	.038	.333	54	.057	.270	54	.078	.223	54	.100
.571	56	.016	.438	56	.030	.346	56	.048	.280	56	.066	.231	56	.087
.633	62	.008	.484	62	.018	.383	62	.031	.310	62	.046	.256	62	.062
.735	72	.004	.562	72	.010	.444	72	.019	.360	72	.030	.298	72	.043
.755	74	.003	.578	74	.008	.457	74	.016	.370	74	.026	.306	74	.037
.796	78	.001	.609	78	.005	.482	78	.010	.390	78	.018	.322	78	.027
.878	86	.000	.672	86	.002	.531	86	.006	.430	86	.012	.355	86	.019
1.000	98	.000	.750	96	.001	.593	96	.004	.480	96	.008	.397	96	.013
			.766	98	.001	.605	98	.003	.490	98	.006	.405	98	.011
			.812	104	.000	.642	104	.001	.520	104	.003	.430	104	.007
			.891	114	.000	.704	114	.001	.570	114	.002	.471	114	.005
			1.000	128	.000	.753	122	.000	.610	122	.001	.504	122	.003
						.778	126	.000	.630	126	.001	.521	126	.002
						.790	128	.000	.640	128	.001	.529	128	.002
						.827	134	.000	.670	134	.000	.554	134	.001
						.901	146	.000	.730	146	.000	.603	146	.001
						1.000	162	.000	.750	150	.000	.620	150	.000
									.760	152	.000	.628	152	.000
									.790	158	.000	.653	158	.000
									.810	162	.000	.669	162	.000
									.840	168	.000	.694	168	.000
									.910	182	.000	.752	182	.000
									1.000	200	.000	.769	186	.000
												.802	194	.000
												.826	200	.000
												.851	206	.000
												.917	222	.000
												1.000	242	.000

Table G. Friedman's *m* Rankings or Kendall's Coefficient of Concordance Distributions

(Upper Tail)

Number of Columns = 3

Number of Rows

12

x	S	P
.000	0	1.000
.007	2	.978
.021	6	.856
.028	8	.751
.049	14	.654
.062	18	.500
.083	24	.434
.090	26	.383
.111	32	.287
.132	38	.249
.146	42	.191
.174	50	.141
.188	54	.123
.194	56	.108
.215	62	.080
.250	72	.058
.257	74	.050
.271	78	.038
.299	86	.028
.333	96	.019
.340	98	.017
.361	104	.011
.396	114	.008
.424	122	.005
.438	126	.004
.444	128	.004
.465	134	.002
.507	146	.002
.521	150	.001
.528	152	.001
.549	158	.001
.562	162	.001
.583	168	.000
.632	182	.000
.646	186	.000
.674	194	.000
.694	200	.000
.715	206	.000
.757	218	.000
.771	222	.000
.778	224	.000
.812	234	.000
.840	242	.000
.861	248	.000
.924	266	.000
1.000	288	.000

13

x	S	P
.000	0	1.000
.006	2	.980
.018	6	.866
.024	8	.767
.041	14	.675
.053	18	.527
.071	24	.463
.077	26	.412
.095	32	.316
.112	38	.278
.124	42	.217
.148	50	.165
.160	54	.145
.166	56	.129
.183	62	.098
.213	72	.073
.219	74	.064
.231	78	.050
.254	86	.038
.284	96	.027
.290	98	.025
.308	104	.016
.337	114	.012
.361	122	.008
.373	126	.007
.379	128	.006
.396	134	.004
.432	146	.003
.444	150	.002
.450	152	.002
.467	158	.001
.479	162	.001
.497	168	.001
.538	182	.001
.550	186	.000
.574	194	.000
.592	200	.000
.609	206	.000
.639	216	.000
.645	218	.000
.657	222	.000
.663	224	.000
.692	234	.000
.716	242	.000
.734	248	.000
.751	254	.000
.763	258	.000
.787	266	.000
.822	278	.000
.852	288	.000
.870	294	.000
.929	314	.000
1.000	338	.000

14

x	S	P	x	S	P
.000	0	1.000	.403	158	.003
.005	2	.981	.413	162	.002
.015	6	.874	.429	168	.002
.020	8	.781	.464	182	.001
.036	14	.694	.474	186	.001
.046	18	.551	.495	194	.000
.061	24	.489	.510	200	.000
.066	26	.438	.526	206	.000
.082	32	.344	.551	216	.000
.097	38	.305	.556	218	.000
.107	42	.242	.566	222	.000
.128	50	.188	.571	224	.000
.138	54	.167	.597	234	.000
.143	56	.150	.617	242	.000
.158	62	.117	.633	248	.000
.184	72	.089	.648	254	.000
.189	74	.079	.658	258	.000
.199	78	.063	.679	266	.000
.219	86	.049	.709	278	.000
.245	96	.036	.735	288	.000
.250	98	.033	.750	294	.000
.265	104	.023	.755	296	.000
.291	114	.018	.770	302	.000
.311	122	.011	.796	312	.000
.321	126	.010	.801	314	.000
.327	128	.009	.832	326	.000
.342	134	.007	.862	338	.000
.372	146	.005	.878	344	.000
.383	150	.003	.934	366	.000
.388	152	.003	1.000	392	.000

15

x	S	P	x	S	P
.000	0	1.000	.413	186	.001
.004	2	.982	.431	194	.001
.013	6	.882	.444	200	.001
.018	8	.794	.458	206	.001
.031	14	.711	.480	216	.000
.040	18	.573	.484	218	.000
.053	24	.513	.493	222	.000
.058	26	.463	.498	224	.000
.071	32	.369	.520	234	.000
.084	38	.330	.538	242	.000
.093	42	.267	.551	248	.000
.111	50	.211	.564	254	.000
.120	54	.189	.573	258	.000
.124	56	.170	.591	266	.000
.138	62	.136	.618	278	.000
.160	72	.106	.640	288	.000
.164	74	.096	.653	294	.000
.173	78	.077	.658	296	.000
.191	86	.059	.671	302	.000
.213	96	.047	.693	312	.000
.218	98	.043	.698	314	.000
.231	104	.030	.724	326	.000
.253	114	.022	.751	338	.000
.271	122	.018	.760	342	.000
.280	126	.015	.764	344	.000
.284	128	.011	.778	350	.000
.298	134	.010	.804	362	.000
.324	146	.007	.813	366	.000
.333	150	.005	.840	378	.000
.338	152	.005	.871	392	.000
.351	158	.004	.884	398	.000
.360	162	.004	.938	422	.000
.373	168	.003	1.000	450	.000
.404	182	.002			

Table G. Friedman's m Rankings or Kendall's Coefficient of Concordance Distributions

(Upper Tail)

Number of Columns = 4

Number of Rows

2			3			4			5		
x	S	P	x	S	P	x	S	P	x	S	P
.000	0	1.000	.022	1	1.000	.000	0	1.000	.008	1	1.000
.100	2	.958	.067	3	.958	.025	2	.992	.024	3	.974
.200	4	.833	.111	5	.910	.050	4	.930	.040	5	.944
.300	6	.792	.200	9	.727	.075	6	.898	.072	9	.857
.400	8	.625	.244	11	.615	.100	8	.794	.088	11	.769
.500	10	.542	.289	13	.524	.125	10	.753	.104	13	.710
.600	12	.458	.378	17	.446	.150	12	.680	.136	17	.652
.700	14	.375	.422	19	.328	.175	14	.651	.152	19	.563
.800	16	.208	.467	21	.293	.200	16	.528	.168	21	.520
.900	18	.167	.556	25	.207	.225	18	.513	.200	25	.443
1.000	20	.042	.600	27	.182	.250	20	.432	.216	27	.406
			.644	29	.161	.275	22	.390	.232	29	.368
			.733	33	.075	.300	24	.352	.264	33	.301
			.778	35	.054	.325	26	.321	.280	35	.266
			.822	37	.026	.375	30	.237	.296	37	.232
			.911	41	.017	.400	32	.199	.328	41	.213
			1.000	45	.002	.425	34	.188	.344	43	.162
						.450	36	.159	.360	45	.151
						.475	38	.141	.392	49	.119
						.500	40	.106	.408	51	.102
						.525	42	.093	.424	53	.089
						.550	44	.077	.456	57	.071
						.575	46	.069	.472	59	.067
						.600	48	.058	.488	61	.057
						.625	50	.054	.520	65	.049
						.650	52	.036	.536	67	.033
						.675	54	.035	.552	69	.032
						.700	56	.020	.584	73	.024
						.725	58	.013	.600	75	.021
						.775	62	.011	.616	77	.015
						.800	64	.006	.648	81	.011
						.825	66	.005	.664	83	.009
						.850	68	.002	.680	85	.008
						.900	72	.002	.712	89	.006
						.925	74	.001	.728	91	.003
						1.000	80	.000	.744	93	.002
									.776	97	.002
									.792	99	.001
									.808	101	.001
									.840	105	.000
									.856	107	.000
									.872	109	.000
									.904	113	.000
									.936	117	.000
									1.000	125	.000

Table G. Friedman's m Rankings or Kendall's Coefficient of Concordance Distributions

(Upper Tail)

Number of Columns = 4

Number of Rows

6						7					
x	S	P	x	S	P	x	S	P	x	S	P
.000	0	1.000	.456	82	.033	.004	1	1.000	.469	115	.014
.011	2	.996	.467	84	.031	.012	3	.984	.478	117	.013
.022	4	.952	.478	86	.027	.020	5	.964	.494	121	.009
.033	6	.938	.489	88	.021	.037	9	.905	.502	123	.008
.044	8	.878	.500	90	.021	.045	11	.846	.510	125	.008
.056	10	.843	.522	94	.017	.053	13	.795	.527	129	.007
.067	12	.797	.533	96	.015	.069	17	.754	.535	131	.006
.078	14	.779	.544	98	.015	.078	19	.678	.543	133	.004
.089	16	.676	.556	100	.011	.086	21	.652	.559	137	.004
.100	18	.666	.567	102	.010	.102	25	.596	.567	139	.003
.111	20	.608	.578	104	.009	.110	27	.564	.576	141	.003
.122	22	.566	.589	106	.008	.118	29	.533	.592	145	.003
.133	24	.541	.600	108	.006	.135	33	.460	.600	147	.002
.144	26	.517	.611	110	.006	.143	35	.420	.608	149	.002
.167	30	.427	.633	114	.004	.151	37	.378	.624	153	.001
.178	32	.385	.644	116	.003	.167	41	.358	.633	155	.001
.189	34	.374	.656	118	.003	.176	43	.306	.641	157	.001
.200	36	.337	.667	120	.002	.184	45	.300	.657	161	.001
.211	38	.321	.678	122	.002	.200	49	.264	.665	163	.001
.222	40	.274	.700	126	.001	.208	51	.239	.673	165	.001
.233	42	.259	.711	128	.001	.216	53	.216	.690	169	.000
.244	44	.232	.722	130	.001	.233	57	.188	.698	171	.000
.256	46	.221	.733	132	.001	.241	59	.182	.706	173	.000
.267	48	.193	.744	134	.001	.249	61	.163	.722	177	.000
.278	50	.190	.756	136	.000	.265	65	.150	.731	179	.000
.289	52	.162	.767	138	.000	.273	67	.122	.739	181	.000
.300	54	.154	.778	140	.000	.282	69	.118	.755	185	.000
.311	56	.127	.811	146	.000	.298	73	.101	.763	187	.000
.322	58	.113	.822	148	.000	.306	75	.093	.771	189	.000
.344	62	.109	.833	150	.000	.314	77	.081	.788	193	.000
.356	64	.088	.844	152	.000	.331	81	.073	.796	195	.000
.367	66	.087	.856	154	.000	.339	83	.062	.804	197	.000
.378	68	.073	.878	158	.000	.347	85	.058	.820	201	.000
.389	70	.067	.889	160	.000	.363	89	.051	.829	203	.000
.400	72	.063	.900	162	.000	.371	91	.040	.837	205	.000
.411	74	.058	.911	164	.000	.380	93	.037	.853	209	.000
.422	76	.043	.944	170	.000	.396	97	.034	.869	213	.000
.433	78	.041	1.000	180	.000	.404	99	.032	.894	219	.000
.444	80	.036				.412	101	.030	.902	221	.000
						.429	105	.024	.918	225	.000
						.437	107	.021	.951	233	.000
						.445	109	.018	1.000	245	.000
						.461	113	.016			

Table G. Friedman's m Rankings or Kendall's Coefficient of Concordance Distributions

(Upper Tail)

Number of Columns = 4									Number of Columns = 5		
Number of Rows = 8									Number of Rows = 3		
x	S	P	x	S	P	x	S	P	x	S	P
.000	0	1.000	.306	98	.061	.606	194	.001	.000	0	1.000
.006	2	.998	.312	100	.052	.612	196	.000	.022	2	1.000
.012	4	.967	.319	102	.049	.619	198	.000	.044	4	.988
.019	6	.957	.325	104	.046	.625	200	.000	.067	6	.972
.025	8	.914	.331	106	.043	.631	202	.000	.089	8	.941
.031	10	.890	.338	108	.038	.637	204	.000	.111	10	.914
.038	12	.853	.344	110	.037	.644	206	.000	.133	12	.845
.044	14	.842	.356	114	.031	.650	208	.000	.156	14	.831
.050	16	.764	.362	116	.028	.656	210	.000	.178	16	.768
.056	18	.754	.369	118	.026	.662	212	.000	.200	18	.720
.062	20	.709	.375	120	.023	.669	214	.000	.222	20	.682
.069	22	.677	.381	122	.021	.675	216	.000	.244	22	.649
.075	24	.660	.394	126	.019	.681	218	.000	.267	24	.595
.081	26	.637	.400	128	.015	.694	222	.000	.289	26	.559
.094	30	.557	.406	130	.015	.700	224	.000	.311	28	.493
.100	32	.509	.412	132	.013	.706	226	.000	.333	30	.475
.106	34	.500	.419	134	.013	.719	230	.000	.356	32	.432
.112	36	.471	.425	136	.011	.725	232	.000	.378	34	.406
.119	38	.453	.431	138	.010	.731	234	.000	.400	36	.347
.125	40	.404	.438	140	.009	.738	236	.000	.422	38	.326
.131	42	.390	.444	142	.008	.744	238	.000	.444	40	.291
.137	44	.364	.450	144	.008	.756	242	.000	.467	42	.253
.144	46	.348	.456	146	.008	.762	244	.000	.489	44	.236
.156	50	.325	.462	148	.007	.769	246	.000	.511	46	.213
.162	52	.297	.469	150	.007	.775	248	.000	.533	48	.172
.169	54	.283	.475	152	.006	.781	250	.000	.556	50	.163
.175	56	.247	.481	154	.005	.794	254	.000	.578	52	.127
.181	58	.231	.494	158	.004	.806	258	.000	.600	54	.117
.194	62	.217	.500	160	.004	.812	260	.000	.622	56	.096
.200	64	.185	.506	162	.004	.819	262	.000	.644	58	.080
.206	66	.182	.512	164	.003	.825	264	.000	.667	60	.063
.212	68	.162	.519	166	.003	.831	266	.000	.689	62	.056
.219	70	.155	.525	168	.002	.844	270	.000	.711	64	.045
.225	72	.153	.531	170	.002	.850	272	.000	.733	66	.038
.231	74	.144	.538	172	.002	.856	274	.000	.756	68	.028
.238	76	.122	.544	174	.002	.862	276	.000	.778	70	.026
.244	78	.120	.550	176	.002	.869	278	.000	.800	72	.017
.250	80	.112	.556	178	.002	.881	282	.000	.822	74	.015
.256	82	.106	.562	180	.001	.906	290	.000	.844	76	.008
.262	84	.098	.569	182	.001	.912	292	.000	.867	78	.005
.269	86	.091	.575	184	.001	.925	296	.000	.889	80	.004
.281	90	.077	.581	186	.001	.956	306	.000	.911	82	.003
.294	94	.067	.594	190	.001	1.000	320	.000	.956	86	.001
.300	96	.062							1.000	90	.000

TABLE **H**

χ^2 DISTRIBUTIONS*

Table H gives, for each of the degrees of freedom from 1 to 20, the areas under the χ^2 curve. The table is cumulative from the right-hand extreme to zero. The relation between the areas under curve and the table is as for the following example for 2 degrees of freedom.

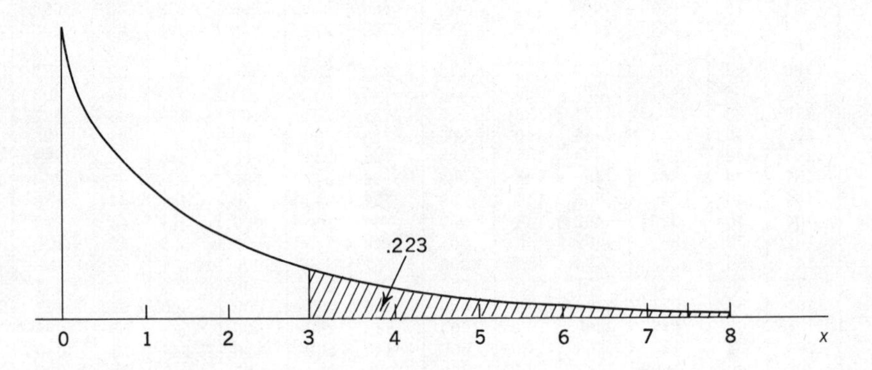

For more than 20 degrees of freedom, it is usual to approximate areas under a χ^2 curve by those from a normal distribution with

$$\mu = n = \text{(degrees of freedom)},$$
$$\sigma = \sqrt{2n}.$$

In particular, $P\{\chi^2 \leq t\}$ is approximately the area below $(t - n)/\sqrt{2n}$ under a unit normal curve (Table E).

* With kind permission of the Biometrika Trustees, adapted from "Tables of the χ^2-Integral and of the Cumulative Poisson Distribution," by H. O. Hartley and E. S. Pearson, *Biometrika*, **37** (1950), 313–325.

Table H. χ^2 Distributions

(Upper Tail)

Number of Degrees of Freedom													
1		2		3		4		5		6		7	
x	P	x	P	x	P	x	P	x	P	x	P	x	P
0	1.000	0	1.000	0	1.000	0	1.000	0	1.000	0	1.000	0	1.000
.01	.920	.2	.905	.5	.919	1	.910	1.5	.913	2	.920	2	.960
.05	.823	.3	.861	1	.801	1.5	.827	2	.849	3	.809	3	.885
.1	.752	.4	.819	1.5	.682	2	.736	3	.700	4	.677	4	.780
.2	.655	.5	.779	2	.572	3	.558	4	.549	5	.544	5	.660
.3	.584	1	.607	3	.392	4	.406	5	.416	6	.423	6	.540
.4	.527	1.5	.472	4	.261	5	.287	6	.306	7	.321	7	.429
.5	.480	2	.368	5	.172	6	.199	7	.221	8	.238	8	.333
1	.317	3	.223	6	.112	7	.136	8	.156	9	.174	9	.253
1.5	.221	4	.135	7	.072	8	.092	9	.109	10	.125	10	.189
2	.157	5	.082	8	.046	9	.061	10	.075	11	.088	11	.139
3	.083	6	.050	9	.029	10	.040	11	.051	12	.062	12	.101
4	.046	7	.030	10	.019	11	.027	12	.035	13	.043	13	.072
5	.025	8	.018	11	.012	12	.017	13	.023	14	.030	14	.051
6	.014	9	.011	12	.007	13	.011	14	.016	15	.020	15	.036
7	.008	10	.007	13	.005	14	.007	15	.010	16	.014	16	.025
8	.005	11	.004	14	.003	15	.005	16	.007	17	.009	17	.017
9	.003	12	.002	15	.002	16	.003	17	.004	18	.006	18	.012
10	.002	13	.002	16	.001	17	.002	18	.003	19	.004	19	.008
11	.001	14	.001	17	.001	18	.001	19	.002	20	.003	20	.006
12	.001	15	.001	18	.000	19	.001	20	.001	21	.002	21	.004
13	.000	16	.000			20	.000	21	.001	22	.001	22	.003
								22	.001	23	.001	23	.002
								23	.000	24	.001	24	.001
										25	.000	25	.001
												26	.000

Table H. χ^2 Distributions

(Upper Tail)

Number of Degrees of Freedom													
8		9		10		11		12		13		14	
x	P	x	P	x	P	x	P	x	P	x	P	x	P
0	1.000	0	1.000	0	1.000	0	1.000	0	1.000	0	1.000	0	1.000
3	.934	4	.911	4	.947	5	.931	6	.916	7	.902	7	.935
4	.857	5	.834	5	.891	6	.873	7	.858	8	.844	8	.889
5	.758	6	.740	6	.815	7	.799	8	.785	9	.773	9	.831
6	.647	7	.637	7	.725	8	.713	9	.703	10	.694	10	.762
7	.537	8	.534	8	.629	9	.622	10	.616	11	.611	11	.686
8	.433	9	.437	9	.532	10	.530	11	.529	12	.528	12	.606
9	.342	10	.350	10	.440	11	.443	12	.446	13	.448	13	.527
10	.265	11	.276	11	.358	12	.364	13	.369	14	.374	14	.450
11	.202	12	.213	12	.285	13	.293	14	.301	15	.307	15	.378
12	.151	13	.163	13	.224	14	.233	15	.241	16	.249	16	.313
13	.112	14	.122	14	.173	15	.182	16	.191	17	.199	17	.256
14	.082	15	.091	15	.132	16	.141	17	.150	18	.158	18	.207
15	.059	16	.067	16	.100	17	.108	18	.116	19	.123	19	.165
16	.042	17	.049	17	.074	18	.082	19	.089	20	.095	20	.130
17	.030	18	.035	18	.055	19	.061	20	.067	21	.073	21	.102
18	.021	19	.025	19	.040	20	.045	21	.050	22	.055	22	.079
19	.015	20	.018	20	.029	21	.033	22	.038	23	.042	23	.060
20	.010	21	.013	21	.021	22	.024	23	.028	24	.031	24	.046
21	.007	22	.009	22	.015	23	.018	24	.020	25	.023	25	.035
22	.005	23	.006	23	.011	24	.013	25	.015	26	.017	26	.026
23	.003	24	.004	24	.008	25	.009	26	.011	27	.012	27	.019
24	.002	25	.003	25	.005	26	.006	27	.008	28	.009	28	.014
25	.002	26	.002	26	.004	27	.005	28	.006	29	.007	29	.010
26	.001	27	.001	27	.003	28	.003	29	.004	30	.005	30	.008
27	.001	28	.001	28	.002	29	.002	30	.003	31	.003	31	.006
28	.000	29	.001	29	.001	30	.002	31	.002	32	.002	32	.004
		30	.000	30	.001	31	.001	32	.001	33	.002	33	.003
				31	.001	32	.001	33	.001	34	.001	34	.002
				32	.000	33	.001	34	.001	35	.001	35	.001
						34	.000	35	.000	36	.001	36	.001
										37	.000	37	.001
												38	.001
												39	.000

Table H. χ^2 Distributions

(Upper Tail)

Number of Degrees of Freedom											
15		16		17		18		19		20	
x	P	x	P	x	P	x	P	x	P	x	P
0	1.000	0	1.000	0	1.000	0	1.000	0	1.000	0	1.000
8	.924	9	.913	10	.904	10	.932	11	.924	12	.916
9	.878	10	.867	11	.857	11	.894	12	.886	13	.877
10	.820	11	.809	12	.800	12	.847	13	.839	14	.830
11	.753	12	.744	13	.736	13	.792	14	.784	15	.776
12	.679	13	.673	14	.667	14	.729	15	.723	16	.717
13	.602	14	.599	15	.595	15	.662	16	.657	17	.653
14	.526	15	.525	16	.524	16	.593	17	.590	18	.587
15	.451	16	.453	17	.454	17	.523	18	.522	19	.522
16	.382	17	.386	18	.389	18	.456	19	.457	20	.458
17	.319	18	.324	19	.329	19	.392	20	.395	21	.397
18	.263	19	.269	20	.274	20	.333	21	.337	22	.341
19	.214	20	.220	21	.226	21	.279	22	.284	23	.289
20	.172	21	.179	22	.185	22	.232	23	.237	24	.242
21	.137	22	.143	23	.149	23	.191	24	.196	25	.201
22	.108	23	.114	24	.119	24	.155	25	.161	26	.166
23	.084	24	.090	25	.095	25	.125	26	.130	27	.135
24	.065	25	.070	26	.074	26	.100	27	.105	28	.109
25	.050	26	.054	27	.058	27	.079	28	.083	29	.088
26	.038	27	.041	28	.045	28	.062	29	.066	30	.070
27	.029	28	.032	29	.035	29	.048	30	.052	31	.055
28	.022	29	.024	30	.026	30	.037	31	.040	32	.043
29	.016	30	.018	31	.020	31	.029	32	.031	33	.034
30	.012	31	.013	32	.015	32	.022	33	.024	34	.026
31	.009	32	.010	33	.011	33	.017	34	.018	35	.020
32	.006	33	.007	34	.008	34	.013	35	.014	36	.015
33	.005	34	.005	35	.006	35	.009	36	.011	37	.012
34	.003	35	.004	36	.005	36	.007	37	.008	38	.009
35	.002	36	.003	37	.003	37	.005	38	.006	39	.007
36	.002	37	.002	38	.002	38	.004	39	.004	40	.005
37	.001	38	.002	39	.002	39	.003	40	.003	42	.003
38	.001	39	.001	40	.001	40	.002	42	.002	44	.002
39	.001	40	.001	42	.001	42	.001	44	.001	46	.001
40	.000	42	.000	44	.000	44	.001	46	.000	48	.000
						46	.000				

TABLE I

F DISTRIBUTIONS*

Table I gives the areas under the curve for F distributions with ν_1 and ν_2 degrees of freedom. When F is computed as the ratio of two mean squares, ν_1 is the degrees of freedom for the numerator and ν_2 is that for the denominator. The table is cumulative from the right-hand extreme to zero. The relation between the table and the areas under the curve is as for the following example for $\nu_1 = 8$ and $\nu_2 = 3$.

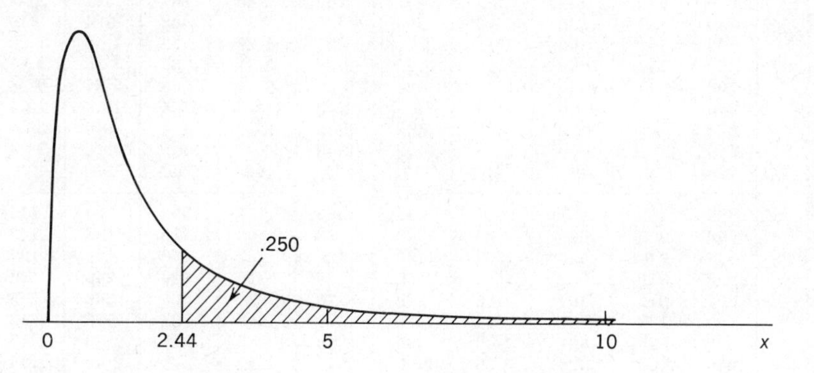

The range for either ν_1 or ν_2 is 1(1)10, 12, 15, 20, 30, 40, 60, 120, and ∞. In this table, .000062 is written $.0^4 62$; 16,200 is written 162^2. The distributions for $\nu_1 = 1$ are those of Student's t^2 with ν_2 degrees of freedom.

* With kind permission of the Biometrika Trustees, adapted from "Tables of Percentage Points of the Inverted Beta (F) Distribution," by Maxime Merrington and Catherine M. Thompson, *Biometrika*, **33** (1943), 73–88.

Table I. F Distributions

(Upper Tail)

ν_2	P	x								
		$\nu_1 = 1$	$\nu_1 = 2$	$\nu_1 = 3$	$\nu_1 = 4$	$\nu_1 = 5$	$\nu_1 = 6$	$\nu_1 = 7$	$\nu_1 = 8$	$\nu_1 = 9$
1	.995	$.0^4 62$	$.0^2 50$	.018	.032	.044	.054	.062	.068	.073
	.990	$.0^3 25$	.010	.029	.047	.062	.073	.082	.089	.095
	.975	$.0^2 15$	.026	.057	.082	.100	.113	.124	.132	.139
	.950	$.0^2 62$	.054	.099	.130	.151	.167	.179	.188	.195
	.900	.025	.117	.181	.220	.246	.265	.279	.289	.298
	.750	.172	.389	.494	.553	.591	.617	.636	.650	.661
	.500	1.00	1.50	1.71	1.82	1.89	1.94	1.98	2.00	2.02
	.250	5.83	7.50	8.20	8.58	8.82	8.98	9.10	9.19	9.26
	.100	39.9	49.5	53.6	55.8	57.2	58.2	58.9	59.4	59.9
	.050	161	200	216	225	230	234	237	239	241
	.025	648	800	864	900	922	937	948	957	963
	.010	405^1	500^1	540^1	562^1	576^1	586^1	593^1	598^1	602^1
	.005	162^2	200^2	216^2	225^2	231^2	234^2	237^2	239^2	241^2
2	.995	$.0^4 50$	$.0^2 50$	.020	.038	.055	.069	.081	.091	.099
	.990	$.0^3 20$	.010	.032	.056	.075	.092	.105	.116	.125
	.975	$.0^2 13$	.026	.062	.094	.119	.138	.153	.165	.175
	.950	$.0^2 50$	.053	.105	.144	.173	.194	.211	.224	.235
	.900	.020	.111	.183	.231	.265	.289	.307	.321	.333
	.750	.133	.333	.439	.500	.540	.567	.588	.604	.616
	.500	.667	1.00	1.13	1.21	1.25	1.28	1.30	1.32	1.33
	.250	2.57	3.00	3.15	3.23	3.28	3.31	3.34	3.35	3.37
	.100	8.53	9.00	9.16	9.24	9.29	9.33	9.35	9.37	9.38
	.050	18.5	19.0	19.2	19.2	19.3	19.3	19.4	19.4	19.4
	.025	38.5	39.0	39.2	39.2	39.3	39.3	39.4	39.4	39.4
	.010	98.5	99.0	99.2	99.2	99.3	99.3	99.4	99.4	99.4
	.005	198	199	199	199	199	199	199	199	199
3	.995	$.0^4 46$	$.0^2 50$	.021	.041	.060	.077	.092	.104	.115
	.990	$.0^3 19$	.010	.034	.060	.083	.102	.118	.132	.143
	.975	$.0^2 12$	.026	.065	.100	.129	.152	.170	.185	.197
	.950	$.0^2 46$	.052	.108	.152	.185	.210	.230	.246	.259
	.900	.019	.109	.186	.239	.276	.304	.325	.342	.356
	.750	.122	.317	.425	.489	.531	.560	.582	.599	.613
	.500	.585	.881	1.00	1.06	1.10	1.13	1.15	1.16	1.17
	.250	2.02	2.28	2.36	2.39	2.41	2.42	2.43	2.44	2.44
	.100	5.54	5.46	5.39	5.34	5.31	5.28	5.27	5.25	5.24
	.050	10.1	9.55	9.28	9.12	9.01	8.94	8.89	8.85	8.81
	.025	17.4	16.0	15.4	15.1	14.9	14.7	14.6	14.5	14.5
	.010	34.1	30.8	29.5	28.7	28.2	27.9	27.7	27.5	27.3
	.005	55.6	49.8	47.5	46.2	45.4	44.8	44.4	44.1	43.9

Table I. F Distributions

(Upper Tail)

ν_2	P	x								
		$\nu_1 = 10$	$\nu_1 = 12$	$\nu_1 = 15$	$\nu_1 = 20$	$\nu_1 = 30$	$\nu_1 = 40$	$\nu_1 = 60$	$\nu_1 = 120$	$\nu_1 = \infty$
1	.995	.078	.085	.093	.101	.109	.113	.118	.122	.127
	.990	.100	.107	.115	.124	.132	.137	.141	.146	.151
	.975	.144	.153	.161	.170	.180	.184	.189	.194	.199
	.950	.201	.211	.220	.230	.240	.245	.250	.255	.260
	.900	.304	.315	.325	.336	.347	.353	.358	.364	.370
	.750	.670	.684	.698	.712	.727	.734	.741	.748	.756
	.500	2.04	2.07	2.09	2.12	2.15	2.16	2.17	2.18	2.20
	.250	9.32	9.41	9.49	9.58	9.67	9.71	9.76	9.80	9.85
	.100	60.2	60.7	61.2	61.7	62.3	62.5	62.8	63.1	63.3
	.050	242	244	246	248	250	251	252	253	254
	.025	969	977	985	993	100^{1}	101^{1}	101^{1}	101^{1}	102^{1}
	.010	606^{1}	611^{1}	616^{1}	621^{1}	626^{1}	629^{1}	631^{1}	634^{1}	637^{1}
	.005	242^{2}	244^{2}	246^{2}	248^{2}	250^{2}	251^{2}	253^{2}	254^{2}	255^{2}
2	.995	.106	.118	.130	.143	.157	.165	.173	.181	.189
	.990	.132	.144	.157	.171	.186	.193	.201	.209	.217
	.975	.183	.196	.210	.224	.239	.247	.255	.263	.271
	.950	.244	.257	.272	.286	.302	.309	.317	.326	.334
	.900	.342	.356	.371	.386	.402	.410	.418	.426	.434
	.750	.626	.641	.657	.672	.689	.697	.705	.713	.721
	.500	1.34	1.36	1.38	1.39	1.41	1.42	1.43	1.43	1.44
	.250	3.38	3.39	3.41	3.43	3.44	3.45	3.46	3.47	3.48
	.100	9.39	9.41	9.42	9.44	9.46	9.47	9.47	9.48	9.49
	.050	19.4	19.4	19.4	19.4	19.5	19.5	19.5	19.5	19.5
	.025	39.4	39.4	39.4	39.4	39.5	39.5	39.5	39.5	39.5
	.010	99.4	99.4	99.4	99.4	99.5	99.5	99.5	99.5	99.5
	.005	199	199	199	199	199	199	199	199	200
3	.995	.124	.138	.154	.172	.191	.201	.211	.222	.234
	.990	.153	.168	.185	.203	.222	.232	.242	.253	.264
	.975	.207	.224	.241	.259	.279	.289	.299	.310	.321
	.950	.270	.287	.304	.323	.342	.352	.363	.373	.384
	.900	.367	.384	.402	.420	.439	.449	.459	.469	.480
	.750	.624	.641	.658	.675	.693	.702	.711	.721	.730
	.500	1.18	1.20	1.21	1.23	1.24	1.25	1.25	1.26	1.27
	.250	2.44	2.45	2.46	2.46	2.46	2.47	2.47	2.47	2.47
	.100	5.23	5.22	5.20	5.18	5.17	5.16	5.15	5.14	5.13
	.050	8.79	8.74	8.70	8.66	8.62	8.59	8.57	8.55	8.53
	.025	14.4	14.3	14.3	14.2	14.1	14.0	14.0	13.9	13.9
	.010	27.2	27.1	26.9	26.7	26.5	26.4	26.3	26.2	26.1
	.005	43.7	43.4	43.1	42.8	42.5	42.3	42.1	42.0	41.8

Table I. F Distributions

(Upper Tail)

ν_2	P	x								
		$\nu_1 = 1$	$\nu_1 = 2$	$\nu_1 = 3$	$\nu_1 = 4$	$\nu_1 = 5$	$\nu_1 = 6$	$\nu_1 = 7$	$\nu_1 = 8$	$\nu_1 = 9$
4	.995	$.0^{4}44$	$.0^{2}50$	.022	.043	.064	.083	.100	.114	.126
	.990	$.0^{3}18$	.010	.035	.063	.088	.109	.127	.143	.156
	.975	$.0^{2}11$	.025	.066	.104	.135	.161	.181	.198	.212
	.950	$.0^{2}44$	.052	.110	.157	.193	.221	.243	.261	.275
	.900	.018	.108	.187	.243	.284	.314	.338	.356	.371
	.750	.117	.309	.418	.484	.528	.560	.583	.601	.615
	.500	.549	.828	.941	1.00	1.04	1.06	1.08	1.09	1.10
	.250	1.81	2.00	2.05	2.06	2.07	2.08	2.08	2.08	2.08
	.100	4.54	4.32	4.19	4.11	4.05	4.01	3.98	3.95	3.94
	.050	7.71	6.94	6.59	6.39	6.26	6.16	6.09	6.04	6.00
	.025	12.2	10.6	9.98	9.60	9.36	9.20	9.07	8.98	8.90
	.010	21.2	18.0	16.7	16.0	15.5	15.2	15.0	14.8	14.7
	.005	31.3	26.3	24.3	23.2	22.5	22.0	21.6	21.4	21.1
5	.995	$.0^{4}43$	$.0^{2}50$	.022	.045	.067	.087	.105	.120	.134
	.990	$.0^{3}17$	.010	.035	.064	.091	.114	.134	.151	.165
	.975	$.0^{2}11$	.025	.067	.107	.140	.167	.189	.208	.223
	.950	$.0^{2}43$	.052	.111	.160	.198	.228	.252	.271	.287
	.900	.017	.108	.188	.247	.290	.322	.347	.367	.383
	.750	.113	.305	.415	.483	.528	.560	.584	.603	.618
	.500	.528	.799	.907	.965	1.00	1.02	1.04	1.05	1.06
	.250	1.69	1.85	1.88	1.89	1.89	1.89	1.89	1.89	1.89
	.100	4.06	3.78	3.62	3.52	3.45	3.40	3.37	3.34	3.32
	.050	6.61	5.79	5.41	5.19	5.05	4.95	4.88	4.82	4.77
	.025	10.0	8.43	7.76	7.39	7.15	6.98	6.85	6.76	6.68
	.010	16.3	13.3	12.1	11.4	11.0	10.7	10.5	10.3	10.2
	.005	22.8	18.3	16.5	15.6	14.9	14.5	14.2	14.0	13.8
6	.995	$.0^{4}43$	$.0^{2}50$	.022	.046	.069	.090	.109	.126	.140
	.990	$.0^{3}17$	.010	.036	.066	.094	.118	.139	.157	.172
	.975	$.0^{2}11$	.025	.068	.109	.143	.172	.195	.215	.231
	.950	$.0^{2}43$	.052	.112	.162	.202	.233	.259	.279	.296
	.900	.017	.107	.189	.249	.294	.327	.354	.375	.392
	.750	.111	.302	.413	.482	.528	.561	.586	.606	.621
	.500	.515	.780	.886	.942	.977	1.00	1.02	1.03	1.04
	.250	1.62	1.76	1.78	1.79	1.79	1.78	1.78	1.78	1.77
	.100	3.78	3.46	3.29	3.18	3.11	3.05	3.01	2.98	2.96
	.050	5.99	5.14	4.76	4.53	4.39	4.28	4.21	4.15	4.10
	.025	8.81	7.26	6.60	6.23	5.99	5.82	5.70	5.60	5.52
	.010	13.7	10.9	9.78	9.15	8.75	8.47	8.26	8.10	7.98
	.005	18.6	14.5	12.9	12.0	11.5	11.1	10.8	10.6	10.4

Table I. F Distributions

(Upper Tail)

ν_2	P	x								
		$\nu_1 = 10$	$\nu_1 = 12$	$\nu_1 = 15$	$\nu_1 = 20$	$\nu_1 = 30$	$\nu_1 = 40$	$\nu_1 = 60$	$\nu_1 = 120$	$\nu_1 = \infty$
4	.995	.136	.153	.172	.193	.216	.229	.242	.255	.269
	.990	.167	.185	.204	.226	.249	.261	.274	.287	.301
	.975	.224	.243	.263	.285	.308	.320	.332	.346	.359
	.950	.288	.307	.327	.349	.372	.384	.396	.409	.422
	.900	.384	.403	.423	.445	.467	.478	.490	.502	.514
	.750	.627	.645	.664	.683	.702	.712	.722	.732	.743
	.500	1.11	1.13	1.14	1.15	1.16	1.17	1.18	1.18	1.19
	.250	2.08	2.08	2.08	2.08	2.08	2.08	2.08	2.08	2.08
	.100	3.92	3.90	3.87	3.84	3.82	3.80	3.79	3.78	3.76
	.050	5.96	5.91	5.86	5.80	5.75	5.72	5.69	5.66	5.63
	.025	8.84	8.75	8.66	8.56	8.46	8.41	8.36	8.31	8.26
	.010	14.5	14.4	14.2	14.0	13.8	13.7	13.7	13.6	13.5
	.005	21.0	20.7	20.4	20.2	19.9	19.8	19.6	19.5	19.3
5	.995	.146	.165	.186	.210	.237	.251	.266	.282	.299
	.990	.177	.197	.220	.244	.270	.285	.299	.315	.331
	.975	.236	.257	.280	.304	.330	.344	.359	.374	.390
	.950	.301	.322	.345	.369	.395	.408	.422	.437	.452
	.900	.397	.418	.440	.463	.488	.501	.514	.527	.541
	.750	.631	.650	.669	.690	.711	.721	.732	.743	.755
	.500	1.07	1.09	1.10	1.11	1.12	1.13	1.14	1.14	1.15
	.250	1.89	1.89	1.89	1.88	1.88	1.88	1.87	1.87	1.87
	.100	3.30	3.27	3.24	3.21	3.17	3.16	3.14	3.12	3.10
	.050	4.74	4.68	4.62	4.56	4.50	4.46	4.43	4.40	4.36
	.025	6.62	6.52	6.43	6.33	6.23	6.18	6.12	6.07	6.02
	.010	10.1	9.89	9.72	9.55	9.38	9.29	9.20	9.11	9.02
	.005	13.6	13.4	13.1	12.9	12.7	12.5	12.4	12.3	12.1
6	.995	.153	.174	.197	.224	.253	.269	.286	.304	.323
	.990	.186	.207	.232	.258	.288	.304	.321	.338	.357
	.975	.246	.268	.293	.320	.349	.364	.381	.398	.415
	.950	.311	.334	.358	.385	.413	.428	.444	.460	.477
	.900	.406	.429	.453	.478	.505	.519	.533	.548	.564
	.750	.634	.654	.675	.696	.718	.730	.741	.753	.765
	.500	1.05	1.06	1.07	1.08	1.10	1.10	1.11	1.12	1.12
	.250	1.77	1.77	1.76	1.76	1.75	1.75	1.74	1.74	1.74
	.100	2.94	2.90	2.87	2.84	2.80	2.78	2.76	2.74	2.72
	.050	4.06	4.00	3.94	3.87	3.81	3.77	3.74	3.70	3.67
	.025	5.46	5.37	5.27	5.17	5.07	5.01	4.96	4.90	4.85
	.010	7.87	7.72	7.56	7.40	7.23	7.14	7.06	6.97	6.88
	.005	10.2	10.0	9.81	9.59	9.36	9.24	9.12	9.00	8.88

Table I. F Distributions

(Upper Tail)

		x								
ν_2	P	$\nu_1 = 1$	$\nu_1 = 2$	$\nu_1 = 3$	$\nu_1 = 4$	$\nu_1 = 5$	$\nu_1 = 6$	$\nu_1 = 7$	$\nu_1 = 8$	$\nu_1 = 9$
7	.995	$.0^{4}42$	$.0^{2}50$	.023	.046	.070	.093	.113	.130	.145
	.990	$.0^{3}17$	.010	.036	.067	.096	.121	.143	.162	.178
	.975	$.0^{2}11$	.025	.068	.110	.146	.176	.200	.221	.238
	.950	$.0^{2}42$	.052	.113	.164	.205	.238	.264	.286	.304
	.900	.017	.107	.190	.251	.297	.332	.359	.381	.399
	.750	.110	.300	.411	.481	.528	.562	.588	.608	.624
	.500	.506	.767	.871	.926	.960	.983	1.00	1.01	1.02
	.250	1.57	1.70	1.72	1.72	1.71	1.71	1.70	1.70	1.69
	.100	3.59	3.26	3.07	2.96	2.88	2.83	2.78	2.75	2.72
	.050	5.59	4.74	4.35	4.12	3.97	3.87	3.79	3.73	3.68
	.025	8.07	6.54	5.89	5.52	5.29	5.12	4.99	4.90	4.82
	.010	12.2	9.55	8.45	7.85	7.46	7.19	6.99	6.84	6.72
	.005	16.2	12.4	10.9	10.0	9.52	9.16	8.89	8.68	8.51
8	.995	$.0^{4}42$	$.0^{2}50$	.023	.047	.072	.095	.115	.133	.149
	.990	$.0^{3}17$	.010	.036	.068	.097	.123	.146	.166	.183
	.975	$.0^{2}10$	.025	.069	.111	.148	.179	.204	.226	.244
	.950	$.0^{2}42$	.052	.113	.166	.208	.241	.268	.291	.310
	.900	.017	.107	.190	.253	.299	.335	.363	.386	.405
	.750	.109	.298	.410	.481	.528	.563	.589	.610	.627
	.500	.499	.757	.860	.915	.948	971	.988	1.00	1.01
	.250	1.54	1.66	1.67	1.66	1.66	1.65	1.64	1.64	1.64
	.100	3.46	3.11	2.92	2.81	2.73	2.67	2.62	2.59	2.56
	.050	5.32	4.46	4.07	3.84	3.69	3.58	3.50	3.44	3.39
	.025	7.57	6.06	5.42	5.05	4.82	4.65	4.53	4.43	4.36
	.010	11.3	8.65	7.59	7.01	6.63	6.37	6.18	6.03	5.91
	.005	14.7	11.0	9.60	8.81	8.30	7.95	7.69	7.50	7.34
9	.995	$.0^{4}42$	$.0^{2}50$	.023	.047	.073	.096	.117	.136	.153
	.990	$.0^{3}17$	.010	.037	.068	.098	.125	.149	.169	.187
	.975	$.0^{2}10$	.025	.069	.112	.150	.181	.207	.230	.248
	.950	$.0^{2}42$	.052	.113	.167	.210	.244	.272	.295	.315
	.900	.017	.107	.191	.254	.302	.338	.367	.390	.410
	.750	.108	.297	.410	.480	.529	.564	.591	.612	.629
	.500	.494	.749	.852	.906	.939	.962	.978	.990	1.00
	.250	1.51	1.62	1.63	1.63	1.62	1.61	1.60	1.60	1.59
	.100	3.36	3.01	2.81	2.69	2.61	2.55	2.51	2.47	2.44
	.050	5.12	4.26	3.86	3.63	3.48	3.37	3.29	3.23	3.18
	.025	7.21	5.71	5.08	4.72	4.48	4.32	4.20	4.10	4.03
	.010	10.6	8.02	6.99	6.42	6.06	5.80	5.61	5.47	5.35
	.005	13.6	10.1	8.72	7.96	7.47	7.13	6.88	6.69	6.54

Table I. F Distributions

(Upper Tail)

		x								
ν_2	P	$\nu_1 = 10$	$\nu_1 = 12$	$\nu_1 = 15$	$\nu_1 = 20$	$\nu_1 = 30$	$\nu_1 = 40$	$\nu_1 = 60$	$\nu_1 = 120$	$\nu_1 = \infty$
7	.995	.159	.181	.206	.235	.267	.285	.304	.324	.345
	.990	.192	.216	.241	.270	.303	.320	.339	.358	.379
	.975	.253	.277	.304	.333	.364	.381	.399	.418	.437
	.950	.319	.343	.369	.398	.428	.445	.462	.479	.498
	.900	.414	.438	.463	.490	.519	.534	.550	.566	.583
	.750	.637	.658	.679	.702	.725	.737	.749	.762	.775
	.500	1.03	1.04	1.05	1.07	1.08	1.08	1.09	1.10	1.10
	.250	1.69	1.68	1.68	1.67	1.66	1.66	1.65	1.65	1.65
	.100	2.70	2.67	2.63	2.59	2.56	2.54	2.51	2.49	2.47
	.050	3.64	3.57	3.51	3.44	3.38	3.34	3.30	3.27	3.23
	.025	4.76	4.67	4.57	4.47	4.36	4.31	4.25	4.20	4.14
	.010	6.62	6.47	6.31	6.16	5.99	5.91	5.82	5.74	5.65
	.005	8.38	8.18	7.97	7.75	7.53	7.42	7.31	7.19	7.08
8	.995	.164	.187	.214	.244	.279	.299	.319	.341	.364
	.990	.198	.222	.250	.281	.315	.334	.354	.376	.398
	.975	.259	.285	.313	.343	.377	.395	.415	.435	.456
	.950	.326	.351	.379	.409	.441	.459	.477	.496	.516
	.900	.421	.446	.472	.500	.531	.547	.563	.581	.599
	.750	.640	.661	.683	.707	.731	.743	.756	.769	.783
	.500	1.02	1.03	1.04	1.05	1.07	1.07	1.08	1.08	1.09
	.250	1.63	1.62	1.62	1.61	1.60	1.59	1.59	1.58	1.58
	.100	2.54	2.50	2.46	2.42	2.38	2.36	2.34	2.32	2.29
	.050	3.35	3.28	3.22	3.15	3.08	3.04	3.01	2.97	2.93
	.025	4.30	4.20	4.10	4.00	3.89	3.84	3.78	3.73	3.67
	.010	5.81	5.67	5.52	5.36	5.20	5.12	5.03	4.95	4.86
	.005	7.21	7.01	6.81	6.61	6.40	6.29	6.18	6.06	5.95
9	.995	.168	.192	.220	.253	.290	.310	.332	.356	.382
	.990	.202	.228	.257	.289	.326	.346	.368	.391	.415
	.975	.265	.291	.320	.353	.388	.408	.428	.450	.473
	.950	.331	.358	.386	.418	.452	.471	.490	.511	.532
	.900	.426	.452	.479	.509	.541	.558	.575	.594	.613
	.750	.643	.664	.687	.711	.736	.749	.762	.776	.790
	.500	1.01	1.02	1.03	1.04	1.05	1.06	1.07	1.07	1.08
	.250	1.59	1.58	1.57	1.56	1.55	1.54	1.54	1.53	1.53
	.100	2.42	2.38	2.34	2.30	2.25	2.23	2.21	2.18	2.16
	.050	3.14	3.07	3.01	2.94	2.86	2.83	2.79	2.75	2.71
	.025	3.96	3.87	3.77	3.67	3.56	3.51	3.45	3.39	3.33
	.010	5.26	5.11	4.96	4.81	4.65	4.57	4.48	4.40	4.31
	.005	6.42	6.23	6.03	5.83	5.62	5.52	5.41	5.30	5.19

Table I. F Distributions

(Upper Tail)

ν_2	P	x								
		$\nu_1 = 1$	$\nu_1 = 2$	$\nu_1 = 3$	$\nu_1 = 4$	$\nu_1 = 5$	$\nu_1 = 6$	$\nu_1 = 7$	$\nu_1 = 8$	$\nu_1 = 9$
10	.995	$.0^441$	$.0^250$	.023	.048	.073	.098	.119	.139	.156
	.990	$.0^317$	.010	.037	.069	.099	.127	.151	.172	.190
	.975	$.0^210$	.025	.069	.113	.151	.183	.210	.233	.252
	.950	$.0^241$	.052	.114	.168	.211	.246	.275	.299	.319
	.900	.017	.106	.191	.255	.303	.340	.370	.394	.414
	.750	.107	.296	.409	.480	.529	.565	.592	.613	.630
	.500	.490	.743	.845	.899	.932	.954	.971	.983	.992
	.250	1.49	1.60	1.60	1.59	1.59	1.58	1.57	1.56	1.56
	.100	3.28	2.92	2.73	2.61	2.52	2.46	2.41	2.38	2.35
	.050	4.96	4.10	3.71	3.48	3.33	3.22	3.14	3.07	3.02
	.025	6.94	5.46	4.83	4.47	4.24	4.07	3.95	3.85	3.78
	.010	10.0	7.56	6.55	5.99	5.64	5.39	5.20	5.06	4.94
	.005	12.8	9.43	8.08	7.34	6.87	6.54	6.30	6.12	5.97
12	.995	$.0^441$	$.0^250$	.023	.048	.075	.100	.122	.143	.161
	.990	$.0^316$	.010	.037	.070	.101	.130	.155	.176	.196
	.975	$.0^210$	.025	.070	.114	.153	.186	.214	.238	.259
	.950	$.0^241$	.052	.114	.169	.214	.250	.280	.305	.325
	.900	.016	.106	.192	.257	.306	.344	.375	.400	.420
	.750	.106	.295	.408	.480	.530	.566	.594	.616	.633
	.500	.484	.735	.835	.888	.921	.943	.959	.972	.981
	.250	1.46	1.56	1.56	1.55	1.54	1.53	1.52	1.51	1.51
	.100	3.18	2.81	2.61	2.48	2.39	2.33	2.28	2.24	2.21
	.050	4.75	3.89	3.49	3.26	3.11	3.00	2.91	2.85	2.80
	.025	6.55	5.10	4.47	4.12	3.89	3.73	3.61	3.51	3.44
	.010	9.33	6.93	5.95	5.41	5.06	4.82	4.64	4.50	4.39
	.005	11.8	8.51	7.23	6.52	6.07	5.76	5.52	5.35	5.20
15	.995	$.0^441$	$.0^250$	.023	.049	.076	.102	.126	.147	.166
	.990	$.0^316$	.010	.037	.070	.103	.132	.158	.181	.202
	.975	$.0^210$	.025	.070	.116	.156	.190	.219	.244	.265
	.950	$.0^241$	.051	.115	.171	.217	.254	.285	.311	.333
	.900	.016	.106	.192	.258	.309	.348	.380	.406	.427
	.750	.105	.293	.407	.480	.530	.568	.596	.618	.637
	.500	.478	.726	.826	.878	.911	.933	.948	.960	.970
	.250	1.43	1.52	1.52	1.51	1.49	1.48	1.47	1.46	1.46
	.100	3.07	2.70	2.49	2.36	2.27	2.21	2.16	2.12	2.09
	.050	4.54	3.68	3.29	3.06	2.90	2.79	2.71	2.64	2.59
	.025	6.20	4.76	4.15	3.80	3.58	3.41	3.29	3.20	3.12
	.010	8.68	6.36	5.42	4.89	4.56	4.32	4.14	4.00	3.89
	.005	10.8	7.70	6.48	5.80	5.37	5.07	4.85	4.67	4.54

Table I. F Distributions

(Upper Tail)

ν_2	P	x								
		$\nu_1 = 10$	$\nu_1 = 12$	$\nu_1 = 15$	$\nu_1 = 20$	$\nu_1 = 30$	$\nu_1 = 40$	$\nu_1 = 60$	$\nu_1 = 120$	$\nu_1 = \infty$
10	.995	.171	.197	.226	.260	.299	.321	.344	.370	.397
	.990	.206	.233	.263	.297	.336	.357	.380	.405	.431
	.975	.269	.296	.327	.361	.398	.419	.440	.464	.488
	.950	.336	.363	.393	.426	.462	.481	.502	.523	.546
	.900	.431	.457	.486	.516	.550	.567	.586	.605	.626
	.750	.645	.667	.690	.715	.740	.754	.768	.782	.797
	.500	1.00	1.01	1.02	1.03	1.05	1.05	1.06	1.06	1.07
	.250	1.55	1.54	1.53	1.52	1.51	1.51	1.50	1.49	1.48
	.100	2.32	2.28	2.24	2.20	2.16	2.13	2.11	2.08	2.06
	.050	2.98	2.91	2.84	2.77	2.70	2.66	2.62	2.58	2.54
	.025	3.72	3.62	3.52	3.42	3.31	3.26	3.20	3.14	3.08
	.010	4.85	4.71	4.56	4.41	4.25	4.17	4.08	4.00	3.91
	.005	5.85	5.66	5.47	5.27	5.07	4.97	4.86	4.75	4.64
12	.995	.177	.204	.235	.272	.315	.339	.365	.393	.424
	.990	.212	.241	.273	.309	.352	.375	.401	.428	.458
	.975	.276	.305	.337	.374	.415	.437	.461	.487	.514
	.950	.343	.372	.404	.439	.478	.499	.522	.545	.571
	.900	.438	.466	.496	.528	.564	.583	.603	.625	.647
	.750	.648	.671	.695	.721	.748	.762	.777	.792	.808
	.500	.989	1.00	1.01	1.02	1.03	1.04	1.05	1.05	1.06
	.250	1.50	1.49	1.48	1.47	1.45	1.45	1.44	1.43	1.42
	.100	2.19	2.15	2.10	2.06	2.01	1.99	1.96	1.93	1.90
	.050	2.75	2.69	2.62	2.54	2.47	2.43	2.38	2.34	2.30
	.025	3.37	3.28	3.18	3.07	2.96	2.91	2.85	2.79	2.72
	.010	4.30	4.16	4.01	3.86	3.70	3.62	3.54	3.45	3.36
	.005	5.09	4.91	4.72	4.53	4.33	4.23	4.12	4.01	3.90
15	.995	.183	.212	.246	.286	.333	.360	.389	.421	.457
	.990	.219	.249	.284	.324	.370	.397	.425	.456	.491
	.975	.284	.315	.349	.389	.433	.458	.485	.514	.546
	.950	.351	.382	.416	.454	.496	.520	.545	.571	.600
	.900	.446	.475	.507	.542	.581	.602	.624	.647	.672
	.750	.652	.676	.701	.728	.757	.772	.788	.805	.822
	.500	.977	.989	1.00	1.01	1.02	1.03	1.03	1.04	1.05
	.250	1.45	1.44	1.43	1.41	1.40	1.39	1.38	1.37	1.36
	.100	2.06	2.02	1.97	1.92	1.87	1.85	1.82	1.79	1.76
	.050	2.54	2.48	2.40	2.33	2.25	2.20	2.16	2.11	2.07
	.025	3.06	2.96	2.86	2.76	2.64	2.58	2.52	2.46	2.40
	.010	3.80	3.67	3.52	3.37	3.21	3.13	3.05	2.96	2.87
	.005	4.42	4.25	4.07	3.88	3.69	3.58	3.48	3.37	3.26

Table I. F Distributions

(Upper Tail)

ν_2	P	x								
		$\nu_1 = 1$	$\nu_1 = 2$	$\nu_1 = 3$	$\nu_1 = 4$	$\nu_1 = 5$	$\nu_1 = 6$	$\nu_1 = 7$	$\nu_1 = 8$	$\nu_1 = 9$
20	.995	$.0^{4}40$	$.0^{2}50$	.023	.050	.078	.104	.129	.151	.171
	.990	$.0^{3}16$	.010	.037	.071	.105	.135	.162	.187	.208
	.975	$.0^{2}10$	.025	.071	.117	.158	.193	.224	.250	.273
	.950	$.0^{2}40$	.051	.115	.172	.219	.258	.290	.317	.341
	.900	.016	.106	.193	.260	.312	.353	.385	.412	.435
	.750	.104	.292	.406	.480	.531	.569	.598	.622	.641
	.500	.472	.718	.816	.868	.900	.922	.938	.950	.959
	.250	1.40	1.49	1.48	1.47	1.45	1.44	1.43	1.42	1.41
	.100	2.97	2.59	2.38	2.25	2.16	2.09	2.04	2.00	1.96
	.050	4.35	3.49	3.10	2.87	2.71	2.60	2.51	2.45	2.39
	.025	5.87	4.46	3.86	3.51	3.29	3.13	3.01	2.91	2.84
	.010	8.10	5.85	4.94	4.43	4.10	3.87	3.70	3.56	3.46
	.005	9.94	6.99	5.82	5.17	4.76	4.47	4.26	4.09	3.96
30	.995	$.0^{4}40$	$.0^{2}50$	.024	.050	.079	.107	.133	.156	.178
	.990	$.0^{3}16$	.010	.038	.072	.107	.138	.167	.192	.215
	.975	$.0^{2}10$	.025	.071	.118	.161	.197	.229	.257	.281
	.950	$.0^{2}40$	.051	.116	.174	.222	.263	.296	.325	.349
	.900	.016	.106	.193	.262	.315	.357	.391	.420	.444
	.750	.103	.290	.406	.480	.532	.571	.601	.625	.645
	.500	.466	.709	.807	.858	.890	.912	.927	.939	.948
	.250	1.38	1.45	1.44	1.42	1.41	1.39	1.38	1.37	1.36
	.100	2.88	2.49	2.28	2.14	2.05	1.98	1.93	1.88	1.85
	.050	4.17	3.32	2.92	2.69	2.53	2.42	2.33	2.27	2.21
	.025	5.57	4.18	3.59	3.25	3.03	2.87	2.75	2.65	2.57
	.010	7.56	5.39	4.51	4.02	3.70	3.47	3.30	3.17	3.07
	.005	9.18	6.35	5.24	4.62	4.23	3.95	3.74	3.58	3.45
40	.995	$.0^{4}40$	$.0^{2}50$	.024	.051	.080	.108	.135	.159	.181
	.990	$.0^{3}16$	.010	.038	.073	.108	.140	.169	.195	.219
	.975	$.0^{3}99$	.025	.071	.119	.162	.200	.232	.260	.285
	.950	$.0^{2}40$	.051	.116	.175	.224	.265	.299	.329	.354
	.900	.016	.106	.194	.263	.317	.360	.394	.423	.448
	.750	.103	.290	.405	.480	.533	.572	.603	.627	.647
	.500	.463	.705	.802	.854	.885	.907	.922	.934	.943
	.250	1.36	1.44	1.42	1.40	1.39	1.37	1.36	1.35	1.34
	.100	2.84	2.44	2.23	2.09	2.00	1.93	1.87	1.83	1.79
	.050	4.08	3.23	2.84	2.61	2.45	2.34	2.25	2.18	2.12
	.025	5.42	4.05	3.46	3.13	2.90	2.74	2.62	2.53	2.45
	.010	7.31	5.18	4.31	3.83	3.51	3.29	3.12	2.99	2.89
	.005	8.83	6.07	4.98	4.37	3.99	3.71	3.51	3.35	3.22

Table I. F Distributions

(Upper Tail)

ν_2	P	x								
		$\nu_1 = 10$	$\nu_1 = 12$	$\nu_1 = 15$	$\nu_1 = 20$	$\nu_1 = 30$	$\nu_1 = 40$	$\nu_1 = 60$	$\nu_1 = 120$	$\nu_1 = \infty$
20	.995	.190	.221	.258	.301	.354	.385	.419	.457	.500
	.990	.227	.259	.297	.340	.392	.422	.455	.491	.532
	.975	.293	.325	.363	.406	.456	.484	.514	.548	.585
	.950	.360	.393	.430	.471	.518	.544	.572	.603	.637
	.900	.454	.486	.520	.557	.600	.623	.648	.675	.704
	.750	.656	.681	.708	.736	.767	.784	.801	.820	.839
	.500	.966	.977	.989	1.00	1.01	1.02	1.02	1.03	1.03
	.250	1.40	1.39	1.37	1.36	1.34	1.33	1.32	1.31	1.29
	.100	1.94	1.89	1.84	1.79	1.74	1.71	1.68	1.64	1.61
	.050	2.35	2.28	2.20	2.12	2.04	1.99	1.95	1.90	1.84
	.025	2.77	2.68	2.57	2.46	2.35	2.29	2.22	2.16	2.09
	.010	3.37	3.23	3.09	2.94	2.78	2.69	2.61	2.52	2.42
	.005	3.85	3.68	3.50	3.32	3.12	3.02	2.92	2.81	2.69
30	.995	.197	.231	.271	.320	.381	.416	.457	.504	.559
	.990	.235	.270	.311	.360	.419	.454	.493	.538	.589
	.975	.302	.337	.378	.426	.482	.515	.551	.592	.639
	.950	.370	.405	.445	.490	.543	.573	.606	.643	.685
	.900	.464	.497	.534	.575	.622	.649	.678	.710	.745
	.750	.661	.688	.716	.746	.780	.798	.818	.839	.862
	.500	.955	.966	.978	.989	1.00	1.01	1.01	1.02	1.02
	.250	1.35	1.34	1.32	1.30	1.28	1.27	1.26	1.24	1.23
	.100	1.82	1.77	1.72	1.67	1.61	1.57	1.54	1.50	1.46
	.050	2.16	2.09	2.01	1.93	1.84	1.79	1.74	1.68	1.62
	.025	2.51	2.41	2.31	2.20	2.07	2.01	1.94	1.87	1.79
	.010	2.98	2.84	2.70	2.55	2.39	2.30	2.21	2.11	2.01
	.005	3.34	3.18	3.01	2.82	2.63	2.52	2.42	2.30	2.18
40	.995	.201	.237	.279	.331	.396	.436	.481	.535	.599
	.990	.240	.276	.319	.371	.435	.473	.517	.567	.628
	.975	.307	.344	.387	.437	.498	.533	.573	.620	.674
	.950	.376	.412	.454	.502	.558	.591	.627	.669	.717
	.900	.469	.503	.542	.585	.636	.664	.696	.731	.772
	.750	.664	.691	.720	.752	.787	.807	.828	.851	.877
	.500	.950	.961	.972	.983	.994	1.00	1.01	1.01	1.02
	.250	1.33	1.31	1.30	1.28	1.25	1.24	1.22	1.21	1.19
	.100	1.76	1.71	1.66	1.61	1.54	1.51	1.47	1.43	1.38
	.050	2.08	2.00	1.92	1.84	1.74	1.69	1.64	1.58	1.51
	.025	2.39	2.29	2.18	2.07	1.94	1.88	1.80	1.72	1.64
	.010	2.80	2.66	2.52	2.37	2.20	2.11	2.02	1.92	1.80
	.005	3.12	2.95	2.78	2.60	2.40	2.30	2.18	2.06	1.93

Table I. F Distributions

(Upper Tail)

ν_2	P	x								
		$\nu_1 = 1$	$\nu_1 = 2$	$\nu_1 = 3$	$\nu_1 = 4$	$\nu_1 = 5$	$\nu_1 = 6$	$\nu_1 = 7$	$\nu_1 = 8$	$\nu_1 = 9$
60	.995	$.0^{4}40$	$.0^{2}50$	.024	.051	.081	.110	.137	.162	.185
	.990	$.0^{3}16$	.010	.038	.073	.109	.142	.172	.199	.223
	.975	$.0^{3}99$	.025	.071	.120	.163	.202	.235	.264	.290
	.950	$.0^{2}40$	.051	.117	.176	.226	.267	.303	.333	.359
	.900	.016	.106	.194	.264	.318	.362	.398	.428	.453
	.750	.102	.289	.405	.480	.534	.573	.604	.629	.650
	.500	.461	.701	.798	.849	.880	.901	.917	.928	.937
	.250	1.35	1.42	1.41	1.38	1.37	1.35	1.33	1.32	1.31
	.100	2.79	2.39	2.18	2.04	1.95	1.87	1.82	1.77	1.74
	.050	4.00	3.15	2.76	2.53	2.37	2.25	2.17	2.10	2.04
	.025	5.29	3.93	3.34	3.01	2.79	2.63	2.51	2.41	2.33
	.010	7.08	4.98	4.13	3.65	3.34	3.12	2.95	2.82	2.72
	.005	8.49	5.80	4.73	4.14	3.76	3.49	3.29	3.13	3.01
120	.995	$.0^{4}39$	$.0^{2}50$	.024	.051	.081	.111	.139	.165	.189
	.990	$.0^{3}16$	.010	.038	.074	.110	.143	.174	.202	.227
	.975	$.0^{3}99$	.025	.072	.120	.165	.204	.238	.268	.295
	.950	$.0^{2}39$	.051	.117	.177	.227	.270	.306	.337	.364
	.900	.016	.105	.194	.265	.320	.365	.401	.432	.458
	.750	.102	.288	.405	.480	.534	.574	.606	.631	.653
	.500	.458	.697	.793	.844	.875	.896	.912	.923	.932
	.250	1.34	1.40	1.39	1.37	1.35	1.33	1.31	1.30	1.29
	.100	2.75	2.35	2.13	1.99	1.90	1.82	1.77	1.72	1.68
	.050	3.92	3.07	2.68	2.45	2.29	2.18	2.09	2.02	1.96
	.025	5.15	3.80	3.23	2.89	2.67	2.52	2.39	2.30	2.22
	.010	6.85	4.79	3.95	3.48	3.17	2.96	2.79	2.66	2.56
	.005	8.18	5.54	4.50	3.92	3.55	3.28	3.09	2.93	2.81
∞	.995	$.0^{4}39$	$.0^{2}50$	.024	.052	.082	.113	.141	.168	.193
	.990	$.0^{3}16$	.010	.038	.074	.111	.145	.177	.206	.232
	.975	$.0^{3}98$	.025	.072	.121	.166	.206	.241	.272	.300
	.950	$.0^{2}39$	.051	.117	.178	.229	.273	.310	.342	.369
	.900	.016	.105	.195	.266	.322	.367	.405	.436	.463
	.750	.102	.288	.404	.481	.535	.576	.608	.634	.655
	.500	.455	.693	.789	.839	.870	.891	.907	.918	.927
	.250	1.32	1.39	1.40	1.35	1.33	1.31	1.29	1.28	1.27
	.100	2.71	2.30	2.08	1.94	1.85	1.77	1.72	1.67	1.63
	.050	3.84	3.00	2.60	2.37	2.21	2.10	2.01	1.94	1.88
	.025	5.02	3.69	3.12	2.79	2.57	2.41	2.29	2.19	2.11
	.010	6.63	4.61	3.78	3.32	3.02	2.80	2.64	2.51	2.41
	.005	7.88	5.30	4.28	3.72	3.35	3.09	2.90	2.74	2.62

Table I. F Distributions

(Upper Tail)

ν_2	P	x								
		$\nu_1 = 10$	$\nu_1 = 12$	$\nu_1 = 15$	$\nu_1 = 20$	$\nu_1 = 30$	$\nu_1 = 40$	$\nu_1 = 60$	$\nu_1 = 120$	$\nu_1 = \infty$
60	.995	.206	.243	.287	.343	.414	.458	.510	.572	.653
	.990	.245	.283	.328	.383	.453	.495	.545	.604	.679
	.975	.313	.351	.396	.450	.515	.555	.600	.654	.720
	.950	.382	.419	.463	.514	.575	.611	.652	.700	.759
	.900	.475	.510	.550	.596	.650	.682	.717	.757	.806
	.750	.667	.695	.725	.758	.795	.816	.839	.865	.896
	.500	.945	.956	.967	.978	.989	.994	1.00	1.01	1.01
	.250	1.30	1.29	1.27	1.25	1.22	1.21	1.19	1.17	1.15
	.100	1.71	1.66	1.60	1.54	1.48	1.44	1.40	1.35	1.29
	.050	1.99	1.92	1.84	1.75	1.65	1.59	1.53	1.47	1.39
	.025	2.27	2.17	2.06	1.94	1.82	1.74	1.67	1.58	1.48
	.010	2.63	2.50	2.35	2.20	2.03	1.94	1.84	1.73	1.60
	.005	2.90	2.74	2.57	2.39	2.19	2.08	1.96	1.83	1.69
120	.995	.211	.249	.297	.356	.435	.485	.545	.623	.733
	.990	.250	.290	.338	.397	.474	.522	.579	.652	.755
	.975	.318	.359	.406	.464	.536	.580	.633	.698	.788
	.950	.382	.419	.463	.514	.575	.611	.652	.700	.759
	.900	.480	.518	.560	.609	.667	.702	.742	.791	.856
	.750	.670	.699	.730	.765	.805	.828	.854	.884	.923
	.500	.939	.950	.961	.972	.983	.989	.994	1.00	1.01
	.250	1.28	1.26	1.24	1.22	1.19	1.18	1.16	1.13	1.10
	.100	1.65	1.60	1.54	1.48	1.41	1.37	1.32	1.26	1.19
	.050	1.91	1.83	1.75	1.66	1.55	1.50	1.43	1.35	1.25
	.025	2.16	2.05	1.94	1.82	1.69	1.61	1.53	1.43	1.31
	.010	2.47	2.34	2.19	2.03	1.86	1.76	1.66	1.53	1.38
	.005	2.71	2.54	2.37	2.19	1.98	1.87	1.75	1.61	1.43
∞	.995	.216	.256	.307	.372	.460	.518	.592	.699	1.00
	.990	.256	.298	.349	.413	.498	.554	.625	.724	1.00
	975	.325	.367	.417	.480	.560	.611	.675	.763	1.00
	.950	.394	.436	.484	.543	.616	.663	.720	.798	1.00
	.900	.487	.525	.570	.622	.687	.726	.774	.839	1.00
	.750	.674	.703	.736	.773	.816	.842	.872	.910	1.00
	.500	.934	.945	.956	.967	.978	.983	.989	.994	1.00
	.250	1.25	1.24	1.22	1.19	1.16	1.14	1.12	1.08	1.00
	.100	1.60	1.55	1.49	1.42	1.34	1.30	1.24	1.17	1.00
	.050	1.83	1.75	1.67	1.57	1.46	1.39	1.32	1.22	1.00
	.025	2.05	1.94	1.83	1.71	1.57	1.48	1.39	1.27	1.00
	.010	2.32	2.18	2.04	1.88	1.70	1.59	1.47	1.32	1.00
	.005	2.52	2.36	2.19	2.00	1.79	1.67	1.53	1.36	1.00

TABLE J

SPEARMAN'S RANK CORRELATION DISTRIBUTIONS*

Table J gives the distribution of Spearman's rank correlation coefficient X, computed as the coefficient of linear correlation between two independent sets of n paired untied ranks. The table is cumulative from each extreme to, but not beyond, the mean. That is, the relation between the table and the distribution is as for the example below, where $n = 4$. The table also contains the distribution of the equivalent function $\sum d^2$, where $d_1, \ldots, d_n$ are the differences between the two ranks of a pair. The relation between X and $\sum d^2$ is given by $X = 1 - [6 \sum d^2/n(n^2 - 1)]$. (See Table J.1.) The range of n is $4 \leq n \leq 11$.

If $n > 11$, an approximation is obtained by referring $\sqrt{n-2}X/\sqrt{1-X^2}$ to a Student's t distribution with $n - 2$ degrees of freedom, or, equivalently, by referring $[(n-2)X^2]/(1 - X^2)$ to an F distribution with $\nu_1 = 1$ and $\nu_2 = n - 2$ degrees of freedom (Table I).

Another approximation, which can be used when n is fairly large, say, $n > 20$, is a normal approximation. The mean and standard deviation of X are

$$\mu_X = 0,$$

$$\sigma_X = \frac{1}{\sqrt{n-1}},$$

that is, $P\{X \leq k\}$ is approximately the area under the unit normal curve (Table E) below

$$\frac{(X + [6/n(n^2-1)]) - \mu}{\sigma} = \left(X + \frac{6}{n(n^2-1)}\right)\sqrt{n-1}.$$

* With kind permission of the publisher, adapted from *Handbook of Statistical Tables*, by D. B. Owen, Addison-Wesley Publishing Company (1962).

Distribution

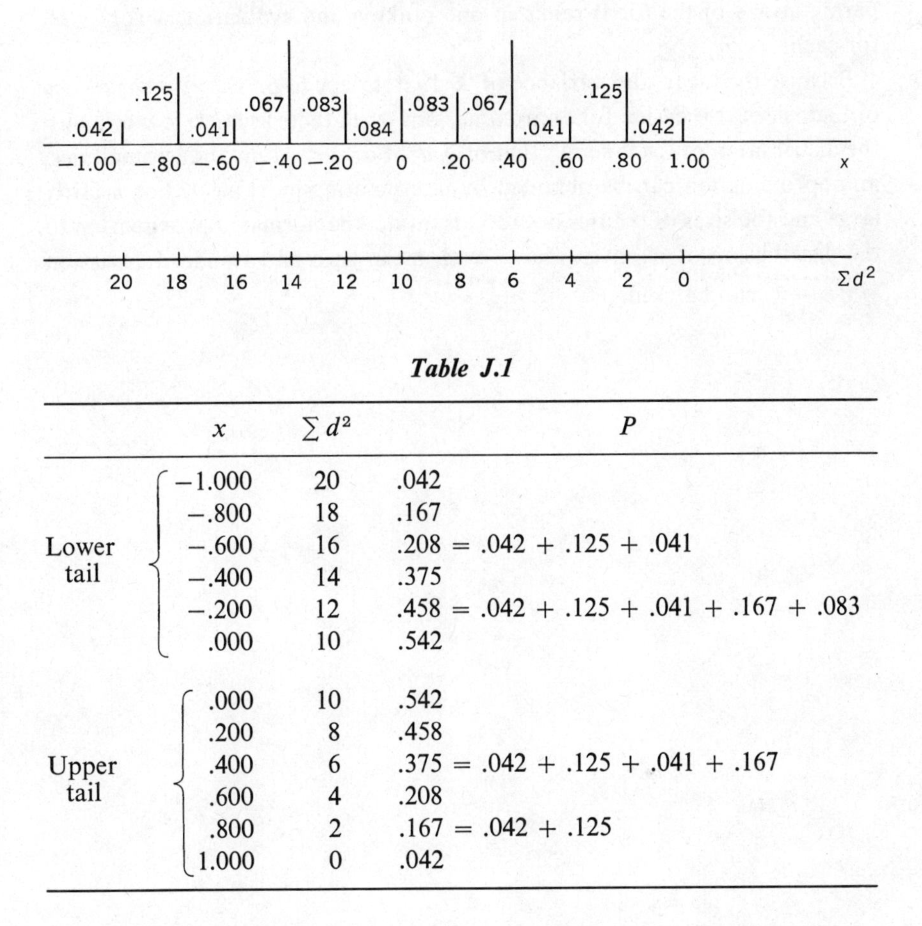

Table J.1

	x	$\sum d^2$	P
Lower tail	−1.000	20	.042
	−.800	18	.167
	−.600	16	.208 = .042 + .125 + .041
	−.400	14	.375
	−.200	12	.458 = .042 + .125 + .041 + .167 + .083
	.000	10	.542
Upper tail	.000	10	.542
	.200	8	.458
	.400	6	.375 = .042 + .125 + .041 + .167
	.600	4	.208
	.800	2	.167 = .042 + .125
	1.000	0	.042

When there are ties in one or both rankings, the ranks within each are found by averaging within each tie (see the introduction to Table B). X is the coefficient of linear correlation between these two sets of tied ranks. It can also be found by computing $\sum d^2$ for the two sets of tied ranks and making use of the formula

$$X = \frac{N^3 - [(D_1 + D_2)/2] - 6 \sum d^2}{\sqrt{(N^3 - D_1)(N^3 - D_2)}},$$

where $D_1(D_2)$ is the sum of the cubes of the sizes of the ties in the first (second) ranking.

The exact distribution of X (or $\sum d^2$) can be found by enumerating all permutations of the (tied) ranks in one ranking and evaluating X (or $\sum d^2$) for each.

Because the mean and variance of X do not depend on the number of ties or their sizes, it is easier, for approximations when there are ties, to work with the distribution of X than with that of $\sum d^2$. For $n \leq 11$ and a few small ties, an approximation can be obtained by interpolating in Table J. For n fairly large and the sizes of the ties not too disparate, the normal approximation to the distribution of X, given above, with mean zero and standard deviation $1/\sqrt{n-1}$, can be used.

Table J. Spearman's Rank Correlation Distributions

$n = 4$			$n = 5$			$n = 6$		
x	Σd^2	P	x	Σd^2	P	x	Σd^2	P
−1.000	20	.042	−1.000	40	.008	−1.000	70	.001
−.800	18	.167	−.900	38	.042	−.943	68	.008
−.600	16	.208	−.800	36	.067	−.886	66	.017
−.400	14	.375	−.700	34	.117	−.829	64	.029
−.200	12	.458	−.600	32	.175	−.771	62	.051
.000	10	.542	−.500	30	.225	−.714	60	.068
			−.400	28	.258	−.657	58	.088
.000	10	.542	−.300	26	.342	−.600	56	.121
.200	8	.458	−.200	24	.392	−.543	54	.149
.400	6	.375	−.100	22	.475	−.486	52	.178
.600	4	.208	.000	20	.525	−.429	50	.210
.800	2	.167				−.371	48	.249
1.000	0	.042	.000	20	.525	−.314	46	.282
			.100	18	.475	−.257	44	.329
			.200	16	.392	−.200	42	.357
			.300	14	.342	−.143	40	.401
			.400	12	.258	−.086	38	.460
			.500	10	.225	−.029	36	.500
			.600	8	.175			
			.700	6	.117	.029	34	.500
			.800	4	.067	.086	32	.460
			.900	2	.042	.143	30	.401
			1.000	0	.008	.200	28	.357
						.257	26	.329
						.314	24	.282
						.371	22	.249
						.429	20	.210
						.486	18	.178
						.543	16	.149
						.600	14	.121
						.657	12	.088
						.714	10	.068
						.771	8	.051
						.829	6	.029
						.886	4	.017
						.943	2	.008
						1.000	0	.001

Table J. Spearman's Rank Correlation Distributions

(Lower Tail)

$n = 7$			$n = 8$			$n = 9$					
x	Σd^2	P	x	Σd^2	P	x	Σd^2	P	x	Σd^2	P
-1.000	112	.000	-1.000	168	.000	-1.000	240	.000	-.483	178	.097
-.964	110	.001	-.976	166	.000	-.983	238	.000	-.467	176	.106
-.929	108	.003	-.952	164	.001	-.967	236	.000	-.450	174	.115
-.893	106	.006	-.929	162	.001	-.950	234	.000	-.433	172	.125
-.857	104	.012	-.905	160	.002	-.933	232	.000	-.417	170	.135
-.821	102	.017	-.881	158	.004	-.917	230	.001	-.400	168	.146
-.786	100	.024	-.857	156	.005	-.900	228	.001	-.383	166	.156
-.750	98	.033	-.833	154	.008	-.883	226	.002	-.367	164	.168
-.714	96	.044	-.810	152	.011	-.867	224	.002	-.350	162	.179
-.679	94	.055	-.786	150	.014	-.850	222	.003	-.333	160	.193
-.643	92	.069	-.762	148	.018	-.833	220	.004	-.317	158	.205
-.607	90	.083	-.738	146	.023	-.817	218	.005	-.300	156	.218
-.571	88	.100	-.714	144	.029	-.800	216	.007	-.283	154	.231
-.536	86	.118	-.690	142	.035	-.783	214	.009	-.267	152	.247
-.500	84	.133	-.667	140	.042	-.767	212	.011	-.250	150	.260
-.464	82	.151	-.643	138	.048	-.750	210	.013	-.233	148	.276
-.429	80	.177	-.619	136	.057	-.733	208	.016	-.217	146	.290
-.393	78	.198	-.595	134	.066	-.717	206	.018	-.200	144	.307
-.357	76	.222	-.571	132	.076	-.700	204	.022	-.183	142	.322
-.321	74	.249	-.548	130	.085	-.683	202	.025	-.167	140	.339
-.286	72	.278	-.524	128	.098	-.667	200	.029	-.150	138	.354
-.250	70	.297	-.500	126	.108	-.650	198	.033	-.133	136	.372
-.214	68	.331	-.476	124	.122	-.633	196	.038	-.117	134	.388
-.179	66	.357	-.452	122	.134	-.617	194	.043	-.100	132	.405
-.143	64	.391	-.429	120	.150	-.600	192	.048	-.083	130	.422
-.107	62	.420	-.405	118	.163	-.583	190	.054	-.067	128	.440
-.071	60	.453	-.381	116	.180	-.567	188	.060	-.050	126	.456
-.036	58	.482	-.357	114	.195	-.550	186	.066	-.033	124	.474
.000	56	.518	-.333	112	.214	-.533	184	.074	-.017	122	.491
			-.310	110	.231	-.517	182	.081	.000	120	.509
			-.286	108	.250	-.500	180	.089			
			-.262	106	.268						
			-.238	104	.291						
			-.214	102	.310						
			-.190	100	.332						
			-.167	98	.352						
			-.143	96	.376						
			-.119	94	.397						
			-.095	92	.420						
			-.071	90	.441						
			-.048	88	.467						
			-.024	86	.488						
			.000	84	.512						

Table J. Spearman's Rank Correlation Distributions

(Upper Tail)

$n = 7$		
x	Σd^2	P
.000	56	.518
.036	54	.482
.071	52	.453
.107	50	.420
.143	48	.391
.179	46	.357
.214	44	.331
.250	42	.297
.286	40	.278
.321	38	.249
.357	36	.222
.393	34	.198
.429	32	.177
.464	30	.151
.500	28	.133
.536	26	.118
.571	24	.100
.607	22	.083
.643	20	.069
.679	18	.055
.714	16	.044
.750	14	.033
.786	12	.024
.821	10	.017
.857	8	.012
.893	6	.006
.929	4	.003
.964	2	.001
1.000	0	.000

$n = 8$		
x	Σd^2	P
.000	84	.512
.024	82	.488
.048	80	.467
.071	78	.441
.095	76	.420
.119	74	.397
.143	72	.376
.167	70	.352
.190	68	.332
.214	66	.310
.238	64	.291
.262	62	.268
.286	60	.250
.310	58	.231
.333	56	.214
.357	54	.195
.381	52	.180
.405	50	.163
.429	48	.150
.452	46	.134
.476	44	.122
.500	42	.108
.524	40	.098
.548	38	.085
.571	36	.076
.595	34	.066
.619	32	.057
.643	30	.048
.667	28	.042
.690	26	.035
.714	24	.029
.738	22	.023
.762	20	.018
.786	18	.014
.810	16	.011
.833	14	.008
.857	12	.005
.881	10	.004
.905	8	.002
.929	6	.001
.952	4	.001
.976	2	.000
1.000	0	.000

$n = 9$					
x	Σd^2	P	x	Σd^2	P
.000	120	.509	.517	58	.081
.017	118	.491	.533	56	.074
.033	116	.474	.550	54	.066
.050	114	.456	.567	52	.060
.067	112	.440	.583	50	.054
.083	110	.422	.600	48	.048
.100	108	.405	.617	46	.043
.117	106	.388	.633	44	.038
.133	104	.372	.650	42	.033
.150	102	.354	.667	40	.029
.167	100	.339	.683	38	.025
.183	98	.322	.700	36	.022
.200	96	.307	.717	34	.018
.217	94	.290	.733	32	.016
.233	92	.276	.750	30	.013
.250	90	.260	.767	28	.011
.267	88	.247	.783	26	.009
.283	86	.231	.800	24	.007
.300	84	.218	.817	22	.005
.317	82	.205	.833	20	.004
.333	80	.193	.850	18	.003
.350	78	.179	.867	16	.002
.367	76	.168	.883	14	.002
.383	74	.156	.900	12	.001
.400	72	.146	.917	10	.001
.417	70	.135	.933	8	.000
.433	68	.125	.950	6	.000
.450	66	.115	.967	4	.000
.467	64	.106	.983	2	.000
.483	62	.097	1.000	0	.000
.500	60	.089			

Table J. Spearman's Rank Correlation Distributions

(Lower Tail)

n = 10					
x	Σd^2	P	x	Σd^2	P
−1.000	330	.000	−.491	246	.077
−.988	328	.000	−.479	244	.083
−.976	326	.000	−.467	242	.089
−.964	324	.000	−.455	240	.096
−.952	322	.000	−.442	238	.102
−.939	320	.000	−.430	236	.109
−.927	318	.000	−.418	234	.116
−.915	316	.000	−.406	232	.124
−.903	314	.000	−.394	230	.132
−.891	312	.001	−.382	228	.139
−.879	310	.001	−.370	226	.148
−.867	308	.001	−.358	224	.156
−.855	306	.001	−.345	222	.165
−.842	304	.002	−.333	220	.174
−.830	302	.002	−.321	218	.184
−.818	300	.003	−.309	216	.193
−.806	298	.004	−.297	214	.203
−.794	296	.004	−.285	212	.214
−.782	294	.005	−.273	210	.224
−.770	292	.006	−.261	208	.235
−.758	290	.008	−.248	206	.246
−.745	288	.009	−.236	204	.257
−.733	286	.010	−.224	202	.268
−.721	284	.012	−.212	200	.280
−.709	282	.013	−.200	198	.292
−.697	280	.015	−.188	196	.304
−.685	278	.017	−.176	194	.316
−.673	276	.019	−.164	192	.328
−.661	274	.022	−.152	190	.341
−.648	272	.024	−.139	188	.354
−.636	270	.027	−.127	186	.367
−.624	268	.030	−.115	184	.379
−.612	266	.033	−.103	182	.393
−.600	264	.037	−.091	180	.406
−.588	262	.040	−.079	178	.419
−.576	260	.044	−.067	176	.433
−.564	258	.048	−.055	174	.446
−.552	256	.052	−.042	172	.459
−.539	254	.057	−.030	170	.473
−.527	252	.062	−.018	168	.486
−.515	250	.067	−.006	166	.500
−.503	248	.072			

n = 11					
x	Σd^2	P	x	Σd^2	P
−1.000	440	.000	−.491	328	.065
−.991	438	.000	−.482	326	.069
−.982	436	.000	−.473	324	.073
−.973	434	.000	−.464	322	.077
−.964	432	.000	−.455	320	.082
−.955	430	.000	−.445	318	.087
−.945	428	.000	−.436	316	.091
−.936	426	.000	−.427	314	.096
−.927	424	.000	−.418	312	.102
−.918	422	.000	−.409	310	.107
−.909	420	.000	−.400	308	.112
−.900	418	.000	−.391	306	.118
−.891	416	.000	−.382	304	.124
−.882	414	.000	−.373	302	.130
−.873	412	.000	−.364	300	.137
−.864	410	.001	−.355	298	.143
−.855	408	.001	−.345	296	.150
−.845	406	.001	−.336	294	.157
−.836	404	.001	−.327	292	.163
−.827	402	.001	−.318	290	.171
−.818	400	.002	−.309	288	.178
−.809	398	.002	−.300	286	.186
−.800	396	.002	−.291	284	.193
−.791	394	.003	−.282	282	.201
−.782	392	.003	−.273	280	.209
−.773	390	.004	−.264	278	.217
−.764	388	.004	−.255	276	.226
−.755	386	.005	−.245	274	.234
−.745	384	.006	−.236	272	.243
−.736	382	.006	−.227	270	.252
−.727	380	.007	−.218	268	.260
−.718	378	.008	−.209	266	.270
−.709	376	.009	−.200	264	.279
−.700	374	.010	−.191	262	.288
−.691	372	.011	−.182	260	.298
−.682	370	.013	−.173	258	.307
−.673	368	.014	−.164	256	.317
−.664	366	.015	−.155	254	.327
−.655	364	.017	−.145	252	.337
−.645	362	.018	−.136	250	.347
−.636	360	.020	−.127	248	.357
−.627	358	.022	−.118	246	.367
−.618	356	.024	−.109	244	.377
−.609	354	.026	−.100	242	.388
−.600	352	.028	−.091	240	.398
−.591	350	.030	−.082	238	.409
−.582	348	.033	−.073	236	.419
−.573	346	.035	−.064	234	.430
−.564	344	.038	−.055	232	.441
−.555	342	.041	−.045	230	.452
−.545	340	.044	−.036	228	.462
−.536	338	.047	−.027	226	.473
−.527	336	.050	−.018	224	.484
−.518	334	.054	−.009	222	.495
−.509	332	.057	.000	220	.505
−.500	330	.061			

Table J. Spearman's Rank Correlation Distributions

(Upper Tail)

n = 10						n = 11					
x	Σd^2	P	x	Σd^2	P	x	Σd^2	P	x	Σd^2	P
.006	164	.500	.515	80	.067	.000	220	.505	.509	108	.057
.018	162	.486	.527	78	.062	.009	218	.495	.518	106	.054
.030	160	.473	.539	76	.057	.018	216	.484	.527	104	.050
.042	158	.459	.552	74	.052	.027	214	.473	.536	102	.047
.055	156	.446	.564	72	.048	.036	212	.462	.545	100	.044
.067	154	.433	.576	70	.044	.045	210	.452	.555	98	.041
.079	152	.419	.588	68	.040	.055	208	.441	.564	96	.038
.091	150	.406	.600	66	.037	.064	206	.430	.573	94	.035
.103	148	.393	.612	64	.033	.073	204	.419	.582	92	.033
.115	146	.379	.624	62	.030	.082	202	.409	.591	90	.030
.127	144	.367	.636	60	.027	.091	200	.398	.600	88	.028
.139	142	.354	.648	58	.024	.100	198	.388	.609	86	.026
.152	140	.341	.661	56	.022	.109	196	.377	.618	84	.024
.164	138	.328	.673	54	.019	.118	194	.367	.627	82	.022
.176	136	.316	.685	52	.017	.127	192	.357	.636	80	.020
.188	134	.304	.697	50	.015	.136	190	.347	.645	78	.018
.200	132	.292	.709	48	.013	.145	188	.337	.655	76	.017
.212	130	.280	.721	46	.012	.155	186	.327	.664	74	.015
.224	128	.268	.733	44	.010	.164	184	.317	.673	72	.014
.236	126	.257	.745	42	.009	.173	182	.307	.682	70	.013
.248	124	.246	.758	40	.008	.182	180	.298	.691	68	.011
.261	122	.235	.770	38	.006	.191	178	.288	.700	66	.010
.273	120	.224	.782	36	.005	.200	176	.279	.709	64	.009
.285	118	.214	.794	34	.004	.209	174	.270	.718	62	.008
.297	116	.203	.806	32	.004	.218	172	.260	.727	60	.007
.309	114	.193	.818	30	.003	.227	170	.252	.736	58	.006
.321	112	.184	.830	28	.002	.236	168	.243	.745	56	.006
.333	110	.174	.842	26	.002	.245	166	.234	.755	54	.005
.345	108	.165	.855	24	.001	.255	164	.226	.764	52	.004
.358	106	.156	.867	22	.001	.264	162	.217	.773	50	.004
.370	104	.148	.879	20	.001	.273	160	.209	.782	48	.003
.382	102	.139	.891	18	.001	.282	158	.201	.791	46	.003
.394	100	.132	.903	16	.000	.291	156	.193	.800	44	.002
.406	98	.124	.915	14	.000	.300	154	.186	.809	42	.002
.418	96	.116	.927	12	.000	.309	152	.178	.818	40	.002
.430	94	.109	.939	10	.000	.318	150	.171	.827	38	.001
.442	92	.102	.952	8	.000	.327	148	.163	.836	36	.001
.455	90	.096	.964	6	.000	.336	146	.157	.845	34	.001
.467	88	.089	.976	4	.000	.345	144	.150	.855	32	.001
.479	86	.083	.988	2	.000	.355	142	.143	.864	30	.001
.491	84	.077	1.000	0	.000	.364	140	.137	.873	28	.000
.503	82	.072				.373	138	.130	.882	26	.000
						.382	136	.124	.891	24	.000
						.391	134	.118	.900	22	.000
						.400	132	.112	.909	20	.000
						.409	130	.107	.918	18	.000
						.418	128	.102	.927	16	.000
						.427	126	.096	.936	14	.000
						.436	124	.091	.945	12	.000
						.445	122	.087	.955	10	.000
						.455	120	.082	.964	8	.000
						.464	118	.077	.973	6	.000
						.473	116	.073	.982	4	.000
						.482	114	.069	.991	2	.000
						.491	112	.065	1.000	0	.000
						.500	110	.061			

TABLE K

HYPERGEOMETRIC DISTRIBUTIONS*

Table K gives the distribution of one of the entries in a two-by-two table with fixed marginals when the two classifications are independent. More specifically, for a two-by-two table,

X		r
		s
n	m	N

arranged so that $r \leq s$ and $n \leq m$, Table K gives the distribution of X for $r \leq N/2$ and $n \leq N/2$. In the tables, the notation p = minimum of (n, m) and q = minimum of (r, s) is used.

Table K also gives the distribution for X = no. of red chips, where n chips are drawn at random, and without replacement, from an urn containing r red chips and $s = N - r$ black chips. If the inequalities above are not satisfied, appropriate interchanges of the colors of the chips and/or whether the n chips are drawn or $N - n$ are drawn permit the use of the table (see page 110). The table is cumulative from each extreme to, but not beyond, the mean. That is, the relations between the two-by-two table, the distribution, and Table K is as for the following example, where $N = 8$, $n = 3$, and $r = 2$.

X		$r = 2$ (smaller marginal)
$n = 3$ (larger marginal)		$N = 8$

* With kind permission of the publisher, adapted from *Tables of the Hypergeometric Probability Distribution*, by G. Lieberman and D. B. Owen, Stanford University Press (1961).

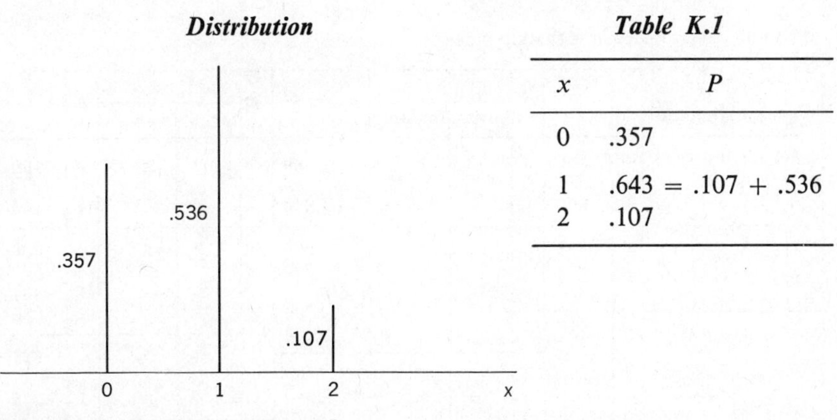

Table K.1

x	P
0	.357
1	.643 = .107 + .536
2	.107

The range of N is $2 \leq N \leq 15$.

For N larger than 15, various approximations are given below. It is not possible to give simple conditions under which these approximations are reasonable. If the exact values of the probabilities are important, they can be obtained from the table by Lieberman and Owen (from which this table is an excerpt), in which $2 \leq N \leq 100$. If nearly the same values of p, q, and N are being repeatedly encountered, then it is often possible to select one of the approximations below after comparing the approximations with some exact values.

The following statements can be used as some guide to the use of approximations.

If neither p nor q is extreme, that is, close to 0, then X will be approximately normal with mean, $\mu = pq/N$ and standard deviation

$$\sigma = \sqrt{\frac{pq(N - p)(N - q)}{N^2(N - 1)}}.$$

In particular, the probability that X is at most k is approximately the area below $[(k + 1/2) - \mu]/\sigma$ from Table E.

If one of p, q is near zero and the other not, then X will have, approximately, a binomial distribution with the number of trials equal to the minimum of (p, q) and the probability of success on a single trial equal to [maximum of (p, q)]$/N$.

If both p and q are near zero, X will have, approximately, a Poisson distribution with $\lambda = pq/N$.

These approximations are for large N, and the meaning above of extreme, or close to zero, depends upon N, as well as upon p and q. For example, if p and q are each $N/2$, the normal approximation is quite close for N as large as 10. As another example, if $N = 10$, and p and q are each 2, the Poisson approximation is not very good, for $N = 30$ and the same p and q the Poisson approximation is quite good.

Table K. Hypergeometric Distributions

N	(p, q) larger	(p, q) smaller	x	P
2	1	1	0	.500
			1	.500
3	1	1	0	.667
			1	.333
4	1	1	0	.750
			1	.250
4	2	1	0	.500
			1	.500
4	2	2	0	.167
			1	.833
			1	.833
			2	.167
5	1	1	0	.800
			1	.200
5	2	1	0	.600
			1	.400
5	2	2	0	.300
			1	.700
			2	.100
6	1	1	0	.833
			1	.167
6	2	1	0	.667
			1	.333
6	2	2	0	.400
			1	.600
			2	.067

N	(p, q) larger	(p, q) smaller	x	P
6	3	1	0	.500
			1	.500
6	3	2	0	.200
			1	.800
			1	.800
			2	.200
6	3	3	0	.050
			1	.500
			2	.500
			3	.050
7	1	1	0	.857
			1	.143
7	2	1	0	.714
			1	.286
7	2	2	0	.476
			1	.524
			2	.048
7	3	1	0	.571
			1	.429
7	3	2	0	.286
			1	.714
			2	.143
7	3	3	0	.114
			1	.629
			2	.371
			3	.029
8	1	1	0	.875
			1	.125

N	(p, q) larger	(p, q) smaller	x	P
8	2	1	0	.750
			1	.250
8	2	2	0	.536
			1	.464
			2	.036
8	3	1	0	.625
			1	.375
8	3	2	0	.357
			1	.643
			2	.107
8	3	3	0	.179
			1	.714
			2	.286
			3	.018
8	4	1	0	.500
			1	.500
8	4	2	0	.214
			1	.786
			1	.786
			2	.214
8	4	3	0	.071
			1	.500
			2	.500
			3	.071
8	4	4	0	.014
			1	.243
			2	.757
			2	.757
			3	.243
			4	.014

Table K. Hypergeometric Distributions

N	(p, q) larger	(p, q) smaller	x	P
9	1	1	0	.889
			1	.111
9	2	1	0	.778
			1	.222
9	2	2	0	.583
			1	.417
			2	.028
9	3	1	0	.667
			1	.333
9	3	2	0	.417
			1	.583
			2	.083
9	3	3	0	.238
			1	.774
			1	.762
			2	.226
			3	.012
9	4	1	0	.556
			1	.444
9	4	2	0	.278
			1	.722
			2	.167
9	4	3	0	.119
			1	.595
			2	.405
			3	.048
9	4	4	0	.040
			1	.357
			2	.643
			3	.167
			4	.008
10	1	1	0	.900
			1	.100
10	2	1	0	.800
			1	.200
10	2	2	0	.622
			1	.378
			2	.022
10	3	1	0	.700
			1	.300
10	3	2	0	.467
			1	.533
			2	.067
10	3	3	0	.292
			1	.708
			2	.183
			3	.008
10	4	1	0	.600
			1	.400
10	4	2	0	.333
			1	.667
			2	.133
10	4	3	0	.167
			1	.667
			2	.333
			3	.033
10	4	4	0	.071
			1	.452
			2	.548
			3	.119
			4	.005
10	5	1	0	.500
			1	.500
10	5	2	0	.222
			1	.778
			1	.778
			2	.222
10	5	3	0	.083
			1	.500
			2	.500
			3	.083
10	5	4	0	.024
			1	.262
			2	.738
			2	.738
			3	.262
			4	.024
10	5	5	0	.004
			1	.103
			2	.500
			3	.500
			4	.103
			5	.004

Table K. Hypergeometric Distributions

N	(p, q) larger	(p, q) smaller	x	P
11	1	1	0	.909
			1	.091
11	2	1	0	.818
			1	.182
11	2	2	0	.655
			1	.345
			2	.018
11	3	1	0	.727
			1	.273
11	3	2	0	.509
			1	.491
			2	.055
11	3	3	0	.339
			1	.661
			2	.152
			3	.006
11	4	1	0	.636
			1	.364
11	4	2	0	.382
			1	.618
			2	.109
11	4	3	0	.212
			1	.721
			2	.279
			3	.024
11	4	4	0	.106
			1	.530
			2	.470
			3	.088
			4	.003
11	5	1	0	.545
			1	.455
11	5	2	0	.273
			1	.727
			2	.182
11	5	3	0	.121
			1	.576
			2	.424
			3	.061
11	5	4	0	.045
			1	.348
			2	.652
			3	.197
			4	.015
11	5	5	0	.013
			1	.175
			2	.608
			3	.392
			4	.067
			5	.002
12	1	1	0	.917
			1	.083
12	2	1	0	.833
			1	.167
12	2	2	0	.682
			1	.318
			2	.015
12	3	1	0	.750
			1	.250
12	3	2	0	.545
			1	.455
			2	.045
12	3	3	0	.382
			1	.618
			2	.127
			3	.005
12	4	1	0	.667
			1	.333
12	4	2	0	.424
			1	.576
			2	.091
12	4	3	0	.255
			1	.764
			1	.745
			2	.236
			3	.018
12	4	4	0	.141
			1	.594
			2	.406
			3	.067
			4	.002
12	5	1	0	.583
			1	.417

Table K. Hypergeometric Distributions

N	(p, q)		x	P
	larger	smaller		
12	5	2	0	.318
			1	.682
			2	.152
12	5	3	0	.159
			1	.636
			2	.364
			3	.045
12	5	4	0	.071
			1	.424
			2	.576
			3	.152
			4	.010
12	5	5	0	.027
			1	.247
			2	.689
			3	.311
			4	.045
			5	.001
12	6	1	0	.500
			1	.500
12	6	2	0	.227
			1	.773
			1	.773
			2	.227
12	6	3	0	.091
			1	.500
			2	.500
			3	.091
12	6	4	0	.030
			1	.273
			2	.727
			2	.727
			3	.273
			4	.030
12	6	5	0	.008
			1	.121
			2	.500
			3	.500
			4	.121
			5	.008
12	6	6	0	.001
			1	.040
			2	.284
			3	.716
			3	.716
			4	.284
			5	.040
			6	.001
13	1	1	0	.923
			1	.077
13	2	1	0	.846
			1	.154
13	2	2	0	.705
			1	.295
			2	.013
13	3	1	0	.769
			1	.231
13	3	2	0	.577
			1	.423
			2	.038
13	3	3	0	.420
			1	.580
			2	.108
			3	.003
13	4	1	0	.692
			1	.308
13	4	2	0	.462
			1	.538
			2	.077
13	4	3	0	.294
			1	.706
			2	.203
			3	.014
13	4	4	0	.176
			1	.646
			2	.354
			3	.052
			4	.001
13	5	1	0	.615
			1	.385
13	5	2	0	.359
			1	.641
			2	.128
13	5	3	0	.196
			1	.685
			2	.315
			3	.035

Table K. Hypergeometric Distributions

N	(p, q) larger	(p, q) smaller	x	P
13	5	4	0	.098
			1	.490
			2	.510
			3	.119
			4	.007
13	5	5	0	.044
			1	.315
			2	.685
			3	.249
			4	.032
			5	.001
13	6	1	0	.538
			1	.462
13	6	2	0	.269
			1	.731
			2	.192
13	6	3	0	.122
			1	.563
			2	.437
			3	.070
13	6	4	0	.049
			1	.343
			2	.657
			3	.217
			4	.021
13	6	5	0	.016
			1	.179
			2	.587
			3	.413
			4	.086
			5	.005
13	6	6	0	.004
			1	.078
			2	.383
			3	.617
			4	.209
			5	.025
			6	.001
14	1	1	0	.929
			1	.071
14	2	1	0	.857
			1	.143
14	2	2	0	.725
			1	.275
			2	.011
14	3	1	0	.786
			1	.214
14	3	2	0	.604
			1	.396
			2	.033
14	3	3	0	.453
			1	.547
			2	.093
			3	.003
14	4	1	0	.714
			1	.286
14	4	2	0	.495
			1	.505
			2	.066
14	4	3	0	.330
			1	.670
			2	.176
			3	.011
14	4	4	0	.210
			1	.689
			2	.311
			3	.041
			4	.001
14	5	1	0	.643
			1	.357
14	5	2	0	.396
			1	.604
			2	.110
14	5	3	0	.231
			1	.725
			2	.275
			3	.027
14	5	4	0	.126
			1	.545
			2	.455
			3	.095
			4	.005
14	5	5	0	.063
			1	.378
			2	.622
			3	.203
			4	.023
			5	.000
14	6	1	0	.571
			1	.429

Table K. Hypergeometric Distributions

N	(p, q) larger	(p, q) smaller	x	P
14	6	2	0	.308
			1	.692
			2	.165
14	6	3	0	.154
			1	.615
			2	.385
			3	.055
14	6	4	0	.070
			1	.406
			2	.594
			3	.175
			4	.015
14	6	5	0	.028
			1	.238
			2	.657
			3	.343
			4	.063
			5	.003
14	6	6	0	.009
			1	.121
			2	.471
			3	.529
			4	.156
			5	.016
			6	.000
14	7	1	0	.500
			1	.500
14	7	2	0	.231
			1	.769
			1	.769
			2	.231
14	7	3	0	.096
			1	.500
			2	.500
			3	.096
14	7	4	0	.035
			1	.280
			2	.720
			2	.720
			3	.280
			4	.035
14	7	5	0	.010
			1	.133
			2	.500
			3	.500
			4	.133
			5	.010
14	7	6	0	.002
			1	.051
			2	.296
			3	.704
			3	.704
			4	.296
			5	.051
			6	.002
14	7	7	0	.000
			1	.015
			2	.143
			3	.500
			4	.500
			5	.143
			6	.015
			7	.000
15	1	1	0	.933
			1	.067
15	2	1	0	.867
			1	.133
15	2	2	0	.743
			1	.257
			2	.010
15	3	1	0	.800
			1	.200
15	3	2	0	.629
			1	.371
			2	.029
15	3	3	0	.484
			1	.516
			2	.081
			3	.002
15	4	1	0	.733
			1	.267
15	4	2	0	.524
			1	.476
			2	.057
15	4	3	0	.363
			1	.637
			2	.154
			3	.009
15	4	4	0	.242
			1	.725
			2	.275
			3	.033
			4	.001

Table K. Hypergeometric Distributions

N	(p, q) larger	(p, q) smaller	x	P
15	5	1	0	.667
			1	.333
15	5	2	0	.429
			1	.571
			2	.095
15	5	3	0	.264
			1	.758
			1	.736
			2	.242
			3	.022
15	5	4	0	.154
			1	.593
			2	.407
			3	.077
			4	.004
15	5	5	0	.084
			1	.434
			2	.566
			3	.167
			4	.017
			5	.000
15	6	1	0	.600
			1	.400
15	6	2	0	.343
			1	.657
			2	.143

N	(p, q) larger	(p, q) smaller	x	P
15	6	3	0	.185
			1	.659
			2	.341
			3	.044
15	6	4	0	.092
			1	.462
			2	.538
			3	.143
			4	.011
15	6	5	0	.042
			1	.294
			2	.713
			2	.706
			3	.287
			4	.047
			5	.002
15	6	6	0	.017
			1	.168
			2	.545
			3	.455
			4	.119
			5	.011
			6	.000
15	7	1	0	.533
			1	.467
15	7	2	0	.267
			1	.733
			2	.200

N	(p, q) larger	(p, q) smaller	x	P
15	7	3	0	.123
			1	.554
			2	.446
			3	.077
15	7	4	0	.051
			1	.338
			2	.662
			3	.231
			4	.026
15	7	5	0	.019
			1	.182
			2	.573
			3	.427
			4	.100
			5	.007
15	7	6	0	.006
			1	.084
			2	.378
			3	.622
			4	.231
			5	.035
			6	.001
15	7	7	0	.001
			1	.032
			2	.214
			3	.595
			4	.405
			5	.100
			6	.009
			7	.000

TABLE L

POISSON DISTRIBUTIONS*

Table L gives the Poisson distributions for each of the values of the mean $\lambda = .1$ and .5, by .5 to 5.0, by 1.0 to 15. The table is cumulative from each extreme to, but not beyond, the mean. That is, the relation between the table and the distribution is as for the following example, where $\lambda = .5$.

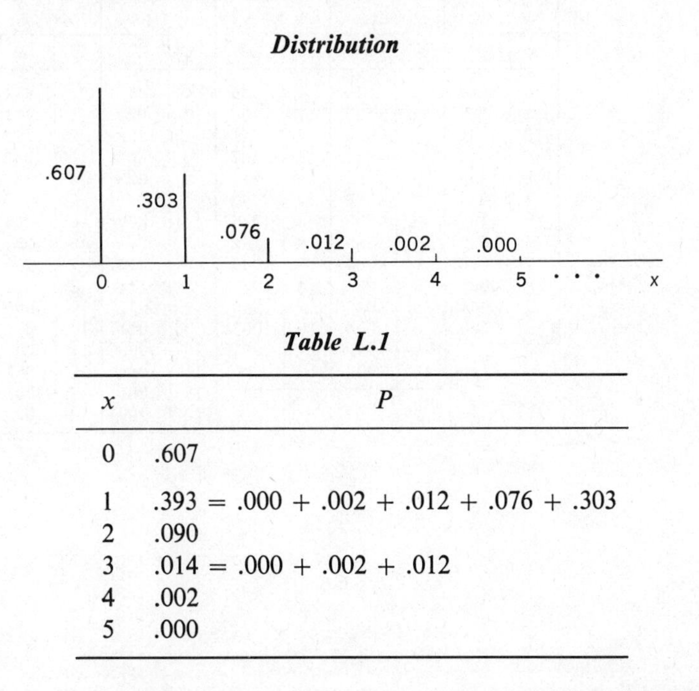

Table L.1

x	P
0	.607
1	.393 = .000 + .002 + .012 + .076 + .303
2	.090
3	.014 = .000 + .002 + .012
4	.002
5	.000

For $\lambda > 15$, the distribution can be approximated by a normal distribution with mean λ and standard deviation $\sqrt{\lambda}$. In particular, $P\{X \le k\}$ is approximately the area under the unit normal curve (Table E) below $[(k + \frac{1}{2}) - \lambda]/\sqrt{\lambda}$.

* With kind permission of the Biometrika Trustees, adapted from "Tables of the χ^2-Integral and the Cumulative Poisson Distribution," by H. O. Hartley and E. S. Pearson, *Biometrika*, **37** (1950), 313–325.

Table L. Poisson Distributions

$\lambda = .1$		$\lambda = .5$		$\lambda = 1.0$		$\lambda = 1.5$		$\lambda = 2.0$	
x	P	x	P	x	P	x	P	x	P
0	.905	0	.607	0	.368	0	.223	0	.135
				1	.736	1	.558	1	.406
1	.095	1	.393					2	.677
2	.005	2	.090	1	.632	2	.442		
3	.000	3	.014	2	.264	3	.191	2	.594
		4	.002	3	.080	4	.066	3	.323
		5	.000	4	.019	5	.019	4	.143
				5	.004	6	.004	5	.053
				6	.001	7	.001	6	.017
				7	.000	8	.000	7	.005
								8	.001
								9	.000

$\lambda = 2.5$		$\lambda = 3.0$		$\lambda = 3.5$		$\lambda = 4.0$		$\lambda = 4.5$	
x	P	x	P	x	P	x	P	x	P
0	.082	0	.050	0	.030	0	.018	0	.011
1	.287	1	.199	1	.136	1	.092	1	.061
2	.544	2	.423	2	.321	2	.238	2	.174
		3	.647	3	.537	3	.433	3	.342
3	.456					4	.629	4	.532
4	.242	3	.577	4	.463				
5	.109	4	.353	5	.275	4	.567	5	.468
6	.042	5	.185	6	.142	5	.371	6	.297
7	.014	6	.084	7	.065	6	.215	7	.169
8	.004	7	.034	8	.027	7	.111	8	.087
9	.001	8	.012	9	.010	8	.051	9	.040
10	.000	9	.004	10	.003	9	.021	10	.017
		10	.001	11	.001	10	.008	11	.007
		11	.000	12	.000	11	.003	12	.002
						12	.001	13	.001
						13	.000	14	.000

Table L. Poisson Distributions

λ = 5		λ = 6		λ = 7		λ = 8		λ = 9		λ = 10	
x	P	x	P	x	P	x	P	x	P	x	P
0	.007	0	.002	0	.001	0	.000	0	.000	0	.000
1	.040	1	.017	1	.007	1	.003	1	.001	1	.000
2	.125	2	.062	2	.030	2	.014	2	.006	2	.003
3	.265	3	.151	3	.082	3	.042	3	.021	3	.010
4	.440	4	.285	4	.173	4	.100	4	.055	4	.029
5	.616	5	.446	5	.301	5	.191	5	.116	5	.067
		6	.606	6	.450	6	.313	6	.207	6	.130
5	.560			7	.599	7	.453	7	.324	7	.220
6	.384	6	.554			8	.593	8	.456	8	.333
7	.238	7	.394	7	.550			9	.587	9	.458
8	.133	8	.256	8	.401	8	.547			10	.583
9	.068	9	.153	9	.271	9	.407	9	.544		
10	.032	10	.084	10	.169	10	.283	10	.413	10	.542
11	.014	11	.043	11	.099	11	.184	11	.294	11	.417
12	.005	12	.020	12	.053	12	.112	12	.197	12	.303
13	.002	13	.009	13	.027	13	.064	13	.124	13	.208
14	.001	14	.004	14	.013	14	.034	14	.074	14	.136
15	.000	15	.001	15	.006	15	.017	15	.041	15	.083
		16	.001	16	.002	16	.008	16	.022	16	.049
		17	.000	17	.001	17	.004	17	.011	17	.027
				18	.000	18	.002	18	.005	18	.014
						19	.001	19	.002	19	.007
						20	.000	20	.001	20	.003
								21	.000	21	.002
										22	.001
										23	.000

Table L. Poisson Distributions

λ = 11		λ = 12		λ = 13		λ = 14		λ = 15	
x	*P*	*x*	*P*	*x*	*P*	*x*	*P*	*x*	*P*
0	.000	0	.000	0	.000	0	.000	0	.000
1	.000	1	.000	1	.000	1	.000	1	.000
2	.001	2	.001	2	.000	2	.000	2	.000
3	.005	3	.002	3	.001	3	.000	3	.000
4	.015	4	.008	4	.004	4	.002	4	.001
5	.038	5	.020	5	.011	5	.006	5	.003
6	.079	6	.046	6	.026	6	.014	6	.008
7	.143	7	.090	7	.054	7	.032	7	.018
8	.232	8	.155	8	.100	8	.062	8	.037
9	.341	9	.242	9	.166	9	.109	9	.070
10	.460	10	.347	10	.252	10	.176	10	.118
11	.579	11	.462	11	.353	11	.260	11	.185
		12	.576	12	.463	12	.358	12	.268
11	.540			13	.573	13	.464	13	.363
12	.421	12	.538			14	.570	14	.466
13	.311	13	.424	13	.537			15	.568
14	.219	14	.318	14	.427	14	.536		
15	.146	15	.228	15	.325	15	.430	15	.534
16	.093	16	.156	16	.236	16	.331	16	.432
17	.056	17	.101	17	.165	17	.244	17	.336
18	.032	18	.063	18	.110	18	.173	18	.251
19	.018	19	.037	19	.070	19	.117	19	.181
20	.009	20	.021	20	.043	20	.076	20	.125
21	.005	21	.012	21	.025	21	.048	21	.083
22	.002	22	.006	22	.014	22	.029	22	.053
23	.001	23	.003	23	.008	23	.017	23	.033
24	.000	24	.001	24	.004	24	.009	24	.019
		25	.001	25	.002	25	.005	25	.011
		26	.000	26	.001	26	.003	26	.006
				27	.000	27	.001	27	.003
						28	.001	28	.002
						29	.000	29	.001
								30	.000

TABLE M

KOLMOGOROV-SMIRNOV DISTRIBUTIONS (ONE SAMPLE)*

Table M gives the distribution of $n \cdot D_n = n \cdot [\sup_t |F_n(t) - F(t)|]$ for samples of size n from the continuous distribution F. F_n is the sample cumulative; that is, $F_n(t) = (\text{no. of } x_i \leq t)/n$ for the sample $(x_1, \ldots, x_n)$. The table is cumulative, from the right-hand extreme to zero; that is, the relation between the table and the distribution of $n \cdot D_n$ is as for the following example for which $n = 4$.

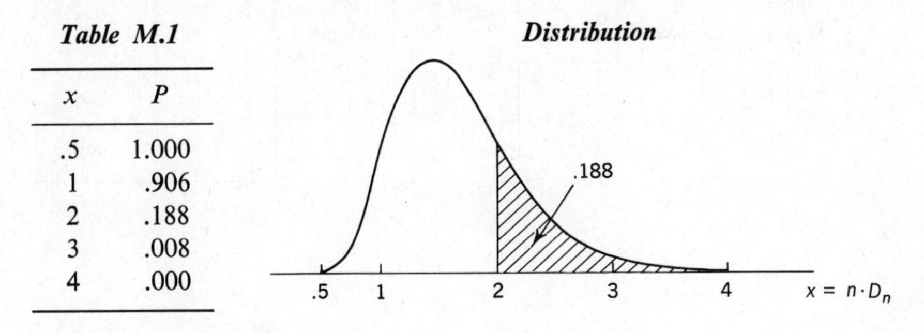

Table M.1

x	P
.5	1.000
1	.906
2	.188
3	.008
4	.000

The range for n is $2 \leq n \leq 40$.

For $n > 40$, Table O can be used. The area above $\sqrt{n}\, D_n = x$ is given there.

* With kind permission of the *Journal of the American Statistical Association*, adapted from Table 1 of "Numerical Tabulation of the Distribution of Kolmogorov's Statistic for Finite Sample Size," by Z. W. Birnbaum, *J.A.S.A.*, **47** (1952), 425–441.

Table M. Kolmogorov-Smirnov Distributions (One Sample)

(Upper Tail)

Sample Size													
2		3		4		5		6		7		8	
x	P	x	P	x	P	x	P	x	P	x	P	x	P
.5	1.000	.5	1.000	.5	1.000	.5	1.000	.5	1.000	.5	1.000	.5	1.000
1	.500	1	.778	1	.906	1	.962	1	.985	1	.994	1	.998
2	.000	2	.074	2	.188	2	.309	2	.423	2	.526	2	.613
		3	.000	3	.008	3	.030	3	.066	3	.111	3	.162
				4	.000	4	.001	4	.004	4	.011	4	.023
						5	.000	5	.000	5	.000	5	.002
												6	.000

Sample Size													
9		10		11		12		13		14		15	
x	P	x	P	x	P	x	P	x	P	x	P	x	P
.5	1.000	.5	1.000	.5	1.000	.5	1.000	.5	1.000	.5	1.000	.5	1.000
1	.999	1	1.000	1	1.000	1	1.000	1	1.000	1	1.000	1	1.000
2	.687	2	.749	2	.799	2	.840	2	.873	2	.899	2	.920
3	.216	3	.271	3	.325	3	.378	3	.429	3	.477	3	.522
4	.039	4	.059	4	.083	4	.109	4	.137	4	.167	4	.197
5	.004	5	.008	5	.014	5	.021	5	.031	5	.042	5	.055
6	.000	6	.001	6	.001	6	.003	6	.005	6	.008	6	.011
		7	.000	7	.000	7	.000	7	.000	7	.001	7	.002
										8	.000	8	.000

Table M. Kolmogorov-Smirnov Distributions (One Sample)

(Upper Tail)

Sample Size													
16		17		18		19		20		21		22	
x	P	x	P	x	P	x	P	x	P	x	P	x	P
.5	1.000	.5	1.000	.5	1.000	.5	1.000	.5	1.000	.5	1.000	.5	1.000
1	1.000	1	1.000	1	1.000	1	1.000	1	1.000	1	1.000	1	1.000
2	.937	2	.951	2	.961	2	.970	2	.976	2	.981	2	.986
3	.564	3	.604	3	.640	3	.674	3	.704	3	.733	3	.759
4	.228	4	.260	4	.291	4	.322	4	.353	4	.383	4	.412
5	.069	5	.085	5	.102	5	.119	5	.138	5	.157	5	.176
6	.016	6	.021	6	.028	6	.035	6	.043	6	.052	6	.062
7	.003	7	.004	7	.006	7	.008	7	.011	7	.014	7	.018
8	.000	8	.001	8	.001	8	.001	8	.002	8	.003	8	.004
		9	.000	9	.000	9	.000	9	.000	9	.001	9	.001
										10	.000	10	.000

Sample Size													
23		24		25		26		27		28		29	
x	P	x	P	x	P	x	P	x	P	x	P	x	P
.5	1.000	.5	1.000	.5	1.000	.5	1.000	.5	1.000	.5	1.000	.5	1.000
1	1.000	1	1.000	1	1.000	1	1.000	1	1.000	1	1.000	1	1.000
2	.989	2	.991	2	.993	2	.995	2	.996	2	.997	2	.997
3	.782	3	.804	3	.823	3	.841	3	.857	3	.871	3	.884
4	.440	4	.468	4	.494	4	.520	4	.545	4	.569	4	.591
5	.196	5	.216	5	.236	5	.257	5	.277	5	.297	5	.317
6	.072	6	.083	6	.094	6	.106	6	.119	6	.131	6	.145
7	.022	7	.027	7	.032	7	.037	7	.043	7	.050	7	.057
8	.005	8	.007	8	.009	8	.011	8	.013	8	.016	8	.019
9	.001	9	.002	9	.002	9	.003	9	.004	9	.004	9	.006
10	.000	10	.000	10	.000	10	.001	10	.001	10	.001	10	.001
						11	.000	11	.000	11	.000	11	.000

Table M. Kolmogorov–Smirnov Distributions (One Sample)

(Upper Tail)

Sample Size													
30		31		32		33		34		35		36	
x	P	x	P	x	P	x	P	x	P	x	P	x	P
.5	1.000	.5	1.000	.5	1.000	.5	1.000	.5	1.000	.5	1.000	.5	1.000
1	1.000	1	1.000	1	1.000	1	1.000	1	1.000	1	1.000	1	1.000
2	.998	2	.998	2	.999	2	.999	2	.999	2	.999	2	1.000
3	.896	3	.907	3	.916	3	.925	3	.933	3	.940	3	.946
4	.613	4	.634	4	.654	4	.673	4	.691	4	.708	4	.724
5	.337	5	.357	5	.376	5	.395	5	.414	5	.433	5	.451
6	.158	6	.172	6	.185	6	.199	6	.213	6	.228	6	.242
7	.064	7	.072	7	.080	7	.088	7	.097	7	.106	7	.115
8	.023	8	.026	8	.030	8	.034	8	.039	8	.043	8	.048
9	.007	9	.008	9	.010	9	.012	9	.014	9	.016	9	.018
10	.002	10	.002	10	.003	10	.003	10	.004	10	.005	10	.006
11	.000	11	.001	11	.001	11	.001	11	.001	11	.001	11	.002
		12	.000	12	.000	12	.000	12	.000	12	.000	12	.000

Sample Size							
37		38		39		40	
x	P	x	P	x	P	x	P
.5	1.000	.5	1.000	.5	1.000	.5	1.000
1	1.000	1	1.000	1	1.000	1	1.000
2	1.000	2	1.000	2	1.000	2	1.000
3	.952	3	.957	3	.961	3	.966
4	.740	4	.755	4	.769	4	.782
5	.468	5	.486	5	.503	5	.519
6	.256	6	.270	6	.284	6	.298
7	.124	7	.133	7	.143	7	.153
8	.054	8	.059	8	.065	8	.070
9	.021	9	.023	9	.026	9	.029
10	.007	10	.008	10	.010	10	.011
11	.002	11	.003	11	.003	11	.004
12	.001	12	.001	12	.001	12	.001
13	.000	13	.000	13	.000	13	.000

TABLE **N**

KOLMOGOROV-SMIRNOV DISTRIBUTIONS (TWO SAMPLE)*

Table N gives the distribution of

$$\frac{2mn}{m+n} D_{n,m} = \frac{2mn}{m+n} [\sup_t |F_n(t) - G_m(t)|],$$

for two independent samples $(x_1, \ldots, x_n)$ and $(y_1, \ldots, y_m)$ from the same continuous distribution. F_n and G_m are the sample cumulatives; that is, $F_n(t) = (\text{no. of } x_i \leq t)/n$ and $G_m(t) = (\text{no. of } y_i \leq t)/m$. The table is cumulative from the right-hand extreme to zero; that is, the relation between the table and the distribution is as for the following example for which $n = m = 6$.

Distribution

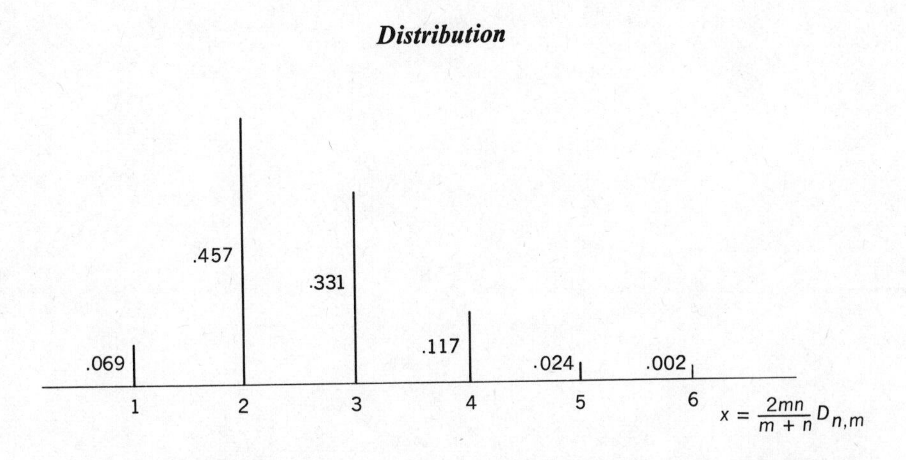

* With kind permission of the *Annals of Mathematical Statistics*, adapted from Table 2 of "Small Sample Distributions for Multi-sample Statistics of the Smirnov-type," by Z. W. Birnbaum and R. A. Hall, *Ann. Math. Stat.*, **31** (1960), 710–720.

Table N.1

x	P
1	1.000
2	.931 = .002 + .024 + .117 + .331 + .457
3	.474
4	.143 = .002 + .024 + .117
5	.026
6	.002

The range for m and n is $2 \leq m = n \leq 40$.

For unequal small sample sizes, a choice has to be made between computing the exact distribution of $D_{n,m}$ or using the approximation of Table O. The exact distribution can be found from the fact that, if the samples are from the same distribution, all permutations of the observations are equally likely. The approximation in Table O gives the approximate area above

$$x = \sqrt{n \cdot m/(n + m)}\, D_{n,m}.$$

Table N. Kolmogorov–Smirnov Distributions (Two Sample)

(Upper Tail)

Sample Sizes													
2		3		4		5		6		7		8	
x	P	x	P	x	P	x	P	x	P	x	P	x	P
1	1.000	1	1.000	1	1.000	1	1.000	1	1.000	1	1.000	1	1.000
2	.333	2	.600	2	.771	2	.873	2	.931	2	.963	2	.980
		3	.100	3	.229	3	.357	3	.474	3	.575	3	.660
				4	.029	4	.079	4	.143	4	.212	4	.283
						5	.008	5	.026	5	.053	5	.087
								6	.002	6	.008	6	.019
										7	.001	7	.002
												8	.000

Sample Sizes													
9		10		11		12		13		14		15	
x	P	x	P	x	P	x	P	x	P	x	P	x	P
1	1.000	1	1.000	1	1.000	1	1.000	1	1.000	1	1.000	1	1.000
2	.989	2	.994	2	.997	2	.998	2	.999	2	1.000	2	1.000
3	.730	3	.787	3	.833	3	.869	3	.898	3	.921	3	.938
4	.352	4	.418	4	.479	4	.536	4	.588	4	.635	4	.678
5	.126	5	.168	5	.211	5	.256	5	.300	5	.343	5	.386
6	.034	6	.052	6	.075	6	.100	6	.126	6	.155	6	.184
7	.006	7	.012	7	.021	7	.031	7	.044	7	.059	7	.075
8	.001	8	.002	8	.004	8	.008	8	.013	8	.019	8	.026
9	.000	9	.000	9	.001	9	.001	9	.003	9	.005	9	.008
		10	.000	10	.000	10	.000	10	.000	10	.001	10	.002
				11	.000	11	.000	11	.000	11	.000	11	.000
						12	.000	12	.000	12	.000	12	.000
								13	.000	13	.000	13	.000
										14	.000	14	.000
												15	.000

Table N. Kolmogorov-Smirnov Distributions (Two Sample)

(Upper Tail)

Sample Sizes													
16		17		18		19		20		21		22	
x	P	x	P	x	P	x	P	x	P	x	P	x	P
1	1.000	1	1.000	1	1.000	1	1.000	1	1.000	1	1.000	1	1.000
2	1.000	2	1.000	2	1.000	2	1.000	2	1.000	2	1.000	2	1.000
3	.952	3	.963	3	.972	3	.978	3	.983	3	.987	3	.990
4	.716	4	.751	4	.781	4	.808	4	.832	4	.853	4	.872
5	.426	5	.465	5	.503	5	.538	5	.571	5	.603	5	.632
6	.215	6	.245	6	.275	6	.306	6	.336	6	.365	6	.394
7	.093	7	.112	7	.132	7	.153	7	.175	7	.196	7	.218
8	.035	8	.045	8	.056	8	.068	8	.081	8	.095	8	.109
9	.011	9	.016	9	.021	9	.027	9	.034	9	.041	9	.049
10	.003	10	.005	10	.007	10	.009	10	.012	10	.016	10	.020
11	.001	11	.001	11	.002	11	.003	11	.004	11	.005	11	.007
12	.000	12	.000	12	.000	12	.001	12	.001	12	.002	12	.002
13	.000	13	.000	13	.000	13	.000	13	.000	13	.000	13	.001
14	.000	14	.000	14	.000	14	.000	14	.000	14	.000	14	.000
15	.000	15	.000	15	.000	15	.000	15	.000	15	.000	15	.000
16	.000	16	.000	16	.000	16	.000	16	.000	16	.000	16	.000
		17	.000	17	.000	17	.000	17	.000	17	.000	17	.000
				18	.000	18	.000	18	.000	18	.000	18	.000
						19	.000	19	.000	19	.000	19	.000
								20	.000	20	.000	20	.000
										21	.000	21	.000
												22	.000

Table N. Kolmogorov-Smirnov Distributions (Two Sample)

(Upper Tail)

Sample Sizes													
23		24		25		26		27		28		29	
x	P	x	P	x	P	x	P	x	P	x	P	x	P
1	1.000	1	1.000	1	1.000	1	1.000	1	1.000	1	1.000	1	1.000
2	1.000	2	1.000	2	1.000	2	1.000	2	1.000	2	1.000	2	1.000
3	.992	3	.994	3	.996	3	.997	3	.997	3	.998	3	.998
4	.888	4	.902	4	.915	4	.926	4	.936	4	.944	4	.951
5	.660	5	.686	5	.710	5	.733	5	.754	5	.773	5	.791
6	.422	6	.449	6	.475	6	.501	6	.526	6	.549	6	.572
7	.241	7	.263	7	.285	7	.307	7	.329	7	.351	7	.372
8	.124	8	.140	8	.156	8	.172	8	.189	8	.205	8	.222
9	.058	9	.068	9	.078	9	.089	9	.100	9	.111	9	.123
10	.025	10	.030	10	.036	10	.042	10	.048	10	.056	10	.063
11	.009	11	.012	11	.015	11	.018	11	.022	11	.026	11	.030
12	.003	12	.004	12	.006	12	.007	12	.009	12	.011	12	.013
13	.001	13	.001	13	.002	13	.003	13	.003	13	.004	13	.005
14	.000	14	.000	14	.001	14	.001	14	.001	14	.002	14	.002
15	.000	15	.000	15	.000	15	.000	15	.000	15	.000	15	.001
16	.000	16	.000	16	.000	16	.000	16	.000	16	.000	16	.000
17	.000	17	.000	17	.000	17	.000	17	.000	17	.000	17	.000
18	.000	18	.000	18	.000	18	.000	18	.000	18	.000	18	.000
19	.000	19	.000	19	.000	19	.000	19	.000	19	.000	19	.000
20	.000	20	.000	20	.000	20	.000	20	.000	20	.000	20	.000
21	.000	21	.000	21	.000	21	.000	21	.000	21	.000	21	.000
22	.000	22	.000	22	.000	22	.000	22	.000	22	.000	22	.000
23	.000	23	.000	23	.000	23	.000	23	.000	23	.000	23	.000
		24	.000	24	.000	24	.000	24	.000	24	.000	24	.000
				25	.000	25	.000	25	.000	25	.000	25	.000
						26	.000	26	.000	26	.000	26	.000
								27	.000	27	.000	27	.000
										28	.000	28	.000
												29	.000

Table N. Kolmogorov–Smirnov Distributions (Two Sample)

(Upper Tail)

Sample Sizes													
30		31		32		33		34		35		36	
x	P	x	P	x	P	x	P	x	P	x	P	x	P
1	1.000	1	1.000	1	1.000	1	1.000	1	1.000	1	1.000	1	1.000
2	1.000	2	1.000	2	1.000	2	1.000	2	1.000	2	1.000	2	1.000
3	.999	3	.999	3	.999	3	.999	3	1.000	3	1.000	3	1.000
4	.958	4	.963	4	.968	4	.973	4	.976	4	.979	4	.982
5	.808	5	.823	5	.838	5	.851	5	.863	5	.874	5	.885
6	.594	6	.615	6	.635	6	.654	6	.673	6	.690	6	.707
7	.393	7	.414	7	.434	7	.453	7	.473	7	.492	7	.510
8	.239	8	.256	8	.273	8	.290	8	.307	8	.323	8	.340
9	.135	9	.147	9	.160	9	.173	9	.186	9	.199	9	.212
10	.071	10	.079	10	.088	10	.097	10	.106	10	.115	10	.125
11	.035	11	.040	11	.045	11	.050	11	.056	11	.063	11	.069
12	.016	12	.018	12	.021	12	.025	12	.028	12	.032	12	.036
13	.007	13	.008	13	.010	13	.011	13	.013	13	.015	13	.018
14	.003	14	.003	14	.004	14	.005	14	.006	14	.007	14	.008
15	.001	15	.001	15	.002	15	.002	15	.002	15	.003	15	.003
16	.000	16	.000	16	.001	16	.001	16	.001	16	.001	16	.001
17	.000	17	.000	17	.000	17	.000	17	.000	17	.000	17	.001
18	.000	18	.000	18	.000	18	.000	18	.000	18	.000	18	.000
19	.000	19	.000	19	.000	19	.000	19	.000	19	.000	19	.000
20	.000	20	.000	20	.000	20	.000	20	.000	20	.000	20	.000
21	.000	21	.000	21	.000	21	.000	21	.000	21	.000	21	.000
22	.000	22	.000	22	.000	22	.000	22	.000	22	.000	22	.000
23	.000	23	.000	23	.000	23	.000	23	.000	23	.000	23	.000
24	.000	24	.000	24	.000	24	.000	24	.000	24	.000	24	.000
25	.000	25	.000	25	.000	25	.000	25	.000	25	.000	25	.000
26	.000	26	.000	26	.000	26	.000	26	.000	26	.000	26	.000
27	.000	27	.000	27	.000	27	.000	27	.000	27	.000	27	.000
28	.000	28	.000	28	.000	28	.000	28	.000	28	.000	28	.000
29	.000	29	.000	29	.000	29	.000	29	.000	29	.000	29	.000
30	.000	30	.000	30	.000	30	.000	30	.000	30	.000	30	.000
		31	.000	31	.000	31	.000	31	.000	31	.000	31	.000
				32	.000	32	.000	32	.000	32	.000	32	.000
						33	.000	33	.000	33	.000	33	.000
								34	.000	34	.000	34	.000
										35	.000	35	.000
												36	.000

Table N. Kolmogorov-Smirnov Distributions (Two Sample)

(Upper Tail)

Sample Sizes							
37		38		39		40	
x	P	x	P	x	P	x	P
1	1.000	1	1.000	1	1.000	1	1.000
2	1.000	2	1.000	2	1.000	2	1.000
3	1.000	3	1.000	3	1.000	3	1.000
4	.985	4	.987	4	.988	4	.990
5	.894	5	.903	5	.911	5	.919
6	.723	6	.738	6	.752	6	.766
7	.528	7	.545	7	.562	7	.579
8	.356	8	.373	8	.389	8	.405
9	.226	9	.239	9	.252	9	.266
10	.135	10	.145	10	.155	10	.165
11	.076	11	.083	11	.090	11	.097
12	.040	12	.045	12	.049	12	.054
13	.020	13	.023	13	.026	13	.029
14	.009	14	.011	14	.013	14	.014
15	.004	15	.005	15	.006	15	.007
16	.002	16	.002	16	.003	16	.003
17	.001	17	.001	17	.001	17	.001
18	.000	18	.000	18	.000	18	.001
19	.000	19	.000	19	.000	19	.000
20	.000	20	.000	20	.000	20	.000
21	.000	21	.000	21	.000	21	.000
22	.000	22	.000	22	.000	22	.000
23	.000	23	.000	23	.000	23	.000
24	.000	24	.000	24	.000	24	.000
25	.000	25	.000	25	.000	25	.000
26	.000	26	.000	26	.000	26	.000
27	.000	27	.000	27	.000	27	.000
28	.000	28	.000	28	.000	28	.000
29	.000	29	.000	29	.000	29	.000
30	.000	30	.000	30	.000	30	.000
31	.000	31	.000	31	.000	31	.000
32	.000	32	.000	32	.000	32	.000
33	.000	33	.000	33	.000	33	.000
34	.000	34	.000	34	.000	34	.000
35	.000	35	.000	35	.000	35	.000
36	.000	36	.000	36	.000	36	.000
37	.000	37	.000	37	.000	37	.000
		38	.000	38	.000	38	.000
				39	.000	39	.000
						40	.000

TABLE O

ASYMPTOTIC KOLMOGOROV-SMIRNOV DISTRIBUTIONS (SUPPLEMENT, FOR $N > 40$, TO TABLE M AND N)*

(Upper Tail)

x	P	x	P	x	P	x	P	x	P	x	P
.35	1.000	.65	.792	.95	.327	1.25	.088	1.55	.016	1.85	.002
.36	.999	.66	.776	.96	.315	1.26	.084	1.56	.015	1.86	.002
.37	.999	.67	.760	.97	.304	1.27	.079	1.57	.014	1.87	.002
.38	.999	.68	.744	.98	.292	1.28	.075	1.58	.014	1.88	.002
.39	.998	.69	.728	.99	.281	1.29	.072	1.59	.013	1.89	.002
.40	.997	.70	.711	1.00	.270	1.30	.068	1.60	.012	1.90	.001
.41	.996	.71	.695	1.01	.259	1.31	.065	1.61	.011	1.91	.001
.42	.995	.72	.678	1.02	.249	1.32	.061	1.62	.011	1.92	.001
.43	.993	.73	.661	1.03	.239	1.33	.058	1.63	.010	1.93	.001
.44	.990	.74	.644	1.04	.230	1.34	.055	1.64	.009	1.94	.001
.45	.987	.75	.627	1.05	.220	1.35	.052	1.65	.009	1.95	.001
.46	.984	.76	.610	1.06	.211	1.36	.049	1.66	.008	1.96	.001
.47	.980	.77	.594	1.07	.202	1.37	.047	1.67	.008	1.97	.001
.48	.975	.78	.577	1.08	.194	1.38	.044	1.68	.007	1.98	.001
.49	.970	.79	.560	1.09	.186	1.39	.042	1.69	.007	1.99	.001
.50	.964	.80	.544	1.10	.178	1.40	.040	1.70	.006	2.00	.001
.51	.957	.81	.528	1.11	.170	1.41	.038	1.71	.006	2.01	.001
.52	.950	.82	.512	1.12	.163	1.42	.035	1.72	.005	2.02	.001
.53	.941	.83	.496	1.13	.155	1.43	.033	1.73	.005	2.03	.001
.54	.933	.84	.481	1.14	.149	1.44	.032	1.74	.005	2.04	.000
.55	.923	.85	.465	1.15	.142	1.45	.030	1.75	.004		
.56	.912	.86	.450	1.16	.136	1.46	.028	1.76	.004		
.57	.901	.87	.435	1.17	.129	1.47	.027	1.77	.004		
.58	.890	.88	.421	1.18	.123	1.48	.025	1.78	.004		
.59	.877	.89	.407	1.19	.118	1.49	.024	1.79	.003		
.60	.864	.90	.393	1.20	.112	1.50	.022	1.80	.003		
.61	.851	.91	.379	1.21	.107	1.51	.021	1.81	.003		
.62	.837	.92	.366	1.22	.102	1.52	.020	1.82	.003		
.63	.822	.93	.353	1.23	.097	1.53	.019	1.83	.002		
.64	.807	.94	.340	1.24	.092	1.54	.017	1.84	.002		

* With kind permission of the *Annals of Mathematical Statistics* adapted from "Table for Estimating the Goodness of Fit of Empirical Distributions," by N. Smirnov, *Ann. Math. Stat.*, **19** (1948), 279–281.

TABLE **P**

SQUARE ROOTS

Table P gives five-digit approximations to the square roots of integers from 1 to 10,000. Square roots for other numbers can be approximated from the relations $\sqrt{10^{2k} \cdot n} = 10^k\sqrt{n}$. For example, $\sqrt{18{,}000} = 10\sqrt{180}$, $\sqrt{.018} = \frac{1}{100}\sqrt{180}$, and $\sqrt{1.80} = \frac{1}{10}\sqrt{180}$.

It is important to recall that it is multiplication by 100 (not 10) that leaves the digits unchanged; that is, $\sqrt{180{,}000} = 100\sqrt{18}$ and $\sqrt{.18} = \frac{1}{10}\sqrt{18}$. There is no immediate relation between the digits of $\sqrt{n}$ and $\sqrt{10n}$; that is, $\sqrt{18} = 4.243$ and $\sqrt{180} = 13.416$.

Table P. Square Roots

n	$\sqrt{n}$	$\sqrt{10n}$	n	$\sqrt{n}$	$\sqrt{10n}$	n	$\sqrt{n}$	$\sqrt{10n}$
1	1.000	3.162	51	7.141	22.583	101	10.050	31.780
2	1.414	4.472	52	7.211	22.804	102	10.100	31.937
3	1.732	5.477	53	7.280	23.022	103	10.149	32.094
4	2.000	6.325	54	7.348	23.238	104	10.198	32.249
5	2.236	7.071	55	7.416	23.452	105	10.247	32.404
6	2.449	7.746	56	7.483	23.664	106	10.296	32.558
7	2.646	8.367	57	7.550	23.875	107	10.344	32.711
8	2.828	8.944	58	7.616	24.083	108	10.392	32.863
9	3.000	9.487	59	7.681	24.290	109	10.440	33.015
10	3.162	10.000	60	7.746	24.495	110	10.488	33.166
11	3.317	10.488	61	7.810	24.698	111	10.536	33.317
12	3.464	10.954	62	7.874	24.900	112	10.583	33.466
13	3.606	11.402	63	7.937	25.100	113	10.630	33.615
14	3.742	11.832	64	8.000	25.298	114	10.677	33.764
15	3.873	12.247	65	8.062	25.495	115	10.724	33.912
16	4.000	12.649	66	8.124	25.690	116	10.770	34.059
17	4.123	13.038	67	8.185	25.884	117	10.817	34.205
18	4.243	13.416	68	8.246	26.077	118	10.863	34.351
19	4.359	13.784	69	8.307	26.268	119	10.909	34.496
20	4.472	14.142	70	8.367	26.458	120	10.954	34.641
21	4.583	14.491	71	8.426	26.646	121	11.000	34.785
22	4.690	14.832	72	8.485	26.833	122	11.045	34.928
23	4.796	15.166	73	8.544	27.019	123	11.091	35.071
24	4.899	15.492	74	8.602	27.203	124	11.136	35.214
25	5.000	15.811	75	8.660	27.386	125	11.180	35.355
26	5.099	16.125	76	8.718	27.568	126	11.225	35.496
27	5.196	16.432	77	8.775	27.749	127	11.269	35.637
28	5.292	16.733	78	8.832	27.928	128	11.314	35.777
29	5.385	17.029	79	8.888	28.107	129	11.358	35.917
30	5.477	17.321	80	8.944	28.284	130	11.402	36.056
31	5.568	17.607	81	9.000	28.460	131	11.446	36.194
32	5.657	17.889	82	9.055	28.636	132	11.489	36.332
33	5.745	18.166	83	9.110	28.810	133	11.533	36.469
34	5.831	18.439	84	9.165	28.983	134	11.576	36.606
35	5.916	18.708	85	9.220	29.155	135	11.619	36.742
36	6.000	18.974	86	9.274	29.326	136	11.662	36.878
37	6.083	19.235	87	9.327	29.496	137	11.705	37.014
38	6.164	19.494	88	9.381	29.665	138	11.747	37.148
39	6.245	19.748	89	9.434	29.833	139	11.790	37.283
40	6.325	20.000	90	9.487	30.000	140	11.832	37.417
41	6.403	20.248	91	9.539	30.166	141	11.874	37.550
42	6.481	20.494	92	9.592	30.332	142	11.916	37.683
43	6.557	20.736	93	9.644	30.496	143	11.958	37.815
44	6.633	20.976	94	9.695	30.659	144	12.000	37.947
45	6.708	21.213	95	9.747	30.822	145	12.042	38.079
46	6.782	21.448	96	9.798	30.984	146	12.083	38.210
47	6.856	21.679	97	9.849	31.145	147	12.124	38.341
48	6.928	21.909	98	9.899	31.305	148	12.166	38.471
49	7.000	22.136	99	9.950	31.464	149	12.207	38.601
50	7.071	22.361	100	10.000	31.623	150	12.247	38.730

Table P. Square Roots

n	$\sqrt{n}$	$\sqrt{10n}$
151	12.288	38.859
152	12.329	38.987
153	12.369	39.115
154	12.410	39.243
155	12.450	39.370
156	12.490	39.497
157	12.530	39.623
158	12.570	39.749
159	12.610	39.875
160	12.649	40.000
161	12.689	40.125
162	12.728	40.249
163	12.767	40.373
164	12.806	40.497
165	12.845	40.620
166	12.884	40.743
167	12.923	40.866
168	12.961	40.988
169	13.000	41.110
170	13.038	41.231
171	13.077	41.352
172	13.115	41.473
173	13.153	41.593
174	13.191	41.713
175	13.229	41.833
176	13.266	41.952
177	13.304	42.071
178	13.342	42.190
179	13.379	42.308
180	13.416	42.426
181	13.454	42.544
182	13.491	42.661
183	13.528	42.778
184	13.565	42.895
185	13.601	43.012
186	13.638	43.128
187	13.675	43.243
188	13.711	43.359
189	13.748	43.474
190	13.784	43.589
191	13.820	43.704
192	13.856	43.818
193	13.892	43.932
194	13.928	44.045
195	13.964	44.159
196	14.000	44.272
197	14.036	44.385
198	14.071	44.497
199	14.107	44.609
200	14.142	44.721

n	$\sqrt{n}$	$\sqrt{10n}$
201	14.177	44.833
202	14.213	44.944
203	14.248	45.056
204	14.283	45.166
205	14.318	45.277
206	14.353	45.387
207	14.387	45.497
208	14.422	45.607
209	14.457	45.717
210	14.491	45.826
211	14.526	45.935
212	14.560	46.043
213	14.595	46.152
214	14.629	46.260
215	14.663	46.368
216	14.697	46.476
217	14.731	46.583
218	14.765	46.690
219	14.799	46.797
220	14.832	46.904
221	14.866	47.011
222	14.900	47.117
223	14.933	47.223
224	14.967	47.329
225	15.000	47.434
226	15.033	47.539
227	15.067	47.645
228	15.100	47.749
229	15.133	47.854
230	15.166	47.958
231	15.199	48.062
232	15.232	48.166
233	15.264	48.270
234	15.297	48.374
235	15.330	48.477
236	15.362	48.580
237	15.395	48.683
238	15.427	48.785
239	15.460	48.888
240	15.492	48.990
241	15.524	49.092
242	15.556	49.193
243	15.588	49.295
244	15.620	49.396
245	15.652	49.497
246	15.684	49.598
247	15.716	49.699
248	15.748	49.800
249	15.780	49.900
250	15.811	50.000

n	$\sqrt{n}$	$\sqrt{10n}$
251	15.843	50.100
252	15.875	50.200
253	15.906	50.299
254	15.937	50.398
255	15.969	50.498
256	16.000	50.596
257	16.031	50.695
258	16.062	50.794
259	16.093	50.892
260	16.125	50.990
261	16.155	51.088
262	16.186	51.186
263	16.217	51.284
264	16.248	51.381
265	16.279	51.478
266	16.310	51.575
267	16.340	51.672
268	16.371	51.769
269	16.401	51.865
270	16.432	51.962
271	16.462	52.058
272	16.492	52.154
273	16.523	52.249
274	16.553	52.345
275	16.583	52.440
276	16.613	52.536
277	16.643	52.631
278	16.673	52.726
279	16.703	52.820
280	16.733	52.915
281	16.763	53.009
282	16.793	53.104
283	16.823	53.198
284	16.852	53.292
285	16.882	53.385
286	16.912	53.479
287	16.941	53.572
288	16.971	53.666
289	17.000	53.759
290	17.029	53.852
291	17.059	53.944
292	17.088	54.037
293	17.117	54.129
294	17.146	54.222
295	17.176	54.314
296	17.205	54.406
297	17.234	54.498
298	17.263	54.589
299	17.292	54.681
300	17.321	54.772

Table P. Square Roots

n	$\sqrt{n}$	$\sqrt{10n}$
301	17.349	54.863
302	17.378	54.955
303	17.407	55.045
304	17.436	55.136
305	17.464	55.227
306	17.493	55.317
307	17.521	55.408
308	17.550	55.498
309	17.578	55.588
310	17.607	55.678
311	17.635	55.767
312	17.664	55.857
313	17.692	55.946
314	17.720	56.036
315	17.748	56.125
316	17.776	56.214
317	17.804	56.303
318	17.833	56.391
319	17.861	56.480
320	17.889	56.569
321	17.916	56.657
322	17.944	56.745
323	17.972	56.833
324	18.000	56.921
325	18.028	57.009
326	18.055	57.096
327	18.083	57.184
328	18.111	57.271
329	18.138	57.359
330	18.166	57.446
331	18.193	57.533
332	18.221	57.619
333	18.248	57.706
334	18.276	57.793
335	18.303	57.879
336	18.330	57.966
337	18.358	58.052
338	18.385	58.138
339	18.412	58.224
340	18.439	58.310
341	18.466	58.395
342	18.493	58.481
343	18.520	58.566
344	18.547	58.652
345	18.574	58.737
346	18.601	58.822
347	18.628	58.907
348	18.655	58.992
349	18.682	59.076
350	18.708	59.161

n	$\sqrt{n}$	$\sqrt{10n}$
351	18.735	59.245
352	18.762	59.330
353	18.788	59.414
354	18.815	59.498
355	18.841	59.582
356	18.868	59.666
357	18.894	59.749
358	18.921	59.833
359	18.947	59.917
360	18.974	60.000
361	19.000	60.083
362	19.026	60.166
363	19.053	60.249
364	19.079	60.332
365	19.105	60.415
366	19.131	60.498
367	19.157	60.581
368	19.183	60.663
369	19.209	60.745
370	19.235	60.828
371	19.261	60.910
372	19.287	60.992
373	19.313	61.074
374	19.339	61.156
375	19.365	61.237
376	19.391	61.319
377	19.416	61.400
378	19.442	61.482
379	19.468	61.563
380	19.494	61.644
381	19.519	61.725
382	19.545	61.806
383	19.570	61.887
384	19.596	61.968
385	19.621	62.048
386	19.647	62.129
387	19.672	62.209
388	19.698	62.290
389	19.723	62.370
390	19.748	62.450
391	19.774	62.530
392	19.799	62.610
393	19.824	62.690
394	19.849	62.769
395	19.875	62.849
396	19.900	62.929
397	19.925	63.008
398	19.950	63.087
399	19.975	63.166
400	20.000	63.246

n	$\sqrt{n}$	$\sqrt{10n}$
401	20.025	63.325
402	20.050	63.403
403	20.075	63.482
404	20.100	63.561
405	20.125	63.640
406	20.149	63.718
407	20.174	63.797
408	20.199	63.875
409	20.224	63.953
410	20.248	64.031
411	20.273	64.109
412	20.298	64.187
413	20.322	64.265
414	20.347	64.343
415	20.372	64.420
416	20.396	64.498
417	20.421	64.576
418	20.445	64.653
419	20.469	64.730
420	20.494	64.807
421	20.518	64.885
422	20.543	64.962
423	20.567	65.038
424	20.591	65.115
425	20.616	65.192
426	20.640	65.269
427	20.664	65.345
428	20.688	65.422
429	20.712	65.498
430	20.736	65.574
431	20.761	65.651
432	20.785	65.727
433	20.809	65.803
434	20.833	65.879
435	20.857	65.955
436	20.881	66.030
437	20.905	66.106
438	20.928	66.182
439	20.952	66.257
440	20.976	66.332
441	21.000	66.408
442	21.024	66.483
443	21.048	66.558
444	21.071	66.633
445	21.095	66.708
446	21.119	66.783
447	21.142	66.858
448	21.166	66.933
449	21.190	67.007
450	21.213	67.082

Table P. Square Roots

n	$\sqrt{n}$	$\sqrt{10n}$
451	21.237	67.157
452	21.260	67.231
453	21.284	67.305
454	21.307	67.380
455	21.331	67.454
456	21.354	67.528
457	21.378	67.602
458	21.401	67.676
459	21.424	67.750
460	21.448	67.823
461	21.471	67.897
462	21.494	67.971
463	21.517	68.044
464	21.541	68.118
465	21.564	68.191
466	21.587	68.264
467	21.610	68.337
468	21.633	68.411
469	21.656	68.484
470	21.679	68.557
471	21.703	68.629
472	21.726	68.702
473	21.749	68.775
474	21.772	68.848
475	21.794	68.920
476	21.817	68.993
477	21.840	69.065
478	21.863	69.138
479	21.886	69.210
480	21.909	69.282
481	21.932	69.354
482	21.954	69.426
483	21.977	69.498
484	22.000	69.570
485	22.023	69.642
486	22.045	69.714
487	22.068	69.785
488	22.091	69.857
489	22.113	69.929
490	22.136	70.000
491	22.159	70.071
492	22.181	70.143
493	22.204	70.214
494	22.226	70.285
495	22.249	70.356
496	22.271	70.427
497	22.293	70.498
498	22.316	70.569
499	22.338	70.640
500	22.361	70.711

n	$\sqrt{n}$	$\sqrt{10n}$
501	22.383	70.781
502	22.405	70.852
503	22.428	70.922
504	22.450	70.993
505	22.472	71.063
506	22.494	71.134
507	22.517	71.204
508	22.539	71.274
509	22.561	71.344
510	22.583	71.414
511	22.605	71.484
512	22.627	71.554
513	22.650	71.624
514	22.672	71.694
515	22.694	71.764
516	22.716	71.833
517	22.738	71.903
518	22.760	71.972
519	22.782	72.042
520	22.804	72.111
521	22.825	72.180
522	22.847	72.250
523	22.869	72.319
524	22.891	72.388
525	22.913	72.457
526	22.935	72.526
527	22.956	72.595
528	22.978	72.664
529	23.000	72.732
530	23.022	72.801
531	23.043	72.870
532	23.065	72.938
533	23.087	73.007
534	23.108	73.075
535	23.130	73.144
536	23.152	73.212
537	23.173	73.280
538	23.195	73.348
539	23.216	73.417
540	23.238	73.485
541	23.259	73.553
542	23.281	73.621
543	23.302	73.689
544	23.324	73.756
545	23.345	73.824
546	23.367	73.892
547	23.388	73.959
548	23.409	74.027
549	23.431	74.095
550	23.452	74.162

n	$\sqrt{n}$	$\sqrt{10n}$
551	23.473	74.229
552	23.495	74.297
553	23.516	74.364
554	23.537	74.431
555	23.558	74.498
556	23.580	74.565
557	23.601	74.632
558	23.622	74.699
559	23.643	74.766
560	23.664	74.833
561	23.685	74.900
562	23.707	74.967
563	23.728	75.033
564	23.749	75.100
565	23.770	75.166
566	23.791	75.233
567	23.812	75.299
568	23.833	75.366
569	23.854	75.432
570	23.875	75.498
571	23.896	75.565
572	23.917	75.631
573	23.937	75.697
574	23.958	75.763
575	23.979	75.829
576	24.000	75.895
577	24.021	75.961
578	24.042	76.026
579	24.062	76.092
580	24.083	76.158
581	24.104	76.223
582	24.125	76.289
583	24.145	76.354
584	24.166	76.420
585	24.187	76.485
586	24.207	76.551
587	24.228	76.616
588	24.249	76.681
589	24.269	76.746
590	24.290	76.811
591	24.310	76.877
592	24.331	76.942
593	24.352	77.006
594	24.372	77.071
595	24.393	77.136
596	24.413	77.201
597	24.434	77.266
598	24.454	77.330
599	24.474	77.395
600	24.495	77.460

Table P. Square Roots

n	$\sqrt{n}$	$\sqrt{10n}$
601	24.515	77.524
602	24.536	77.589
603	24.556	77.653
604	24.576	77.717
605	24.597	77.782
606	24.617	77.846
607	24.637	77.910
608	24.658	77.974
609	24.678	78.038
610	24.698	78.102
611	24.718	78.166
612	24.739	78.230
613	24.759	78.294
614	24.779	78.358
615	24.799	78.422
616	24.819	78.486
617	24.839	78.549
618	24.860	78.613
619	24.880	78.677
620	24.900	78.740
621	24.920	78.804
622	24.940	78.867
623	24.960	78.930
624	24.980	78.994
625	25.000	79.057
626	25.020	79.120
627	25.040	79.183
628	25.060	79.246
629	25.080	79.310
630	25.100	79.373
631	25.120	79.436
632	25.140	79.498
633	25.159	79.561
634	25.179	79.624
635	25.199	79.687
636	25.219	79.750
637	25.239	79.812
638	25.259	79.875
639	25.278	79.937
640	25.298	80.000
641	25.318	80.062
642	25.338	80.125
643	25.357	80.187
644	25.377	80.250
645	25.397	80.312
646	25.417	80.374
647	25.436	80.436
648	25.456	80.498
649	25.475	80.561
650	25.495	80.623

n	$\sqrt{n}$	$\sqrt{10n}$
651	25.515	80.685
652	25.534	80.747
653	25.554	80.808
654	25.573	80.870
655	25.593	80.932
656	25.612	80.994
657	25.632	81.056
658	25.652	81.117
659	25.671	81.179
660	25.690	81.240
661	25.710	81.302
662	25.729	81.363
663	25.749	81.425
664	25.768	81.486
665	25.788	81.548
666	25.807	81.609
667	25.826	81.670
668	25.846	81.731
669	25.865	81.792
670	25.884	81.854
671	25.904	81.915
672	25.923	81.976
673	25.942	82.037
674	25.962	82.098
675	25.981	82.158
676	26.000	82.219
677	26.019	82.280
678	26.038	82.341
679	26.058	82.401
680	26.077	82.462
681	26.096	82.523
682	26.115	82.583
683	26.134	82.644
684	26.153	82.704
685	26.173	82.765
686	26.192	82.825
687	26.211	82.885
688	26.230	82.946
689	26.249	83.006
690	26.268	83.066
691	26.287	83.126
692	26.306	83.187
693	26.325	83.247
694	26.344	83.307
6 5	26.363	83.367
696	26.382	83.427
697	26.401	83.487
698	26.420	83.546
699	26.439	83.606
700	26.458	83.666

n	$\sqrt{n}$	$\sqrt{10n}$
701	26.476	83.726
702	26.495	83.785
703	26.514	83.845
704	26.533	83.905
705	26.552	83.964
706	26.571	84.024
707	26.589	84.083
708	26.608	84.143
709	26.627	84.202
710	26.646	84.261
711	26.665	84.321
712	26.683	84.380
713	26.702	84.439
714	26.721	84.499
715	26.739	84.558
716	26.758	84.617
717	26.777	84.676
718	26.796	84.735
719	26.814	84.794
720	26.833	84.853
721	26.851	84.912
722	26.870	84.971
723	26.889	85.029
724	26.907	85.088
725	26.926	85.147
726	26.944	85.206
727	26.963	85.264
728	26.981	85.323
729	27.000	85.381
730	27.019	85.440
731	27.037	85.499
732	27.055	85.557
733	27.074	85.615
734	27.092	85.674
735	27.111	85.732
736	27.129	85.790
737	27.148	85.849
738	27.166	85.907
739	27.185	85.965
740	27.203	86.023
741	27.221	86.081
742	27.240	86.139
743	27.258	86.197
744	27.276	86.255
745	27.295	86.313
746	27.313	86.371
747	27.331	86.429
748	27.350	86.487
749	27.368	86.545
750	27.386	86.603

Table P. Square Roots

n	$\sqrt{n}$	$\sqrt{10n}$	n	$\sqrt{n}$	$\sqrt{10n}$	n	$\sqrt{n}$	$\sqrt{10n}$
751	27.404	86.660	801	28.302	89.499	851	29.172	92.250
752	27.423	86.718	802	28.320	89.554	852	29.189	92.304
753	27.441	86.776	803	28.337	89.610	853	29.206	92.358
754	27.459	86.833	804	28.355	89.666	854	29.223	92.412
755	27.477	86.891	805	28.373	89.722	855	29.240	92.466
756	27.495	86.948	806	28.390	89.778	856	29.257	92.520
757	27.514	87.006	807	28.408	89.833	857	29.275	92.574
758	27.532	87.063	808	28.425	89.889	858	29.292	92.628
759	27.550	87.121	809	28.443	89.944	859	29.309	92.682
760	27.568	87.178	810	28.460	90.000	860	29.326	92.736
761	27.586	87.235	811	28.478	90.056	861	29.343	92.790
762	27.604	87.293	812	28.496	90.111	862	29.360	92.844
763	27.622	87.350	813	28.513	90.167	863	29.377	92.898
764	27.641	87.407	814	28.531	90.222	864	29.394	92.952
765	27.659	87.464	815	28.548	90.277	865	29.411	93.005
766	27.677	87.521	816	28.566	90.333	866	29.428	93.059
767	27.695	87.579	817	28.583	90.388	867	29.445	93.113
768	27.713	87.636	818	28.601	90.443	868	29.462	93.167
769	27.731	87.693	819	28.618	90.499	869	29.479	93.220
770	27.749	87.750	820	28.636	90.554	870	29.496	93.274
771	27.767	87.807	821	28.653	90.609	871	29.513	93.327
772	27.785	87.864	822	28.671	90.664	872	29.530	93.381
773	27.803	87.920	823	28.688	90.719	873	29.547	93.434
774	27.821	87.977	824	28.705	90.774	874	29.563	93.488
775	27.839	88.034	825	28.723	90.830	875	29.580	93.541
776	27.857	88.091	826	28.740	90.885	876	29.597	93.595
777	27.875	88.148	827	28.758	90.940	877	29.614	93.648
778	27.893	88.204	828	28.775	90.995	878	29.631	93.702
779	27.911	88.261	829	28.792	91.049	879	29.648	93.755
780	27.928	88.318	830	28.810	91.104	880	29.665	93.808
781	27.946	88.374	831	28.827	91.159	881	29.682	93.862
782	27.964	88.431	832	28.844	91.214	882	29.698	93.915
783	27.982	88.487	833	28.862	91.269	883	29.715	93.968
784	28.000	88.544	834	28.879	91.324	884	29.732	94.021
785	28.018	88.600	835	28.896	91.378	885	29.749	94.074
786	28.036	88.657	836	28.914	91.433	886	29.766	94.128
787	28.054	88.713	837	28.931	91.488	887	29.783	94.181
788	28.071	88.769	838	28.948	91.542	888	29.799	94.234
789	28.089	88.826	839	28.965	91.597	889	29.816	94.287
790	28.107	88.882	840	28.983	91.652	890	29.833	94.340
791	28.125	88.938	841	29.000	91.706	891	29.850	94.393
792	28.142	88.994	842	29.017	91.761	892	29.866	94.446
793	28.160	89.051	843	29.034	91.815	893	29.883	94.499
794	28.178	89.107	844	29.052	91.869	894	29.900	94.552
795	28.196	89.163	845	29.069	91.924	895	29.917	94.604
796	28.213	89.219	846	29.086	91.978	896	29.933	94.657
797	28.231	89.275	847	29.103	92.033	897	29.950	94.710
798	28.249	89.331	848	29.120	92.087	898	29.967	94.763
799	28.267	89.387	849	29.138	92.141	899	29.983	94.816
800	28.284	89.443	850	29.155	92.195	900	30.000	94.868

Table P. Square Roots

n	$\sqrt{n}$	$\sqrt{10n}$	n	$\sqrt{n}$	$\sqrt{10n}$
901	30.017	94.921	951	30.838	97.519
902	30.033	94.974	952	30.854	97.570
903	30.050	95.026	953	30.871	97.622
904	30.067	95.079	954	30.887	97.673
905	30.083	95.131	955	30.903	97.724
906	30.100	95.184	956	30.919	97.775
907	30.116	95.237	957	30.935	97.826
908	30.133	95.289	958	30.952	97.877
909	30.150	95.341	959	30.968	97.929
910	30.166	95.394	960	30.984	97.980
911	30.183	95.446	961	31.000	98.031
912	30.199	95.499	962	31.016	98.082
913	30.216	95.551	963	31.032	98.133
914	30.232	95.603	964	31.048	98.184
915	30.249	95.656	965	31.064	98.234
916	30.265	95.708	966	31.081	98.285
917	30.282	95.760	967	31.097	98.336
918	30.299	95.812	968	31.113	98.387
919	30.315	95.864	969	31.129	98.438
920	30.332	95.917	970	31.145	98.489
921	30.348	95.969	971	31.161	98.539
922	30.364	96.021	972	31.177	98.590
923	30.381	96.073	973	31.193	98.641
924	30.397	96.125	974	31.209	98.691
925	30.414	96.177	975	31.225	98.742
926	30.430	96.229	976	31.241	98.793
927	30.447	96.281	977	31.257	98.843
928	30.463	96.333	978	31.273	98.894
929	30.480	96.385	979	31.289	98.944
930	30.496	96.437	980	31.305	98.995
931	30.512	96.488	981	31.321	99.045
932	30.529	96.540	982	31.337	99.096
933	30.545	96.592	983	31.353	99.146
934	30.561	96.644	984	31.369	99.197
935	30.578	96.695	985	31.385	99.247
936	30.594	96.747	986	31.401	99.298
937	30.610	96.799	987	31.417	99.348
938	30.627	96.850	988	31.432	99.398
939	30.643	96.902	989	31.448	99.448
940	30.659	96.954	990	31.464	99.499
941	30.676	97.005	991	31.480	99.549
942	30.692	97.057	992	31.496	99.599
943	30.708	97.108	993	31.512	99.649
944	30.725	97.160	994	31.528	99.700
945	30.741	97.211	995	31.544	99.750
946	30.757	97.263	996	31.559	99.800
947	30.773	97.314	997	31.575	99.850
948	30.790	97.365	998	31.591	99.900
949	30.806	97.417	999	31.607	99.950
950	30.822	97.468	1000	31.623	100.000

SOLUTIONS TO EXERCISES

CHAPTER 1

1.3. (Partial answer). If the "five-letter alphabet" is {1, 2, 3, 4, 5}, the 10 assignments, for Example 1, are

Treatment	*Control*
(1, 2, 3)	(4, 5)
(1, 2, 4)	(3, 5)
(1, 2, 5)	(3, 4)
(1, 3, 4)	(2, 5)
(1, 3, 5)	(2, 4)
(1, 4, 5)	(2, 3)
(2, 3, 4)	(1, 5)
(2, 3, 5)	(1, 4)
(2, 4, 5)	(1, 3)
(3, 4, 5)	(1, 2)

CHAPTER 2

2.1.

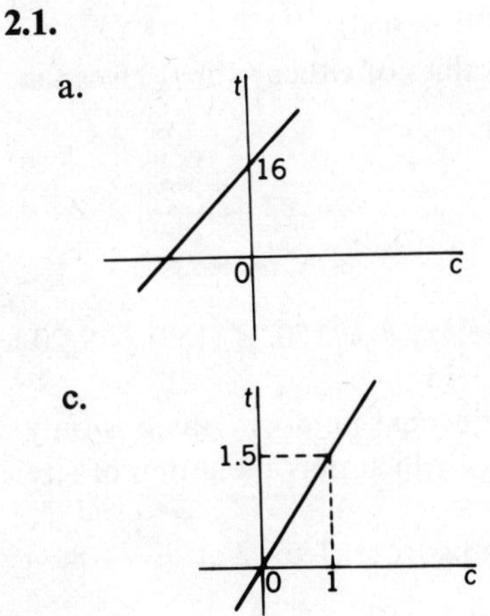

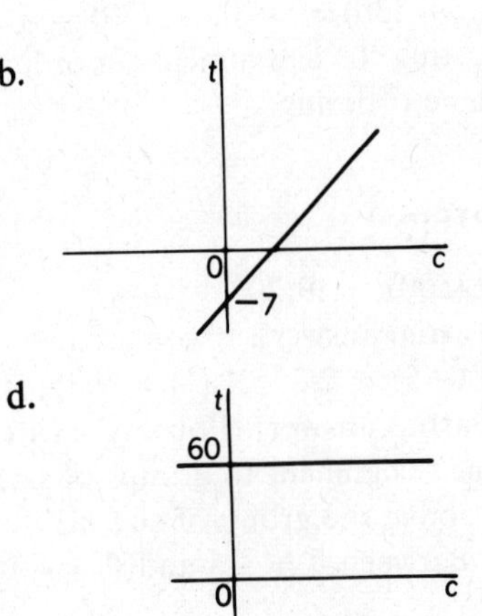

2.2. a. $h(c) = c + 16$ or $t = c + 16$.
b. $h(c) = c - 7$ or $t = c - 7$.
c. $h(c) = \frac{3}{2}c$ or $t = \frac{3}{2}c$.
d. $h(c) = 60$ or $t = 60$.

2.3. a and b.

2.4. No rule for "guessing" is given; hence there is no one "correct" answer. Plotting the treatment and control scores on separate scales and shifting one of them until the treatment scores look about like the control scores will give, for most persons, an "answer" somewhere between 21 and 24 for θ.

2.5. Good arguments can be given that any two of the first, second, fifth, and sixth "look like" no-treatment experiments. Since we are working with constant, for all subjects, effect models, the third "looks like" there was a positive treatment effect and the fourth "looks like" there was a negative effect. Recall that there is no way to know what the control scores would have been, without treatment, for the experimental subjects.

2.6. (Partial answer). $[(t_1', t_2', t_3'), (c_1', c_2')] = [(47, 38, 40), (30, 21)]$ looks most like there was a positive treatment effect, $[(30, 38, 21), (47, 40)]$ looks most like there was a negative effect. Among the other eight there is considerable choice for most plausible no-treatment experiments. "Objective" ways to make distinctions are discussed in Chapter 3.

CHAPTER 3

3.1. f_2: ② < ③ = ①
f_3: ② < ③ = ①

3.2. a. f_1: ④ < ⑥ < ⑨ < ② < ⑤ < ⑩ < ③ < ① < ⑦ < ⑧
f_2: ⑥ = ⑨ < ④ = ② = ⑤ = ⑩ < ③ = ① < ⑦ = ⑧
f_3: ⑥ = ⑨ = ⑤ = ⑩ < ④ = ② = ③ = ① < ⑦ = ⑧
b. $A_{f_1}(30) = 3/10$, $A_{f_2}(30) = 4/10$, $A_{f_3}(30) = 6/10$.

3.3. Listing the assignments in order by the values of either f_2 or f_4 gives the same ordering.

CHAPTER 4

4.3. $A_f(500) = 19/20$.

4.4. (Partial answer). If you are having trouble, try $\theta = 150$. $A_f(150) = 9/20$.

4.5. $A_f(-5) = 2/35$, $A_f(1) = 9/35$, $A_f(16) = 3/35$.

4.6. (Partial answer). For any set of $n + m$ unequal numbers, there is only one assignment to groups of sizes n and m which puts the group of size n above the group of size m.

Between $\theta = -5$ and $\theta = -10$, A_f jumps from .1 to .2 at $\theta = -8$.

CHAPTER 5

5.1. (Partial answer). The value of A_f, for θ below 10, is 2/3. The value at 10 is 1.

5.3. (Partial answer). Use n = smaller sample size = 1, m = larger sample size = 2 for Table B.

5.4. (Partial answer). The intervals are $(-\infty, -5)$, $(-5, 3)$, $(3, 12)$, $(12, 14)$, $(14, 22)$, $(22, 31)$, and $(31, \infty)$. A_f = 2/10 on the first interval and 4/10 on the second interval.

5.5. (Partial answer). The intervals are $(-\infty, -205)$, $(-205, 130)$, $(130, 155)$, $(155, 375)$, $(375, 490)$, $(490, 660)$, $(660, 710)$, $(710, 1020)$, $(1020, 1240)$, and $(1240, \infty)$. A_f = 4/10 on the third interval and 7/10 on the fourth interval.

5.6. (Partial answer). The intervals are $(-\infty, -4)$, $(-4, 0)$, $(0, 1)$, $(1, 5)$, $(5, 8)$, $(8, 9)$, $(9, 10)$, $(10, 12)$, $(12, 14)$, $(14, 17)$, and $(17, \infty)$. A_f = .056 on the first interval and .114 on the second interval.

5.7. $(R_{t_1}, R_{t_2}, R_{t_3}, R_{t_4}) = (5, 2\frac{1}{2}, 5, 7)$. $\bar{R}_t - \bar{R}_c = [(5 + 2.5 + 5 + 7)/4] - [(1 + 5 + 2.5)/3] = 2.042$.

5.9.a. Example 1: (12, 14); Example 2: (375, 660); Example 3: (5, 8).

CHAPTER 6

6.2. (Partial answer).

θ	−10	0	10	15	25	35
A_f	1/3	1	1	1	1	1/3

6.4. (Partial answer). Enter Table K with $N' = 4$, $p = 1$, $q = 2$.

6.5. (Partial answer). The intervals are $(-\infty, -4)$, $(-4, 0)$, $(0, 1)$, $(1, 5)$, $(5, 8)$, $(8, 9)$, $(9, 10)$, $(10, 12)$, $(12, 14)$, $(14, 17)$, and $(17, \infty)$. $A_f(-5) = 1/10$, $A_f(-2) = 4/10$, $A_f(-4) = 1/10$.

CHAPTER 7

7.1.b. The intervals are $(-\infty, -1)$, $(-1, 1)$, $(1, 3)$, $(3, 5)$, and $(5, \infty)$. A_f on these intervals is .333 for the first, .667 for the second, 1 for the third, .667 for the fourth, and .333 for the fifth.

7.2. (Partial answer). Two of the six possible experiments are found as follows.

Scores before treatment (not observed)		*Scores after treatment (observed)*	
Treatment	*Control*	*Treatment*	*Control*
		(t_1, t_2)	(c_1, c_2)
(10, 12)	(15, 19)	(18, 20)	(15, 19)
(10, 15)	(12, 19)	(18, 23)	(12, 19)

The other four are found by finding the other four possible ways of choosing two numbers from (10, 12, 15, 19) and adding 8 to the scores in the treatment group. For the curve A_f for the observed experiment $(t_1, t_2) = (18, 20)$, $(c_1, c_2) = (15, 19)$, the intervals are $(-\infty, -1)$, $(-1, 1)$, $(1, 3)$, $(3, 5)$, and $(5, \infty)$; A_f is 1/3, 1, 1, 1, and 1/3 on these intervals. For the observed experiment $(t_1, t_2) = (18, 23)$, $(c_1, c_2) = (12, 19)$, the intervals are $(-\infty, -1)$, $(-1, 4)$, $(4, 6)$, $(6, 11)$, and $(11, \infty)$; A_f for these intervals is 1/3, 1, 1, 1, and 1/3.

7.5. The probability of inclusion for A and B would be $1\frac{1}{2}$ times the probability of inclusion for C and D.

7.6. For selecting 40 subjects from a set of 100, read two-digit numbers and take the first 40 different ones, from some starting point. For selecting 40 subjects from a set of 80, (a) read two-digit numbers and take the first 40 different ones which are ≤ 80, from some starting point; or (b) read four-digit numbers and take the first 40 different remainders after division by 80, from some starting point.

CHAPTER 8

8.1. (Partial answer). The intervals for the two experiments given in the solution to Exercise 7.2 are $(-1, 5)$ and $(-1, 11)$. The other four are found similarly from their curves A_f. Of the six intervals, only the one corresponding to the experiment with (15, 19) as control scores and the one corresponding to the experiment with (12, 15) as control scores do not contain 8.

8.2. $(-205, 1240)$.

8.3. $(-4, 17)$.

8.5. $A_f(0) = .000$; hence experimentation is continued.

8.6. $A_f(0) = .005$; hence experimentation is continued.

8.7.

	$f = \lvert \bar{R}_t - \bar{R}_c \rvert$	$f = \lvert n_t^+ - n_t^- \rvert$
Example 1	13	13
Example 2	517.5	517.5
Example 3	6.5	7.5

CHAPTER 9

9.1. (Partial answer). For $\theta = 0$, $A_f = 6/16$ (see Table 9.2). For $\theta = 10$, $A_f = 14/16$ (see Table 9.1).

9.3. (Partial answer). Use $n = 5$ for Table C.

9.4. (Partial answer). $A_f(-6) = .250$.

9.5. (Partial answer). The intervals are $(-\infty, -5)$, $(-5, -1.5)$, $(-1.5, .5)$, $(.5, 2)$, $(2, 4)$, $(4, 6)$, and $(6, \infty)$. $A_f = .250$ on the first interval, $A_f = .750$ on the third interval.

9.6. (Partial answer). $A_f(-2) = 5/16$.

9.7. a. $A_f(0) = .624$.
b. (Partial answer). The intervals are $(-\infty, -11)$, $(-11, 7)$, $(7, 16)$, $(16, 20)$, and $(20, \infty)$. A_f on the first interval is .124.

CHAPTER 10

10.1. a. (1) 1/2, 1/2, 1/4.
(2) 1/8, 7/8.
(3) 3/8, 1/8, 1/8.

10.2. a. (1) 1/2, 1/2, 1/4.
(2) 1/16, 15/16.
(3) 11/16, 5/16, 4/16.

10.3. a. .991.
b. .006.
c. .997.

10.4. (Partial answer). For the first population, $\mu_x = 70$, $\sigma_x = 2$. For the third population, direct computation gives $\mu_{(x-60)/12} = 5/6$, $\sigma_{(x-60)/12} = 1/6$. By the formulas

$$\frac{\mu_x - 60}{12} = \frac{70 - 60}{12} = 5/6, \qquad \frac{\sigma_x}{12} = \frac{2}{12} = 1/6.$$

10.5. (As an example). For the distribution

X	$4 \cdot P$
0	1
1	2
2	1

the computation with squared deviations gives

X	$(X-1)^2$	$4 \cdot P$	$(X-1)^2 \cdot 4 \cdot P$
0	1	1	1
1	0	2	0
2	1	1	1
			2

so $\sigma^2 = 2/4 = .5$.

The computation as the mean square minus the squared mean:

X	$4 \cdot P$	$X \cdot 4 \cdot P$	$X^2 \cdot 4 \cdot P$
0	1	0	0
1	2	2	2
2	1	2	4
		4	6

$\mu_X = 4/4 = 1$, $\mu_{X^2} = 6/4 = 1.5$, $\mu_{X^2} - (\mu_X)^2 = 1.5 - (1)^2 = .5$.

10.6. Check your answers by the method of Exercise 10.2.

10.7. c. For the population

X	$4 \cdot P$	$X \cdot 4 \cdot P$	$X^2 \cdot 4 \cdot P$
2	1	2	4
3	1	3	9
5	1	5	25
7	1	7	49
		17	87

$$\mu_X = 17/4, \qquad \mu_{X^2} = 87/4, \qquad \mu_{X^2} - (\mu_X)^2 = \frac{348 - 289}{16} = 59/16.$$

If $S = X_1 + X_2$,

$$\mu_s = 2 \cdot (17/4) = 8.5, \qquad \sigma_s^2 = 2 \cdot \frac{59}{16} \frac{4-2}{4-1} = \frac{59}{12}.$$

d. See the formulas on page 86.

10.8. c. If $S = X_1 + X_2$,

$$\mu_s = 8.5, \qquad \sigma_s^2 = 2 \cdot \frac{59}{16} = \frac{59}{8}.$$

d. See the formulas on page 86.

10.9. For the population

X	$5 \cdot P$
-1	2
0	1
1	2

$$\mu_X = 0, \qquad \sigma_X^2 = 4/5.$$

Hence if three are drawn without replacement, the sum $S = X_1 + X_2 + X_3 = n_t^+ - n_t^-$ will have

$$\mu_s = 3 \cdot \mu_X = 3.0 = 0,$$

$$\sigma_s^2 = 3 \cdot \sigma_X^2 \cdot \frac{5-3}{5-1} = 3 \cdot (4/5) \cdot (2/5) = 6/5.$$

10.10. (partial answer). (1) $f = X_1 + X_2 + X_3 + X_4$ for X as in Exercise 3a.
(2) $f = X_1 + X_2 + X_3 + X_4$ for X as in Exercise 3b.
(3) $f = X_1 + X_2 + X_3 + X_4$ for X as in Exercise 3c.
Hence in each case use

$$\mu_f = 4\mu_X, \qquad \sigma_f^2 = 4 \cdot \sigma_X^2 \cdot \frac{10-4}{10-1}.$$

10.11. $\mu = \dfrac{30 \cdot 101}{2} = 1515, \qquad \sigma^2 = \dfrac{30 \cdot 70 \cdot 101}{12} = 17{,}675.$

10.12. See the answer to Exercise 10.10. Here $\mu_f = 4\mu_X$ and $\sigma_f^2 = 4 \cdot \sigma_X^2$.

10.13. If $S = X_1 + X_2 + \cdots + X_n$ and $\bar{X} = s/n$, $\mu_{\bar{X}} = \mu_{s/n} = \mu_s/n = n\mu_X/n = \mu_X$ with or without replacement and

$$\sigma_{\bar{X}}^2 = \sigma_{s/n}^2 = \frac{\sigma_s^2}{n^2} = \begin{cases} \dfrac{n\sigma_X^2}{n^2}\dfrac{N-n}{N-1} = \dfrac{\sigma_X^2}{n}\dfrac{N-n}{N-1} & \text{without replacement,} \\[2ex] \dfrac{n\sigma_X^2}{n^2} = \dfrac{\sigma_X^2}{n} & \text{with replacement.} \end{cases}$$

10.14. $\sigma_X^2 = \dfrac{\sigma_X^2}{n} = \dfrac{(50)^2}{10{,}000}$; hence $\sigma_{\bar{X}} = \dfrac{50}{100} = 1/2$ with replacement, $\sigma_{\bar{X}}^2 = 0$ without replacement.

CHAPTER 11

11.1. b. If x are taken from n, $n - x$ are left; if $n - x$ are taken from n, x are left.

c. The number of sequences of H's and T's with exactly x H's is the number of different ways to choose x positions to put the H's.

11.2. a. 1/18.

b. 3/30.

c. 17/27.

d. 18/30.

e.

	dt	*no-dt*	
acc.	1.8	1.2	3
no-acc.	16.2	10.8	27
	18	12	30

11.4. a. There is strong dependence among temperatures on successive days.

b. Binomial for all practical purposes.

c. $P\{\text{noon temperature} > 70°\}$ is not constant.

11.6. For the population

X	P
0	$1 - p$
1	p

$\mu_x = p, \quad \sigma_x^2 = p - p^2 = p(1 - p).$

$S = X_1 + \cdots + X_n$ has the binomial distribution for n trials and probability p, so $\mu_s = np$, $\sigma_s^2 = np(1-p)$, and

$$\mu_{s/n} = \frac{np}{n} = p, \qquad \sigma^2_{s/n} = \frac{np(1-p)}{n^2} = \frac{p(1-p)}{n}.$$

11.9. (Partial answer). If $x_0 = 0$ is observed, $A_f(p)$ is

p	0	.1	.2	.3	.4	.5	.6	.7	.8	.9	1
$A_f(p)$	1	1	.591	.331	.165	.062	.010	.002	.000	.000	0

If $x_0 = 1$ is observed, $A_f(p)$ is

p	0	.1	.2	.3	.4	.5	.6	.7	.8	.9	1
$A_f(p)$	0	1	1	1	.654	.376	.165	.031	.007	.000	0

11.11. b. The conditional, given R on the first draw, probability of R on the second is 6/12. The probability of R on the second is 3/5.

11.12. If n are to be drawn so that exactly x are red, x must be drawn from the R red in the urn and $n - x$ must be drawn from the $N - R$ black in the urn.

CHAPTER 12

12.2. $\bar{t} - \bar{c} = 12.83$, $ns_t^2 = \sum (t_i - \bar{t})^2 = 144.78$

$$ms_c^2 = \sum (c_i - \bar{c})^2 = 90.25$$

$$235.03$$

$n + m - 2 = 3.$

For $\theta = -10$,

$$f = \frac{[\bar{t} - \bar{c} - (-10)]^2}{(\frac{1}{2} + \frac{1}{3})[235.03/3]} = \frac{521 \cdot 21}{(5/6)[78.34]} = 8.02.$$

By interpolating in Table I for $\nu_1 = 1$, $\nu_2 = 3$, that is, in

.100	5.54
P	8.02
.05	10.10

$A_f(-10) = P = .07$. For the other values of θ:

θ	$A_f(\theta)$
−10	.07
0	.25
10	.78
20	.47
30	.18

INDEX